Dance in New York

An Indispensable Companion to the Dance Capital of the World

by Ellen Jacob
and Christopher Jonas

quick fox

NEW YORK · TOKYO · LONDON

To the incomparable city of New York

Printed in the United States of America.

International Standard Book Number: 0-8256-3147-5
Library of Congress Catalog Card Number: 78-68482

In Great Britain: Book Sales Ltd., 78 Newman Street, London W1P 3

In Canada: Gage Trade Publishing, P.O. Box 5000, 164 Commander E
Agincourt, Ontario M1S 3C7.

In Japan: Quick Fox, 4-26-22 Jingumae, Shibuya-ku, Tokyo 150.

Cover design: Barry L.S. Mirenburg
Cover photo: David Frazier
Book design: Barbara Hoffman
Dancer on cover: Ann Marie DeAngelo of the Joffrey Ballet
Miss DeAngelo's costume: Eaves Costume Company

This book was produced in cooperation with Danceways, a nonprofit foundation established to educate consumers and promote the growth of dance.

Acknowledgments

We are grateful to the following individuals and groups who helped us assemble the hundreds of disparate ingredients that go into a potpourri of this sort: Joan Jacob and Michaele Salladé for their research assistance; photographer Frank Gimpaya for his poet's touch; editors Jim Charlton and Jeanette Mall for their open-mindedness and patience in undertaking this novel project; Dr. William Liebler and Armando Zetina for their technical advice; Gene Cron of Art Stone Dance and Gymnastics Supply, Michele Wolfe, and of course all the theatres, dance schools, companies, organizations, teachers, local suppliers, and others who have contributed material about themselves. Finally, we'd like to thank the corporations who have sponsored ***Dance in New York*** through their advertising support and in so doing have enabled us to make it available at the lowest possible price.

Contents

James Cunningham's Acme Dance Company at the Chase Manhattan Plaza on Wall Street. ***V. Sladon***

Introduction

To say that New York is the dance capital of the world is not a chauvinistic exaggeration: it's a simple fact. Here can be found more first-rate dance companies, dance schools, and teachers, more dancers, dancegoers, and more dance services and organizations than anywhere else on earth. In no other city can you study with your choice of celebrated teachers alongside principal dancers from the world's leading companies. New York is also peerless for the sheer variety of dance flourishing within its boundaries—ballet, modern, ethnic, musical comedy, and experimental. It houses the largest dance library and film archive in the world, at Lincoln Center. Since the most sophisticated audiences and critics are here, all the world's major dance troupes give regular seasons in New York, making it a nonstop showcase for international dance attractions. (Last spring and summer Lincoln Center alone played host to American Ballet Theatre, the New York City Ballet, the Joffrey Ballet, the Stuttgart Ballet, the National Ballet of Canada, the National Ballet of Cuba, and the Bolshoi Ballet.) Jiri Kylian, the 32-year-old director of the Netherlands Dance Theatre, which had a triumphant run at City Center last July, speaks for many when he says, "Believe me, coming to this city is an act of courage. In fact, I was advised not to come. I was told there was no gasoline, so nobody could drive to the theatre. I was told the summer is a bad time. I was told I'd be playing against such favorites as Nureyev and Alonso. But I said to my well-meaning advisers, as pleasantly as possible, 'Oh, go to hell, everybody.' We ***had*** to come, we had to test ourselves against the best."*

New York, moreover, is probably the only place on the planet where dance is ubiquitous. You can scarcely walk a city block without coming across walls and fences plastered with notices of upcoming concerts, or open a local newspaper without spotting ads for various dance events and classes. Dancewear is everywhere—in shop windows and on people riding to work on the buses. On Broadway in the sixties the streets are thick with dancers hauling their practice gear over their shoulders, hair slicked back from sweat-glistened foreheads. It is also the only place where male dancers are not in desperately short supply. Most New York dance schools have a healthy contingent of men, as do even the smallest companies.

But New York cannot be given the credit for creating all the the dance activity that is concentrated here: there are top-flight companies and schools and knowledgeable audiences in many other locales. Rather, the city has acted as a magnet, drawing dancers and dance enthusiasts with its

*From "New York's Inimitable Audiences," by Lee Edward Stern in ***The New York Times,*** August 12, 1979.

unique spirit, its intoxicating energy, and its matchless opportunites for developing artists. New York has become the place for the world's talents to come and grow. Indeed, most of its professional dancers have received at least their initial training elsewhere.

Choreographer Elaine Summers, who moved to the city from Boston, calls it "an art laboratory for the nation. The close contact between artists gives them emotional support and a chance to exchange ideas," she says. As Veronica Tennant, a principal dancer with the National Ballet of Canada, observed during a recent stay, "You somehow feel that you're at the very center, the actual hub, of everything that's happening when you're in New York. There's something about the circumstances, something in the environment that has brought out of me the best performances I've done anywhere."*

Whether you're already in New York or contemplating a visit,† the purpose of this directory is to show you what's here and how to find it quickly. Conveniently organized listings and consumer information will help you evaluate and compare the city's numerous offerings. Every effort was made to supply current data, but despite our good intentions, some of it will inevitably become outdated in the time it takes to publish these pages. In using the guide, therefore, it's always a good idea to confirm vital information with a brief phone call.

This is the first of a continuing series of updated and more comprehensive editions of ***Dance in New York.*** Although we feel we're off to a good start, we also feel the frustration of not having been able to do everything we had hoped this time around. Undoubtedly, we have missed some new or noteworthy dance theatres, schools, teachers, companies, suppliers, and service organizations. We urge all those not yet included to get in touch with us, and we welcome readers' suggestions as to what they'd like to see in future editions of the guide. Write or call Danceways, 393 West End Avenue, New York, New York, 10024, (212) 799-2860.

In the meantime, we hope you'll give dance in New York a whirl. Welcome and enjoy!

*From "Summertime, and the Arts Are Easy at Lincoln Center," by McCandlish Phillips, in ***The New York Times,*** July 8, 1979.

†For more on the rewards and perils of the New York dance world, see Ellen Jacob's ***Dancing: An Exuberant Invitation and Complete Guide.***

1

Where to See Dance in New York

Theatres that regularly present dance

Lofts

Dance outdoors

Dance on Broadway

Stretching your dance dollars

Until recently most dance events in New York took place in Broadway theatres or opulent concert halls such as the old Metropolitan Opera House or Carnegie Hall. In 1953 Merce Cunningham was virtually ignored by the New York critics when his company presented a week-long season at the off-Broadway Theatre de Lys. Rudolph Nureyev got the same treatment ten years later after making his New York debut with the Chicago Opera Ballet at the Brooklyn Academy of Music, which was not yet an established showcase for dance.

To all but large, prestigious ballet companies and an occasional modern dance troupe* the cost of putting on a New York season was prohibitively expensive. Only Kaufman Concert Hall at the 92nd Street YM-YWHA and the Hunter College Playhouse offered young choreographers an affordable place to perform and adequate press coverage. Likewise, concertgoers had little choice but to pay steep ticket prices or be prepared for a steep climb to the highest balconies of the house.

But the modern dance revolution of the 1960s, together with the general proliferation of small dance companies brought about by the dance explosion of the 1970s, prompted a search for alternative performing spaces. Not content to accept the "Broadway or bust" attitude of their predecessors, avant-garde dancers—in a rebellion very similar to the off-Broadway and off-off-Broadway movements in theatre—performed in all kinds of spaces hitherto considered off limits: churches, industrial lofts, rooftops, museums, and parks. Choreographers like Meredith Monk, Twyla Tharp, Douglas Dunn, Kenneth King, Tricia Brown, and Steve Paxton were looking for more informal performing environments where they could have close contact with their audiences. They needed the artistic freedom to experiment. Others wanted to dance in small houses where they could not only be assured of paying the rent, but of filling most of the seats (there is nothing more depressing than the prospect of playing to a half-empty theatre).

The growing demand for a range of performing spaces has enriched the New York dance scene all around. Small and middle-sized theatres have sprung up all over the city in the past ten years or so, giving small modern dance and ballet companies, ethnic dancers, and soloists—as well as their audiences—a variety of performing environments, theatre locations, ticket prices, and programming to choose from. Oddly enough, most dance is presented off-Broadway now.

You can see dance in New York on proscenium as well as nonproscenium stages. You can pay $25 to watch the internationally famous stars of American Ballet Theatre from a red velvet seat in the Metropolitan Opera House or sit on pillows on the floor and for a $5 charge see the Merce Cunningham Dance Company perform an "event" at their studio

*Even if she couldn't pay her dancers, Martha Graham always managed to get her company on Broadway, and the Denishawn troupe (Ruth St. Denis and Ted Shawn's company) balanced their books by performing with the Ziegfeld Follies.

in Westbeth. For a still smaller contribution you can see a future Cunningham showing his latest avant-garde piece in a loft theatre in Soho.

Large proscenium theatres, such as the Metropolitan Opera House at Lincoln Center or the City Center 55th Street Theatre, generally program major ballet and modern dance companies. At these plush concert halls, which accommodate thousands of patrons, orchestra tickets cost from $9.50 to $25. Be sure to look at a seating plan of the house before buying a ticket; otherwise you're liable to end up with a poor seat, and at those prices! When reserving tickets by phone or mail, ask for a central location. You can pay as little as $5 or $6 for upper-balcony seats, but you'll have to sacrifice detail and a sense of immediacy about the performance. A good pair of opera glasses will help.

Among the most economical places to see dance are small proscenium theatres, such as the Riverside Church and the Marymount Manhattan Theatres. Usually modern or recently remodeled, these are comfortable, well-equipped houses that host established modern dance groups, small ballet companies, and ethnic dance companies. More intimate and informal than the big concert halls, they normally accommodate from 250 to 500 people. Ticket prices range from $4 to $8 and you can usually see well from any seat. Because of the limited seating capacity, however, it's wise to make reservations in advance.

Converted spaces, such as those at Dance Theatre Workshop and the Washington Square Methodist Church are the most plentiful. These are nonproscenium dance theatres set up in churches, studios, and industrial lofts—but with standard sound and lighting equipment. For the most part they present modern, ethnic, and experimental companies, and usually seat from 50 to 200 people. Seating is unreserved, frequently on bleachers or pillows on the floor. The atmosphere is highly informal, and often the audience and dancers linger to talk after the show. Tickets average about $4.50. Unlike many of the proscenium theatres, most converted dance spaces are located outside Manhattan's midtown area.

Loft theatres, such as Eden's Expressway and The Kitchen, are the latest outgrowth of the dance boom. They are strictly for adventurous concertgoers who are interested in the work of young modern dance companies and experimental choreographers. Performers are seen at close range, in a spare but homey setting. Some loft programs are presented as works-in-progress, with no special lighting, makeup, or theatrical effects; others are fully produced concerts. Most loft theatres are located in Soho, accommodate 50 to 75 people, and charge $4 or less for admission.

Outdoor festivals, such as the New York Dance Festival at the Delacorte Theatre in Central Park and the Lincoln Center outdoor concerts, have given many audiences their first taste of dance. Performances usually take place on a temporary platform stage, and seating is on a first come, first served basis. They offer varied programming and are usually free.

Besides all the concert activity in New York, on any given night you can have your pick of Broadway musicals such as Bob Fosse's hit ***Dancin'*** (at the Broadhurst Theatre), and ***Eubie***, a tribute to black songwriter Eubie Blake, choreographed in the jazz dance styles of the 1920s (now playing at the Ambassador). From time to time major dance companies give seasons at Broadway theatres too: most recently Rudolf Nureyev and the Joffrey Ballet appeared in "Homage to Diaghilev" at the Mark Hellinger and Maurice Bejart's Ballet of the Twentieth Century had a run at the Minskoff.

Theatres that regularly present dance

AMERICAN MUSEUM OF NATURAL HISTORY

Central Park West at 79th Street
New York, New York 10024
(212-873-1300)

Type of dance presented: Primarily ethnic and some modern. Recent artists have included Matteo (Indian), Charles Moore (African), Morocco (Middle Eastern), Saeko Ichinohe (Japanese), Noah Hall (Jamaican), Gertrude Ituk (Nigerian), Linda Stanley (Hawaiian), and the Thunderbird Dance Company (American Indian). Performances are ongoing from 1:00 to 4:30 P.M. on Saturdays and Sundays.

What it's like: In conjunction with various anthropological displays, the People's Center at the American Museum of Natural History presents classes and lecture-demonstrations on the dance, theatre, and music of nations all over the world. The colorfully decorated Center has a warm, informal atmosphere that contrasts pleasantly with the imposing columns and large open spaces of the building's exhibition halls. Most dance concerts take place in its eighty-seat theatre, while simultaneous presentations—on songs, storytelling, crafts, history, and the like—are given in the two adjacent mini-amphitheatres. Contact between audience and performers is encouraged, and visitors are urged to sample the different activities by moving from one demonstration area to another. The People's Center is a great place to take the kids on weekends, where they can learn about and participate in the arts of many cultures in a personal way. Soft drinks, snacks, and sandwiches are available in the museum cafeteria.

Tickets: You pay what you wish to get into the museum—the suggested contribution is $1.50 for adults and $.75 for children. Admission to the People's Center is free.

Getting there: The closest subway stop is at 81st Street and Central Park West on the IND local subway line. It lets you off right at the museum. Or you can take the Seventh Avenue IRT local train to 79th Street and Broadway. Walk three blocks east and you're there.

BEACON THEATRE

2124 Broadway (at 74th Street)
New York, New York 10023
(212-874-1718)

Type of dance presented: Mostly ethnic and modern, some ballet. Recent programs have included the Grand Kabuki Theatre of Japan, the Festival of Russian Dance featuring various Russian folk ensembles, and the 28th annual Israel Folk Dance Festival.

Other appearances have been made by Dennis Wayne's Dancers, the Alwin Nikolais Dance Theatre, and Alfonso Catá's Ballet on Broadway.

What it's like: The Beacon is a recently renovated Art Deco theatre built in 1928 and modeled after the old Roxy. Throughout the 1960s and early 1970s it was used for hard-rock concerts, but in 1977, under the direction of Kazuko Hillyer, it returned to theatre productions and also began to present dance. The theatre has an elegant period quality: the lobby has a rotunda with a 1000-light chandelier, and gold statues grace either side of the stage. The seating capacity is 2600, including a mezzanine and balcony. Liquor, soft drinks, popcorn, and candy are sold at the concession stand.

Tickets: Tickets for dance performances range from $5 to $15. TDF vouchers are accepted, and there are student and senior citizen discounts. You can make phone reservations using major credit cards through CHARGIT (212-239-7177); there are also advance sales. Group discounts are sometimes available.

Getting there: The Beacon Theatre is on Broadway at 74th Street. Take the Seventh Avenue IRT express or local to 72nd Street and Broadway; or take the Number 104 bus.

BROOKLYN ACADEMY OF MUSIC (BAM)

30 Lafayette Avenue
Brooklyn, New York 11217
(212-636-4100)

Type of dance presented: Ballet, modern, experimental, and ethnic. The Pennsylvania Ballet is the resident company at BAM, but a host of other major troupes have performed there too, among them the San Francisco Ballet, the Eliot Feld Ballet, Maria Benitez/Estampa Flamenca, the Pilobolus Dance Theatre, Les Ballets Trockadero and the companies of Paul Taylor, José Limón, Merce Cunningham, Twyla Tharp, Meredith Monk, Dan Wagoner, Senta Driver, Lucinda Childs, and Laura Dean. Concerts take place regularly at BAM, October through June.

What it's like: Although it is the oldest performing arts center in the country, the Brooklyn Academy did not produce dance concerts for the first hundred years of its existence. Then in 1962, Rudolf Nureyev made his American debut there with the Chicago Opera Ballet, and by the end of the 1960s, BAM was established as a major showcase for dance in the metropolitan area. Under the direction of Harvey Lichtenstein it has presented a first-rate dance series for the past twelve years. The Brooklyn Academy has three performing spaces for dance: the Opera House, the Helen Carey Playhouse, and the LaPercq Space. The resplendent Opera House seats 2100 and offers orchestra, mezzanine and balcony levels. The Playhouse, a more intimate, smaller stage theatre, seats 1000. The nonproscenium LaPercq Space is a flexible theatre. It can accommodate between 200 and 600 people depending on how the movable seats and bleachers are arranged. The lobby and lounges at BAM were recently remodeled. Better than average fare, such as pastries and fruit and wine, is available from the refreshment bar and foodstuffs carts.

While the Academy's programming is usually excellent, during some of the more popular events when the Opera House was filled to capacity there appeared not to be enough ushers to show people to their seats, and there was much overcrowding on the long, slow-moving ticket lines. Still that seems a small price to pay for such quality productions.

Tickets: Tickets for the Opera House range from $5.00 to $9.50; for the Playhouse, they are $4.50 to $8.50; for the LaPercq Space, they are $5.50 to $6.50. There is reserved seating in the Opera House and the Playhouse, but not in the Lapercq Space. Subscriptions to the dance series are available at a 45% discount; included are discounts on parking and the Express Bus service to Manhattan, as well as local dining. Students and senior citizens can take advantage of discount rush seats. There are advance and group sales, as well as Brooklyn Educational Cultural Alliance (BECA) discounts. Advance reservations may be made with major credit cards through CHARGIT (212-239-7177). Credit cards are also accepted at the box office.

Getting there: BAM runs a special Manhattan Express Bus Service to and from the Academy on the evenings of dance performances at the Opera House and the Playhouse (not the LaPercq Space). One hour before curtain, the bus leaves from 59th Street and Lexington Avenue (in front of Bloomingdale's Department Store) in Manhattan and goes on to make stops at 10 Columbus Circle (near the Coliseum), the Riviera Cafe at Sheridan Square in Greenwich Village, and Cooper Union at Astor Place. The fare is $1.50. If you're going by car, there is BAM attended parking across the street. To get there by subway, take the Seventh Avenue IRT, the Lexington Avenue IRT, or the IND line to Atlantic Avenue. The trip from midtown Manhattan takes less than half an hour. Certain Long Island trains also stop at Atlantic Avenue. Follow the exit signs for the Academy of Music. You will come out just one block away from the front entrance. The Brooklyn Academy is located in a rather rough neighborhood, but if you're on your way to a concert, chances are that you'll find plenty of other dance buffs heading in the same direction. For your first trip, though, you might want to bring a friend.

BROOKLYN COLLEGE CENTER FOR THE PERFORMING ARTS

Guest Artist Series/Dance
Room 154 Gershwin
Brooklyn, New York 11210
(212-780-5291)

Type of dance presented: Ballet, modern, and ethnic. The Joffrey II is the resident company of the Center. Other recent performers have included the Ohio Ballet, Patricia McBride and Jean-Pierre Bonnefous, the Stars of the American Ballet with Suzanne Farrell and Peter Martins, the Cliff Keuter Dance Company, the Eleo Pomare Dance Company, Charles Moore's Dances and Drums of Africa, the Murray Louis Dance Company, the International Afrikan-American Ballet, and Ballet Hispanico of New York. The dance season runs from October through May.

What it's like: The Brooklyn College Center for the Performing Arts has had a Concert Bureau for twenty-six years. All of the country's major orchestras have performed there, but it wasn't until 1975 that dance companies were presented. Performances take place both at the 2500-seat Whitman Hall and the 500-seat Gershwin Theatre. Whitman Hall, which looks like a typical school auditorium, is a deep theatre, with the balcony and last orchestra rows set quite far back from the stage. Seats are best in the first half of the orchestra level. Fruit juice, soda, coffee, and candy are available at the refreshment stand during intermission.

Tickets: Prices vary with performances, but in general orchestra seats range from $7 to $10, mezzanine seats (actually the back half of the orchestra) cost from $6 to $8, and balcony tickets cost $4 to $5. TDF vouchers are accepted, and discount subscriptions are often available. There are also student, senior citizen, and group discounts. Tickets may be charged to major credit cards by phone through CHARGIT (212-239-7177), and there are advance sales at the box office.

Getting there: Brooklyn College is located at the junction of Nostrand and Flatbush Avenues. Take the Number 3 Seventh Avenue IRT train to the end of the line. You will be one block away from the campus.

CARNEGIE HALL

154 West 57th Street
New York, New York 10019
(212-247-7459)

Type of dance presented: Dance concerts are infrequent at Carnegie Hall because it is primarily a music hall. However, several foreign companies have appeared there recently, during the September through June season, among them the Parthenon Dancers of Greece,

Bugaku—Imperial Court Dancers of Japan, the Pearl Primus Afro-American Dancers, the Estrella Morena Flamenco Dancers, the George Tomou Balkan Dancers, and the Anahid Sofian Near East Dancers. In January 1979, a tribute to Katherine Dunham, the dancer and choreographer who popularized Afro-Caribbean dance in America, was held at Carnegie to celebrate Martin Luther King Day. It featured performances by three generations of Dunham dancers, singers, and musicians.

What it's like: Ever since its opening program in 1891, in which Peter Ilyitch Tchaikovsky made his only American appearance, Carnegie Hall has been a symbol of outstanding artistic achievement the world over. It hosted the New York debuts of sixteen-year-old violinist Jascha Heifez and the great Vladimir Horowitz, among others. Pianist-statesman Jan Paderewski gave a benefit concert there for Polish war victims during World War I. Later, distinguished jazz musicians and folk singers performed at Carnegie Hall. It housed the New York Philharmonic until 1962, when Philharmonic Hall (now Avery Fisher Hall) was built at Lincoln Center. Over the decades its unsurpassed acoustics have attracted speakers like Booker T. Washington, Mark Twain, Woodrow Wilson, and both Theodore and Franklin Roosevelt. Bertrand Russell, Albert Einstein, Clarence Darrow, Eugene Debs, and Norman Thomas gave impassioned speeches at Carnegie Hall on the issues of their times.

During the 1920s and 1930s a succession of modern dance giants populated the Carnegie stage: Isadora Duncan, Ruth St. Denis and Ted Shawn, Harold Kreutzberg, Martha Graham, Charles Weidman and Doris Humphrey, Helen Tamiris, and Hanya Holm. But dance performances tapered off with the opening of other theatres. Carnegie Hall is also the headquarters of teaching and rehearsal studios which have equally illustrious histories. Duncan lived and taught there at the turn of the century. Both Agnes de Mille and Jerome Robbins studied at the famous Ballet Arts School, and in 1943 de Mille choreographed the Broadway musical ***Oklahoma!*** in Studio 61.

The 2800-seat theatre, with its curved balconies and carved balustrades, is a model of understated elegance. It was renovated in 1960, after a last-ditch effort by Isaac Stern saved the hall from wrecking crews, and the building was taken over by the City of New York as an historical landmark. Cocktails, light snacks, and soft beverages are served at the charming Cafe Carnegie on the main floor. There are additional refreshment bars on several balcony levels, and the famed Russian Tea Room restaurant, which has been stylishly feeding Carnegie Hall patrons, is right next door.

Tickets: Tickets usually range from $5 to $12. TDF vouchers are not accepted. Student and senior citizen discounts are occasionally available. There are advance sales through CHARGIT (212-239-7177), but no other reservations are taken over the phone. The box office does not accept personal checks, except for purchasing subscriptions to their concert series; it does, however, honor American Express credit cards.

Getting there: Carnegie Hall is located at 57th Street and Seventh Avenue. The closest subway stops are at 57th Street on the BMT "RR" or "N" trains, or at 59th Street and Columbus Circle on the IND and the Seventh Avenue IRT local trains.

CATHEDRAL OF ST. JOHN THE DIVINE

1047 Amsterdam Avenue (at 112th Street)
New York, New York 10027
(212-678-6888)

Type of dance presented: Primarily modern. Dance performances are relatively new at the Cathedral of St. John the Divine. The José Limón Dance Company, featuring guest artist Erik Bruhn, had a critically acclaimed season there in 1978. Bruce King and the Blaska Ballet of Paris were presented as well. In addition, there are periodic appearances by the Renaissance Court Dance Company and the Omega Liturgical Dance Company, a unique modern dance group that bases its work on ecumenical and spiritual themes. The Cathedral hopes to expand its dance program and present a regular series in the near future. At present, though, concerts are held sporadically throughout the year.

What it's like: The Cathedral of St. John the Divine is the largest Gothic cathedral in the world. The building went up at the turn of the century, but is only two-thirds completed due to an interruption of construction in 1941 during the Japanese attack on Pearl Harbor. Plans to finish "Big John" by employing some of the young people from the community got under way in the spring of 1979. The Cathedral clears its pews from the worship space for dance concerts. Its high ceilings, dramatic architecture, and beautiful stained glass make a striking setting. Live organ music was used for the Limón concert. The seating capacity is very large, but unfortunately seats are set up far from the raised platform stage, and it is difficult to get a clear view of the dancers after the first ten or fifteen rows. So arrive there early to claim a good seat. Refreshments are offered occasionally. Since the church is located close to the Columbia University campus, there are also several good, inexpensive, student-style restaurants nearby.

Tickets: Ticket prices and the house policy regarding reservations vary with the performing group. The Bruce King performances were CETA-sponsored and free. The José Limón tickets ranged from $3 to $10. TDF vouchers are usually accepted. It is expected that these practices will become more standardized as the dance series expands.

Getting there: The closest subway stop is at 110th Street on the Seventh Avenue IRT local; or you can take the Number 104 Broadway bus to Broadway and 110th Street.

CITY CENTER 55TH STREET THEATRE

131 West 55th Street
New York, New York 10019
(212-246-8989)

Type of dance presented: The Joffrey Ballet, the Alvin Ailey American Dance Theatre, the Paul Taylor Dance Company, and the Dance Theatre of Harlem regularly perform at City Center. Other groups that have recently given seasons there include Jennifer Muller and the Works, the Ballet of Caracas, and the Louis Falco Dance Company. From November 1, 1979, to March 2, 1980, the companies of Murray Louis, Alvin Ailey, Alwin Nikolais, José Limón, and Merce Cunningham will be appearing in a "Masters of American Dance" series. Dance concerts are held throughout the year, September through mid-June. During the summer months City Center presents primarily foreign troupes, such as the Royal Danish Ballet, the Netherlands Dance Theatre, and the Royal Winnipeg Ballet.

What it's like: Built in 1923, City Center was originally the largest Masonic shrine in New York. The mosque-like structure was taken over by the city under Mayor Fiorello LaGuardia and converted into a concert hall. Although it lost some of its Near Eastern decor in the process, the building still retains a strong Islamic flavor. The New York City Ballet and City Opera were housed at City Center before moving to the New York State Theatre at Lincoln Center. The theatre accommodates three thousand people on orchestra and balcony levels. If you plan to sit in the balcony, bring opera glasses and be prepared for a climb—there are no elevators. During the intermissions, liquor, orange drinks, and candy are sold and some of the dance companies operate their own souvenir gift boutiques.

Tickets: Ticket prices vary somewhat from company to company, but they are generally within the $8.00 to $15.00 range. TDF vouchers are accepted, and there are student rush tickets. Half-price seats for City Center concerts are often available at the TKTS trailer in Times Square (see page 60) Subscriptions and group sales are handled by the individual dance companies. Advance tickets are sold at the City Center box office, through mail order, and by phone through CHARGIT (212-239-7177). Major credit cards are honored.

Getting there: City Center is located on 55th Street between Sixth and Seventh avenues. Take the Seventh Avenue IRT local or an IND train to 59th Street and Columbus Circle. You can also take the BMT subway to 57th Street and Seventh Avenue (use the 55th Street exit).

COOPER UNION GREAT HALL
Astor Place
Third Avenue at 7th Street
New York, New York 10003
(212-254-2003)

Type of dance presented: Mostly modern and ethnic. Recent companies have included Satoru Shimazaki and Dancers, the Thunderbird Dancers (native American), and Dinizulu and His African Dancers, Drummers, and Singers. Only one dance company is presented each semester in the Cooper Union performing arts series. The fall season begins in October and the spring season starts in February.

What it's like: The Cooper Union for the Advancement of Science and Art was founded by Peter Cooper in 1859, and has presented lectures and performances since that time. Abraham Lincoln made a speech in the Great Hall on February 27, 1860, which won him the nomination for the Presidency. During Cooper Union's Centennial 1958-59 season, it was also the site of an historical debate between Doris Humphrey, Ted Shawn, and David Vaughn on the future of modern dance. The renovation of the Great Hall, along with the rest of the building, was undertaken in 1971 by John Hejduk, a graduate of Cooper Union. It has been praised in architectural circles for its breathtaking elegance and purity of form. Unfortunately, the columns on each side of the stage tend to obstruct the view for people sitting on the far right or far left of the theatre. No refreshments are served at dance performances.

Tickets: All tickets are free. There are no phone reservations.

Getting there: The Cooper Union is at Astor Place. Take the Lexington Avenue IRT local to Astor Place station; or the BMT local "RR" train to the 8th Street stop and walk one block east to Astor Place.

THE CUBICULO
National Shakespeare Company
414 West 51st Street
New York, New York 10019
(212-265-2138)

Type of dance presented: Primarily modern, but also tap, mime and ethnic dance. In the past The Cubiculo has presented Rod Rodgers, Phoebe Neville, Barbara Roan, Daniel Nagrin, Cliff Keuter, Elina Mooney, Rudy Perez, Laura Foreman, and Michael Sullivan among others. Recent performers have been Jill Rosenbloom (classical Indian dance) and Candice Christakos (modern).

What it's like: The "Cube," as it is affectionately called by the staff, was established in 1968 by Philip Meister and Maurice Edwards as a showcase for new theatre, dance, music, and poetry pieces. At that time it was one of the few spaces in New York where small dance companies could afford to perform and still be reviewed by the critics. Over the years many now-established artists have had inaugural performances there. The National Shakespeare Company uses the building for its offices and acting conservatory—which, incidentally, also offers classes in dance and mime. The theatre itself is very much like an open loft space, but with more elaborate lighting. It has black brick walls and is located below the ground floor. Chairs stacked on tiered platforms can hold a maximum of seventy-five people. Refreshments are served occasionally.

Tickets: The Cubiculo no longer produces dance concerts, but rents its facilities to individual artists. Ticket prices are therefore up to the performing company. TDF vouchers are usually accepted, and reservations are taken by phone.

Getting there: The Cubiculo is located west of the theatre district, in the former "Hell's Kitchen" area. The neighborhood can still get a bit rough at night. It's best to take the Seventh Avenue IRT local, or an IND train to 50th Street. Walk west on 50th Street until you reach Ninth Avenue. Then walk one block north to 51st Street and continue half a block westward on the south side of 51st Street. The sign on the brownstone building reads "National Shakespeare Company." St. Clare's Hospital is right across the street.

MERCE CUNNINGHAM STUDIO

Westbeth Artists Complex
463 West Street, or 55 Bethune Street (another entrance)
New York, New York 10014
(212-691-9751)

Type of dance presented: Modern and experimental. Merce Cunningham and Dance Company give regular performances there. Other artists who have been presented include Simone Forti, Mel Wong, Albert Reid, Dorothy Vislocky, June Finch, William Dunas, Sandra Stuart, Diane Germaine, and Meg Harper. Dance events take place year round.

What it's like: The Cunningham Studio is located on the 11th floor of Westbeth, a Bell Telephone Laboratories building, overlooking the Hudson River, which has been converted into federally subsidized housing for artists. It is the largest of two classrooms in the Cunningham school used for rehearsals and daily lessons in Cunningham technique. Mirrors cover one of the walls. But the Studio makes an airy, informal dance space for evening performances. Its large windows open out on a lovely starlit view of lower Manhattan. Seating is extremely casual, on a few benches and lots of cushions. The capacity is 150. Visitors are asked to remove their shoes to protect the dance floor. Refreshments are rarely served.

Tickets: Tickets are usually priced between $4 and $5. There are no subscriptions or advance sales. Phone reservations are taken for the Cunningham company performances; otherwise it's up to the individual company. Most groups accept TDF vouchers. There are no other discounts.

Getting there: Take the Seventh Avenue IRT or the Eighth Avenue IND subway to the 14th Street stop. Get off at the south end of the platform, at 12th Street and Seventh Avenue. From Seventh Avenue walk west on 12th Street across Eighth Avenue. (If you've taken the Eighth Avenue subway, you'll already be on Eighth Avenue.) Then go one block south on Eighth Avenue to Bethune Street. Continue west on Bethune Street two and a half blocks to Number 55.

DANCE GALLERY

242 East 14th Street
New York, New York 10003
(212-685-5972)

Type of dance presented: Modern and ethnic dance is presented from September through May. Larry Richardson and Dance Company are based there and other companies rent the space. Recent performances have featured the Viola Farber Dance Company, the José Limón Dance Company, Daniel Nagrin, and Bhaskar—Dances of India.

What it's like: Larry Richardson took over this dance space, which used to be a regulation-size basketball gym, eight years ago. The audience sits on bleachers and plastic molded chairs. The seating capacity is only 261, making advance reservations and getting there early advisable. Coffee or wine is served at performances.

Tickets: Tickets range from $3.50 to $5.00. TDF vouchers are accepted. Student and senior citizen discounts are available. Tickets may be purchased in advance. Phone reservations are accepted occasionally, depending on the performing group.

Getting there: The Dance Gallery is located on 14th Street between Second and Third avenues. It is closest to the Lexington Avenue IRT stop at 14th Street and Union Square. You can also take a Seventh Avenue IRT or Eighth Avenue IND train to 14th Street, and then the 14th Street crosstown bus east to Third Avenue.

DANCE THEATRE WORKSHOP (DTW) AT AMERICAN THEATRE LABORATORY

219 West 19th Street
New York, New York 10010
(212-691-6500, for program information; 924-0077, for reservations)

Type of dance presented: Mostly small but established modern dance companies, occasionally some ethnic or other. Recent performers have been: Rachel Lampert and Dancers, Jane Goldberg and Charles Cook, Albert Reid, Kenneth Rinker, Pat Catterson, Steve Paxton and David Moss, Barbara Roan, Douglas Dunn and Dancers, the Kathryn Posin Dance Company, the Nimbus Dance Company, Marcus Schulkind Dance Company, and Lenore Latimer and John Wilson. DTW also presents out-of-town companies, such as the Concert Dance Company of Boston, Groupe Nouvelle Aire from Montreal, Jan Van Dyke from Washington, D.C., Tandy Beals from San Francisco, and the Albuquerque Dance Theatre. In addition, the work of eighteen new choreographers is shown three times a year in DTW's Choreographer's Showcase. Performances are held year-round, except in July. If you wish to receive notification of upcoming events, ask to be put on their free mailing list.

What it's like: Dance Theatre Workshop is one of the most active and satisfying dance theatres in town. Jeff Duncan and Art Bauman formed the Workshop as a choreographer's cooperative in 1964, and it moved to its present location at the American Theatre Laboratory in 1973, after Jerome Robbins' theatre company, based there, folded. Since its inception, DTW has grown to be a nonprofit membership organization that offers a broad range of technical services to dance companies and their audiences—from funding and management assistance to providing rehearsal space and sponsoring special classes and seminars (see the listing for DTW under dance organizations in Chapter Four). But its main business continues to be producing full evening concerts at a minimum charge or cost-free to new and innovative artists. More than eight hundred dance works have been performed at DTW since its founding, many of them premieres. Dozens of well established modern dance choreographers got their start there, among them Frances Alenikoff, Barbara Roan, Matthew Diamond, Rudy Perez, Kathryn Posin, Kenneth King, William Dunas, Jack Moore, Meredith Monk, Kei Takei, Cliff Keuter, Rachel Lampert, Rosalind Newman, James Cunningham, Ze'va Cohen, Gus Solomons, Jr., and Yvonne Rainer.

Although it is not a proscenium stage, the performing space is roomy and well equipped. Permanent risers accommodate up to 120 people, and at sold-out performances, further seating is provided on the floor. DTW has a homey, relaxed atmosphere. There are seated areas in the lobby for the audience to linger or chat with performers after the show. Tea, coffee, and hot chocolate are served during intermission for a small donation. Often there are craft or photo exhibits on display, and the bulletin board at the front entrance is always crammed with news of local dance classes and events.

Tickets: The standard ticket price is $4.00. TDF vouchers are accepted, and discount subscriptions at 30% off the regular box office price are available for some series. There are no student or senior citizen discounts, however. You cannot buy tickets in advance, but you can make phone reservations, which are recommended because of the limited seating. It's also advisable to arrive early so you can claim a good seat.

Getting there: DTW is located on 19th Street between Seventh and Eighth avenues. Take the Seventh Avenue IRT local subway to 18th Street. The theatre is on the second floor of a two-story building. A tire store is on the street level.

Intermission at Dance Theatre Workshop.
Frank Gimpaya

ENTERMEDIA THEATRE
12th Street at Second Avenue
New York, New York 10003
(212-475-4191)

Type of dance presented: Mostly modern, occasionally other kinds of dance. Recently there have been appearances by Carolyn Lord and Company, the Daniel Lewis Dance Company, Douglas Dunn and Dancers, the Multigravitational Aerodance Group, the Libby Nye Dance Company, and a revue of old-time jazz music and dance called "A Thousand Years of Jazz" (the thousand years refer to the cumulative ages of the veteran hoofers and musicians in the company).

What it's like: The Moorish-style Entermedia Theatre, located on Manhattan's Lower East Side, has had several incarnations. It first opened in 1926 as Murray Schwartz's Yiddish Arts Theatre, and then went on to produce vaudeville and burlesque shows. Later it became a movie theatre. During the 1950s the Entermedia housed the Phoenix Repertory Company, and after that the original off-Broadway productions of ***Oh, Calcutta*** and ***Grease.*** In 1977-78 it was the home of the Dance Umbrella, a collectively packaged series of dance concerts by established modern dance companies. The physical layout of the Entermedia is almost the reverse of the Roundabout Theatre. It has a great deal of seating (500 seats) around a comparatively small stage. There is a mezzanine and balcony that overhang to row H of the orchestra. Refreshments include ***cappuccino,*** fresh fruit, homemade brownies and pastries, and soft drinks.

Tickets: Prices vary according to the event, but on the average, seats cost between $5 and $8. For $10 you can join their new Membership Club, which entitles subscribers to discounts on all Entermedia productions, including dance concerts. Senior citizen and student discounts are also available for most events. There are no phone reservations.

Getting there: The Entermedia is closest to the 14th Street, Union Square subway stop on the Lexington Avenue IRT local and express; or the 8th Street stop on the "RR" local train of the BMT line.

HENRY STREET SETTLEMENT PLAYHOUSE
466 Grand Street
New York, New York 10002
(212-766-9334)

Type of dance presented: Modern, ballet, and ethnic. The Frank Ashley Dance Company is currently in residence, and has a two-week season there each year. Other recent performers have been the Ballet Hispanico of New York and the Fred Benjamin Dance Company. Dance concerts are held from November through May.

What it's like: The Henry Street Settlement was founded at the turn of the century to serve newly arrived immigrants living on the Lower East Side of Manhattan. It has been a social and cultural center for the community since that time. The theatre, located around the corner from the Settlement House, was built in 1915, and it first became known as the Neighborhood Playhouse, from which many renowned actors and playwrights emerged. The Playhouse hosted appearances by Isadora Duncan, Sarah Bernhardt, and Eleanore Duse. It was also there that composer Louis Horst—mentor to Martha Graham, Ted Shawn, and Alwin Nikolais—first taught his famous course in dance composition and its relation to musical structure, called "Pre-Classic Dance Forms."

After the Henry Street Settlement acquired the theatre in 1927, its name was changed to the Henry Street Settlement Playhouse. In 1948 Alwin Nikolais came to head up and revitalize the lagging dance program. He set up a children's dance theatre, for which some of his first important pieces were created, such as the "Lobster Quadrille." Nikolais' present company and school grew out of this, and during the next twenty years many of his finest works were premiered at the Henry Street Playhouse. His lead dancers, Murray Louis and Phyllis Lamhut, also launched their choreographic careers there. Among other things, Nikolais was a technological wizard, who pioneered in the use of elaborate props and lighting design. Not surprisingly, then, the Playhouse has an excellent lighting system. It seats 350 in the orchestra and balcony, but its only drawback is a tiny stage which can accommodate only eight to ten dancers at most. Refreshments are served occasionally.

Tickets: Tickets range from $1.00 to $3.50, with students and senior citizens paying the lowest rates. TDF vouchers are accepted. There are no subscriptions or advance sales. However, phone reservations are taken.

Getting there: Take an IND "D" train to Grand Street; or an IND "F" train to Delancey Street or East Broadway.

HUNTER COLLEGE STUDIO THEATRE

930 Lexington Avenue
New York, New York 10021
(212-570-5434)

Type of dance presented: Primarily young modern companies. Artists who have performed there recently include Emery Hermans, Albert Reid and Dancers, Gale Armiston and Company, Jan Van Dyke and Dancers, Bruce King, and Joan Miller's Dance Players. Performances are usually held two nights a month, September through May. It you wish to be notified of upcoming concerts, ask to be put on the mailing list.

What it's like: The Hunter College Studio Theatre was originally used for student performances, but now hosts a professional dance series which is run independently of the college's dance program. The theatre offers small local and out-of-town companies the opportunity to premiere new pieces in New York City in a large, well-equipped performance space at minimum cost. Also unusual for this informal type of setup, the theatre is located in a rather posh part of town. The performing space has been recently refurbished with a new floor and improved lighting and sound equipment. Chairs placed on risers seat seventy-five people. There are no refreshments.

Tickets: Tickets are $3 to $4 for general admission; $2 for students and senior citizens. TDF vouchers are accepted. There are no subscriptions, reservations, or advance sales at this time.

Getting there: The Hunter College Studio Theatre is located on Lexington Avenue between 68th and 69th streets. Take the Lexington Avenue IRT local train and get off at the 68th Street, Hunter College stop.

JAPAN HOUSE
333 East 47th Street
New York, New York 10017
(212-371-4758)

Type of dance presented: Classical Japanese and American modern dance based on Japanese themes. Groups that have performed here in recent months include the Asakawalker Dance Company, Mariko Sanjo and Company, and Saeko Ichinohe and Company. Performances are held September through May.

What it's like: The Japan Society, which inhabits Japan House, was established in 1907 to strengthen the bonds between Japan and the United States. In keeping with this objective, it has been particularly interested in introducing Japanese art and culture to the American public. The building, designed by Tokyo architect Junzo Yoshimura, blends Japanese design motifs with American construction materials. Since 1970 the well-equipped Japan House theatre has been offering dance, music, theatre, and puppetry performances. It has a proscenium stage and provides a clear view of performers from virtually any one of the 279 seats in the house. No refreshments.

Tickets: Ticket prices range from $3.50 to $5.50. There are no subscriptions, advance sales, or reservations. TDF vouchers are accepted.

Getting there: Japan House is on 47th Street between First and Second avenues. The nearest subway stop is 51st Street on the Lexington Avenue IRT local; from there it's four blocks south and two and a half blocks east.

JUDSON MEMORIAL CHURCH

55 Washington Square South
New York, New York 10012
(212-477-0351)

Type of dance presented: Modern and experimental. The most recent performers have been Elaine Summers, Rudy Perez, Dan Wagoner, and the late Katherine Litz. In 1977, the Judson presented a memorial concert of James Waring's works, many of which had been premiered at the church.

What it's like: Designed by Stanford White in an Italian Renaissance style, the Judson Church has had a long history of social service and political activism. But it wasn't until the early 1960s that Reverend Al Carmines invited avant-garde dancers, theatre groups, and musicians to perform there. Carmines, a musician and actor, appeared in and composed music for several productions himself. Throughout the 1960s the Judson was a haven for experimental modern dancers. It all began when Robert Dunn's movement composition class outgrew its space at the Merce Cunningham Studio and relocated at the Judson. Out of his workshop came the Judson Dance Theatre, a cooperative of young dancers, artists, musicians, and theatre people who changed the face of American modern dance. Among those whose early works were shown at the church were: Yvonne Rainer, Viola Farber, Steve Paxton, Kenneth King, Meredith Monk, Toby Armour, Alex Hay, Lucinda Childs, and Nancy Lewis. Dance performances at the Judson have tapered off considerably in the 1970s because the floor is faulty and many informal, nonproscenium spaces have become available in the last few years. The "stage" is the worship space with the pews removed, complete with marble walls and pillars and marvelous stained glass. Folding chairs accommodate 150 people. Free coffee is often served at intermission.

Tickets: The price of admission is usually \$3.50 to \$4. There are no subscriptions, reservations, or advance sales. TDF vouchers are accepted.

Getting there: The Judson Church is located on Washington Square, off Thompson Street in Greenwich Village. Take the Seventh Avenue IRT local train to Christopher Street, Sheridan Square, and walk east on West Fourth Street; or take an IND train to the West Fourth Street station.

KAUFMAN CONCERT HALL

92nd Street YM-YWHA
1395 Lexington Avenue (at 92nd Street)
New York, New York 10028
(212-427-4410)

Type of dance presented: Mostly modern. Artists who have recently appeared there include Pearl Lang and Dance Company, the Greenhouse

Dance Ensemble (an offshoot of the Erick Hawkins Dance Company), and the Don Redlich Dance Company. Performances take place between September and June, but follow no regular schedule.

What it's like: The 92nd Street YM-YWHA has been a modern dance stronghold for nearly a half a century. During the 1930s and 1940s, under the direction of Dr. William Kolodny, dance, poetry, and music thrived there. Kaufman Concert Hall became one of the few established theatres where young choreographers could be reviewed by the New York critics without the backbreaking expense of putting on a Broadway season. Doris Humphrey was director of the dance division for several years starting in 1946. Through the 1950s concerts were held at Kaufman several nights a week. Many important works were premiered on its stage, including those of Martha Graham, Charles Weidman, Doris Humphrey, José Limón, Sybil Shearer, Donald McKayle, Anna Sokolow, and Alvin Ailey. By the mid-1950s, however, the "Y" was so deluged with requests from artists wishing to rent the hall that it began screening performers stringently. Kolodny's time became divided between his duties at 92nd Street and his work establishing a concert series at the Metropolitan Museum of Art. As a result dance performances at Kaufman dwindled and new choreographers were forced to find other showcases for their pieces. Probably another factor that contributed to the slowdown in dance activity was the theatre's size, considered to be too

The Judson Church was a hotbed of avant-garde dance in the 1960s.
Frank Gimpaya

large for most of today's small dance companies but not large enough for the big ones.

Nonetheless, there are signs of a cultural renaissance at the 92nd Street "Y." Under Omus Hirshbein, who took over as educational director in 1973, Kaufman is once more an active music hall. The José Limón Dance Company was based at the "Y" from 1975 to 1978, and at present the Don Redlich Dance Company is in residence there, teaching classes as well as performing.

The Kaufman Concert Hall is a handsome, wood-paneled stage theatre which seats 916. Two years ago the house was refurbished with new seating and lighting but its original grace and simplicity have been preserved. At intermission, coffee, soda, and cookies are sold.

Tickets: Tickets for concerts produced by the "Y" usually cost $4.00 to $6.50. Companies who rent the space for performances may charge up to $7.50 for seats. TDF vouchers are accepted. Students and senior citizens can get half-price tickets in advance or on the day of the performance; however, no tickets are sold for less than $3.00. There are advance sales and phone reservations through CHARGIT (212-239-7177).

Getting there: The closest subway stop is at Lexington Avenue and 96th Street on the Lexington Avenue IRT (Number 6) local.

Crowd watchers perch along the fountain at Lincoln Center plaza. The Metropolitan Opera House shimmers behind. ***Frank Gimpaya***

MARYMOUNT MANHATTAN THEATRE

Marymount Manhattan College
221 East 71st Street
New York, New York 10021
(212-472-3800)

Type of dance presented: Mostly modern, some ballet. Recent performances have featured the Tricia Brown Company, the Frances Alenikoff Dance Theatre Company, Saeko Ichinohe and Company, Charles Moore Dances and Drums of Africa, the Carol Conway Dance Company, Nimbus, the Solaris Dance Theatre, Gus Solomons, Jr., and Kazuko Hirabayashi, among others. At least six dance concerts are held each year from September through May.

What it's like: The steeply raked seats, small stage, and rich modern décor give performances at the Marymount Manhattan Theatre a jewel-like quality. The seating capacity is 250. It is altogether a comfortable concert hall in a pleasant part of town.

Tickets: Ticket prices average about $5.00. TDF vouchers are accepted, and there are discounts for students and senior citizens. No subscriptions, but there are advance sales and reservations are taken over the phone.

Getting there: The Marymount Manhattan Theatre is on 71st Street between Second and Third avenues. The nearest subway stop is at 68th Street on the Lexington Avenue IRT (Number 6) local train.

METROPOLITAN OPERA HOUSE

Lincoln Center
Broadway at 64th Street
New York, New York 10023
(212-799-4420)

Type of dance presented: The American Ballet Theatre is the company in residence at the Metropolitan Opera House. It has a two-week fall season as well as an extended spring season from April through June. In summer, the Met presents international dance attractions, most recently, the Stuttgart Ballet, the National Ballet of Cuba with Alicia Alonso, the National Ballet of Canada with Rudolf Nureyev, the London Festival Ballet, and the Performing Arts Ensemble of the People's Republic of China.

What it's like: From the Chagall murals and red velvet seats to the crystal chandeliers and marble drinking fountains dedicated to Ezio Pinza, the Met is an elegant house. Built in 1966, it has a mammoth stage and it seats nearly 4000 people. Five balcony levels tower above the orchestra. Bring opera glasses if you plan to sit in the high tiers. The sightlines are good, but you'll be very far away from the stage. American

Ballet Theatre operates a gift boutique during intermission. Refreshments include champagne, cocktails, Perrier, coffee, soft drinks, and Danish pastry. While waiting for the next act, it's nice to buy a glass of champagne and wander through the downstairs portrait gallery of legendary opera stars.

Tickets: Ticket prices vary according to the company performing. Seats for American Ballet Theatre range from $6 to $25. There are no discounts, but standing room tickets are sold on the day of the performance at $4. Subscriptions and group sales are available through the individual dance companies. Tickets may be purchased in advance by mail order, at the box office, and over the phone with major credit cards through CHARGIT (212-239-7177)

Getting there: Take the Seventh Avenue IRT local subway to the 66th Street, Lincoln Center station. The Number 104 Broadway bus also stops nearby.

MINOR LATHAM PLAYHOUSE/DANCE UPTOWN

Columbia University
230 Milbank Hall
New York, New York 10027
(212-280-2079)

Type of dance presented: Modern and experimental. In recent years the companies of Twyla Tharp, Viola Farber, Gus Solomons, Jr., James Cunningham, and the Dance Theatre of Harlem have performed there. Faculty and senior student recitals are given in the spring.

What it's like: Dance Uptown was created twelve years ago to showcase Barnard College's promising young dancers and choreographers, many of whom have become well known dance figures: Twyla Tharp, Sara Rudner, Hannah Kahn, Carol-Rae Kraus and Tobi Tobias, among others. Performances are held most frequently at the Minor Latham Playhouse; however, the Barnard gymnasium and Columbia's Earl Hall are also used on occasion. The Playhouse is a small proscenium stage theatre that accommodates 180 people and, though somewhat worn, is well suited to presenting chamber size dance groups. No refreshments are served.

Tickets: Tickets are either free (in the case of CETA artist performances), or less than $5.00. TDF vouchers are accepted, and there are Columbia student discounts. No advance sales, but occasionally reservations are taken by phone.

Getting there: The Minor Latham Playhouse is at Broadway and 120th Street. Take the Seventh Avenue IRT local train (Number 1) to 116th Street, or the Number 104 bus, which travels up and down Broadway.

New York State Theatre. ***Frank Gimpaya***

NEW YORK STATE THEATRE
Lincoln Center
Broadway at 64th Street
New York, New York 10023
(212-877-4727)

Type of dance presented: Ballet. The New York City Ballet performs at the New York State Theatre from November to February, and from May to July. Other companies, such as the Bolshoi Ballet, the Berlin Opera Ballet, and the National Ballet of Canada, make guests appearances in July and August.

What it's like: The New York City Ballet has been based at the State Theatre since the building's grand opening in 1964. Its ultramodern design makes an apt setting for George Balanchine's sleek, contemporary ballets. Two huge female statues by Elie Nadelman, nineteen feet high and twelve tons each, stand at the first balcony level. On the upper floors the windows facing the fountain in Lincoln Center plaza are covered with beaded curtains that twinkle from the lights in the promenade below. The glass chandeliers resemble clusters of giant rhinestones. Though the New York State Theatre is less formal than the Metropolitan Opera House, it is equally well endowed. It seats 2729 and has standing room as well. Sightlines are fine everywhere, but it is sometimes irksome to sit in the extremely wide center orchestra section because there is no center aisle. Leaving and returning to your seat is a big project. Refreshments include champagne, cocktails, Perrier, coffee, soft drinks, and pastry. During intermission, the New York City Ballet Guild runs a souvenir boutique which benefits the New York City Ballet.

Tickets: Prices range from $3.00 to $20.00. Standing room tickets, sold on the day of the performance, cost $2.50. As at the Met, there are no discounts. Subscriptions and group sales are available through the New York City Ballet. Advance tickets can be purchased by mail order, at the box office, and over the phone with major credit cards through CHARGIT (212-239-7177).

Getting there: Take the Seventh Avenue IRT local subway to the 66th Street, Lincoln Center station; or the Number 104 bus on Broadway to 65th Street.

NEW YORK UNIVERSITY (NYU)

- Eisner and Lubin Auditorium
  566 LaGuardia Place
  New York, New York 10011
  (212-598-2027)
- School of Education, Health, Nursing and Arts Professions (S.E.H.N.A.P.) Theatre
  17 East 4th Street
  New York, New York 10003
  (212-598-3232)
- School of the Arts
  Fifth Floor Theatre and Studio II
  111 Second Avenue
  New York, New York 10003
  (212-598-2401)

Type of dance presented: With two full-time programs in dance—one at the School of the Arts and another at the School of Education—New York University is the center of a lot of concert activity. Three university theatres produce both professional and student modern dance programs; ballet, ethnic dance, and mime are also presented occasionally. At the Eisner and Lubin Auditorium, recent performers have been the People/Dorothy Vislocky Dance Theatre; the Marjorie Gamso Dance Company; Carol Hess—Tap Dances, Rags, and Jazz; and Claudia Gitelman and Helen Kent. Nancy Meehan, Alain Germain, David Hatch Walker, and Balasara Swati have appeared at the S.E.H.N.A.P. Theatre. The School of the Arts primarily offers student performances, but often features the choreography of faculty members such as Rachel Lampert, Bertram Ross, Stuart Hodes, and Deborah Jowitt (the dance critic for the ***Village Voice***). Most concerts take place at the Fifth

Floor Theatre during the academic year. The School of the Arts will be happy to put you on their mailing list if you wish to receive advance notice of events.

What it's like: The Eisner and Lubin Auditorium, built in 1959, is the largest of the NYU theatres and looks like a typical school auditorium. It has a proscenium stage, a balcony level, and seats 800. The more intimate S.E.H.N.A.P. Theatre is a 365-seat hall in art deco style, also with a proscenium stage. The School of the Arts has two nonproscenium performing spaces. The Fifth Floor Theatre is a formally equipped theatre space with permanent blocks of seating (chairs on risers) for up to 150 people. Studio II is more flexible and informal. Seats can be arranged in the round or proscenium fashion to accommodate seventy-five people. Occasionally refreshments are served at S.E.H.N.A.P. concerts, and complimentary wine is sometimes served at the School of the Arts.

Tickets: At the Eisner and Lubin Auditorium tickets range from $ .50 to $5.00. There are no subscriptions, reservations, or advance sales. Tickets cost $3 to $5 on average at the S.E. H.N.A.P. Theatre. There are advance sales and phone reservations. Both theatres accept TDF vouchers and offer student and senior citizen discounts. Admission is always free at the School of the Arts. Phone reservations are accepted.

Getting there: The Eisner and Lubin Auditorium is located off Washington Square, across from the NYU Library, between the south side of Washington Square Park and Third Street. It and the S.E.H.N.A.P. Theatre are closest to the IND subway stop at West 4th Street. The School of the Arts is at Second Avenue between 6th and 7th streets. It is nearest the Astor Place stop on the Lexington Avenue IRT subway line, or the 8th Street stop on the"RR"train of the BMT line.

RADIO CITY MUSIC HALL ENTERTAINMENT CENTER
1260 Avenue of the Americas
New York, New York 10020
(212-246-4600)

Type of dance presented: Musical theatre. Three different ninety-minute stage shows are offered during the Christmas, spring, and summer seasons. These variety extravaganzas feature the famous Radio City Rockettes, a high-kicking precision tap dance ensemble, along with a large cast of other dancers, singers, and actors, and a forty-two piece orchestra. There are matinee and evening performances six days a week. Full-length Broadway-style musicals, such as the recent ***Snow White and the Seven Dwarfs***, are also presented throughout the year, as well as film showings (a retrospective of Hollywood musicals was screened this fall, including such classics as ***Singin' in the Rain, Seven Brides for Seven Brothers,*** and ***Cabaret).***

The world famous Radio City Music Hall Rockettes, the last surviving precision tap dance team. ***courtesy of Radio City Music Hall***

What it's like: Radio City Music Hall, which possesses one of the world's largest stages and indoor motion picture projection facilities, was opened by Roxy Rothafel on December 27, 1932. It soon became a celebrated theatre for motion pictures and lavish stage shows. For generations of New Yorkers a family outing to Radio City was as much a part of celebrating the Christmas holidays as visiting Santa Claus at Macy's or ice skating at Rockefeller Center. When, in 1976, financial troubles loomed and it looked as if this magnificent art deco entertainment palace would be abandoned to the wrecking crews, many people took it as a personal loss. In the spring of 1979, following an eleventh hour declaration of the Music Hall as an historical landmark, the building's interior underwent a massive restoration. At that time Robert F. Jani, a former executive at Walt Disney Productions and head of the newly formed Radio City Music Hall Productions, also announced plans to restore the hall's prior status as the largest broad-based family entertainment center in the world.

Radio City's exterior is made of ripple-finished gray Indiana limestone. Three circular plaques of metal and enamel depict the spirits of song, drama, and dance. The most striking feature of the theatre auditorium, which seats 5981 and has a 24-karat gold ceiling, is an immense proscenium arch. Its semicircular design is repeated throughout the entire auditorium. The walls and ceiling meet in a series of graduated arches that create a sunrise effect. The stage equipment and special effects machinery, which can produce an instant rainstorm or raise the performers thirteen feet high, are said to be among the best anywhere.

The thirty-nine member Rockettes have been a featured attraction at Radio City Music Hall since its inception. The group dates back to 1925, an era when synchronized dance teams and glamorous chorus lines à la Ziegfeld's Follies were the rage. They made their debut in St. Louis as the Missouri Rockets, but assumed their present name with the opening of Radio City. Until 1975 the Rockettes rarely appeared outside their home (they did perform in Paris in 1937, at the behest of the French government, for which they were awarded the Grand Prix of the Republic). Recently they have begun to tour the country during the off-season.

Tickets: For the Christmas, spring, and summer stage shows general admission is $7.50 and reserved seats (first mezzanine only) are $10.50. There are advanced sales, and phone reservations are taken through CHARGIT (212-239-7177) and Ticketron (212-977-9020). The only discounts offered are through group sales to parties of twenty-five or more (for information call 212-541-9436). Other musical productions, concerts, and film events are priced separately.

Getting there: Radio City Music Hall is located at Rockefeller Center on 50th Street between Fifth and Sixth avenues. The IND subway goes directly there (take the "D" train to the 50th Street, Rockefeller Center stop). Or you can take the Seventh Avenue IRT local train to 50th Street and walk east.

ROUNDABOUT STAGE ONE
33 West 23rd Street
New York, New York, 10011
(212-924-7161)

Type of dance presented: Modern, ballet and ethnic. The theatre has hosted the companies of Merce Cunningham, Lar Lubovitch, Paul Sanasardo, and Joyce Trisler, as well as Dennis Wayne's Dancers and the Mariano Parra Spanish Dance Company.

What it's like: The Roundabout Stage One is a converted movie house and the off-Broadway home of the Roundabout Theatre Company. Its excellent oversized stage and close seating arrangement give one a feeling of both space and intimacy. The theatre accommodates 352 people comfortably. All seats are good. Soda, coffee, cookies, and doughnuts are sold at intermission in their cozy lounge area.

Tickets: Prices are usually $6.95 or $7.95. TDF vouchers are accepted upon the discretion of the performing company. Student and senior citizen discounts are frequently offered. There are no subscriptions, but there are advance sales and phone reservations. The box office honors all major credit cards.

Getting there: The Roundabout Stage One is located in the heart of Chelsea, close to the notorious Chelsea Hotel. It's on the north side of 23rd Street, between Eighth and Ninth avenues. Both the Seventh Avenue IRT and the Eighth Avenue IND local trains stop nearby at 23rd Street.

ST. MARK'S CHURCH IN-THE-BOWERY

Danspace
10th Street at Second Avenue
New York, New York 10003
(212-674-6377)

Type of dance presented: Modern and experimental. Artists who have performed there include Merce Cunningham, Meredith Monk, Barbara Dilley, Kenneth King, Steve Paxton, Barbara Roan, Bill Dunas, Sara Rudner, and Becky Arnold.

What it's like: The oldest continuously used worship space in New York City, St. Mark's Church in-the-Bowery has long been known for its innovative arts and community service programs. Isadora Duncan danced in the church's sacristy years ago. Approximately two thousand people participate each week in its poetry, dance, theatre, and art workshops. It also sponsors a Lower East Side historical documentation project and a community youth employment program. In the summer of 1978 historic St. Mark's Church was badly damaged by a tragic fire. Reconstruction is under way, but it is not known how long it will take to be completed. In the meantime, the Danspace series has set up temporary headquarters across the street at the Third Street Music School, 235 East 11th Street. The school's auditorium, where dance performances are held, is an amphitheatre in the round, seating 250 on red-carpeted risers. It is an interesting hall for soloists and small groups, but doesn't compare with the original St. Mark's Danspace, which is tailor-made for dance. No refreshments are served.

Tickets: Dance performances are free, but a contribution of $3 for adults is suggested. TDF vouchers are accepted. There are no phone reservations.

Getting there: Both the St. Mark's Church and the Third Street Music School are closest to the Lexington Avenue IRT subway stop at 14th Street and Union Square, or the 8th Street stop on the "RR" local train of the BMT line.

THEATRE OF THE OPEN EYE

Church of the Holy Trinity
316 East 88th Street
New York, New York 10028
(212-534-6363)

Type of dance presented: Modern and ethnic. Recent performers have been Ari Darom (Indian temple dance), Ritha Devi, Mary Averett Seelye, the Contemporary Chamber Dance Group, the Matteo Ethnoamerican Dance Theatre, the Facets Dance Company, and the Dancers of the Open Eye. The theatre has also presented a revival of choreographer Jean Erdman's award-winning musical production, ***The Coach with the Six Insides***, based on James Joyce's ***Finnegan's Wake.*** Concerts are held from September to June.

What it's like: The lovely brick Church of the Holy Trinity, which houses the Theatre of the Open Eye, is over a century old. As you enter its gates, there is a courtyard and gardens on the way to the theatre. The Open Eye is also the name of the repertory company of dancers, actors, musicians, and puppeteers based there. The theare, which is under the artistic direction of Jean Erdman, is a loft-type space, with a small but handsome floor, miniature wings, and more than adequate lighting and sound system. The audience sits at close range on folding chairs atop risers, which accommodate about 150. There are comfortably wide aisles.

Tickets: Prices range from $3 to $5. TDF vouchers are accepted. Sometimes student and senior citizen discounts are available. Advance tickets are sold for Dancers of the Open Eye performances. Reservations may be made by telephone.

Getting there: The Theatre of the Open Eye is on 88th Street between First and Second avenues. The closest subway stop is 86th Street on the Lexington Avenue IRT line. You can also take the Number 15 bus to 88th Street (it runs uptown on First Avenue and downtown on Second Avenue).

THEATRE OF THE RIVERSIDE CHURCH

Riverside Dance Festival
490 Riverside Drive (121st Street)
New York, New York 10027
(212-864-2929)

Type of dance presented: Primarily modern, but also ballet, tap, jazz, and ethnic. Companies recently presented have included the Kazuko Hirabayashi Dance Theatre, the Pepsi Bethel Authentic Jazz Dance Theatre, the Isadora Duncan Centenary Dance Company, the Theatre Dance Collection the Orlando

Ballet, the Phyllis Lamhut Dance Company, the Sophie Maslow Dance Company, the Solomons Company/Dance, the Pearl Primus Dance Company, the Multigravitational Aerodance Group, the Jerry Ames Tap Dance Company, Tandy Beal and Company, and the Phoebe Neville Dance Company. The Riverside Theatre Dance Festival takes place Thursdays through Sundays, January through July.

What it's like: Riverside Church, with its fine Gothic detail, is perhaps best known for housing the world's largest carillon—seventy-four bells—in its 400-foot tower. The carillon was built by philanthropist John D. Rockefeller III in honor of his mother, for the aural delight of the residents of the surrounding Morningside Heights community. The church established this very successful dance series four years ago with its own funds and support from the National Endowment for the Arts; it had already been producing plays and musicals. The aim of the Festival is to present a diversity of artists from New York City and elsewhere. Over thirty dance companies will have appeared there this year alone. The dancers perform, not in a cleared worship space, but a fully equipped proscenium theatre which seats 250. Conjointly with performances, the Riverside Festival sometimes sponsors master dance classes open to the public. Refreshments are available at some performances.

Tickets: Tickets usually cost $4.50. Subscriptions are available at lower prices. TDF vouchers are accepted, and there are student and senior citizen discounts. Reservations are taken by telephone.

Getting there: Riverside Church is on Riverside Drive between 120th and 122nd streets, two blocks west of Broadway. Take the Seventh Avenue IRT local train to 116th Street, the Number 104 bus on Broadway to 120th Street, or the Number 5 bus along Riverside Drive to 120th Street.

THEATRE OF ST. CLEMENT'S CHURCH

423 West 46th Street
New York, New York 10036
(212-246-7277 or 246-7278)

Type of dance presented: Small modern dance companies and solo performers. Recent concerts have featured Daniel Nagrin, the Elizabeth Keen Dance Company, the Marcus Shulkind Dance Company, Rosalind Newman and Dancers, and Linda Tarnay. Performances are held sporadically throughout the year.

What it's like: The nineteenth-century St. Clement's Church was the home of the American Place Theatre until 1970, and it is still used to premier off-Broadway plays. The theatre began producing dance in 1971. The performing area is the worship space with its thirty-six-foot high ceiling and exposed brick walls. The pews are removed and comfortable seating on risers is brought in to accommodate 160 people. (The farthest seat from the stage is twenty feet away and twelve feet high.) Stained glass windows glow with the light from the street once the house is dark. Concerts are informal, with dancers often coming out to meet the audience after the show. There are usually no refreshments.

Tickets: Prices range from $3 to $5. TDF vouchers are almost always accepted, but it is up to the performing group. The same goes for student and senior citizen discounts. There are no subscriptions or advance sales, but you can make reservations by phone.

Getting there: St. Clement's Church is located just west of the Times Square theatre district, on 46th Street right off Ninth Avenue (between Ninth and Tenth avenues). Take the Seventh Avenue IRT or BMT subway to Times Square. Walk uptown on Broadway to 46th Street, then west on 46th Street until you reach the church. Most of the journey on 46th Street is along well-lit blocks lined with the expensive eateries of Manhattan's "Restaurant Row."

WASHINGTON SQUARE METHODIST CHURCH

133 West 4th Street
New York, New York 10012
(212-777-2528)

Type of dance presented: Primarily modern. The Phoebe Neville Dance Company, Kei Takei's Moving Earth, the Manuel Alum Dance Company, the Laura Foreman Dance Theatre, Margaret Beals, and Claudia Gittleman have performed there in recent years.

What it's like: The church opened its worship space to the community ten years ago, and dance concerts have been presented since that time. Seating, for 75 to 100 people, is arranged very close to the dancers. Although the performance area itself is intimate and informal, it has an imposing setting—a 40-foot vaulted ceiling, huge stained glass windows and a large gold and brass organ. Refreshments are offered occasionally.

Tickets: Tickets range from $3.00 to $4.50, but prices are determined by the individual dance company. There are no subscriptions, reservations, or advance sales. TDF vouchers are accepted, and the church encourages companies to offer student and senior citizen discounts.

Getting there: The Washington Square Methodist Church is located between Sixth Avenue and MacDougal Street in Washington Square, the heart of Greenwich Village. Take the Seventh Avenue IRT local train to the Christopher Street/Sheridan Square stop, or an IND subway to West 4th Street.

Museums in New York

by Fred W. McDarrah

Have you ever been to Wave Hill Center, the American Museum of Immigration, the New York Historical Society, or the Hall of Science?

Have you voyaged to the past at South Street Seaport, or rocketed through the universe at the Hayden Planetarium?

If you've never ventured beyond the Metropolitan Museum of Art or the Museum of Modern Art, get set for some extraordinary adventures throughout the five boroughs of New York City. With *Museums in New York* as your companion, you'll discover 82 great institutions—art museums, local history museums, science museums, botanical and zoological parks, commercial collections, and historic houses and mansions.

From the largest museums, libraries, and zoos, to the tiny out-of-the-way community museums in storefronts and lofts, *Museums in New York* provides everything you need to know about each place: descriptions of major attractions; travel directions; days and hours open; restaurant and gift shop hints; special events; membership information, and more.

More than 200 photographs give you a tantalizing taste of what you can find in the Big Apple. You'll discover a world of entertainment and enlightenment, including Dutch artifacts, Greek icons, Tibetan tankas, Eskimo totem poles, Japanese bonsai trees, California pottery—even moon rocks.

Museums in New York is the book for New Yorkers, permanent residents and week-end visitors alike.

33 West 60th Street
quick fox
New York 10023 (212) 246 0325

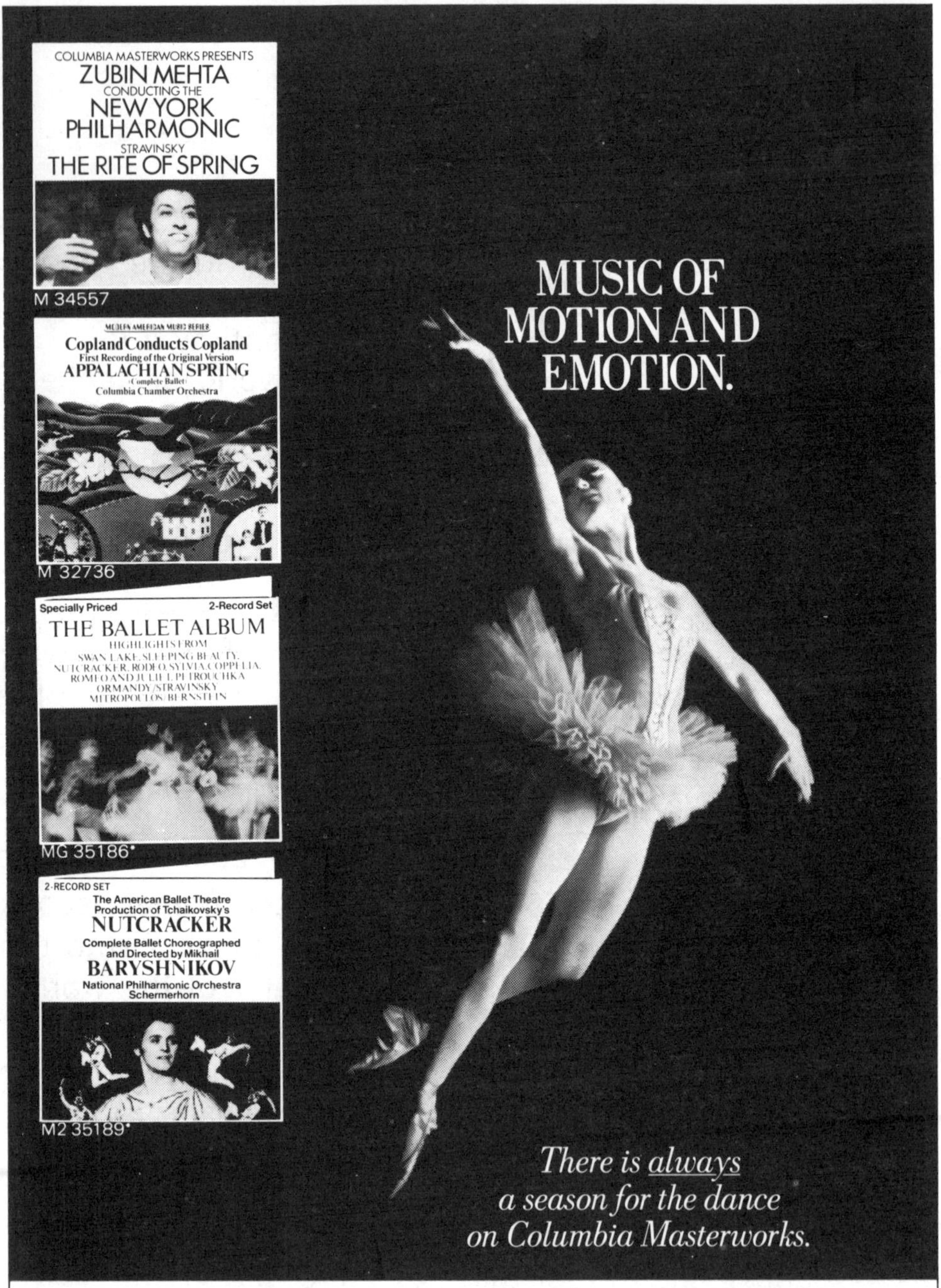

Bartok
The Miraculous Mandarin (Boulez) M 31368

Bernstein
Fancy Free; Candide; On the Town (Bernstein) MS 6677*

Chopin
Les Sylphides (Ormandy) M 31845

Copland
The Copland Album—Includes Billy the Kid; Rodeo; Appalachian Spring (Copland) D3M 33720*

Debussy
The Afternoon of a Faun (Barenboim) M 34500

Dukas
La Peri M 34201

Stravinsky
Apollo; Orpheus (Stravinsky) MS 6646*
Firebird (Complete) (Stravinsky) MS 6328*
Petroushka (Complete) (Stravinsky) MS 6332*
Pulcinella Suite (Boulez) M 35105

Tchaikovsky
Aurora's Wedding (Stokowski) M 34560
The Tchaikovsky Ballet Album (Ormandy) MG 30297*
Excerpts from Swan Lake, Sleeping Beauty (Ormandy) M 31838

Ravel
Daphnis et Chloé (Complete) (Boulez) M 33523

A loft concert at The Kitchen. ***Babette Mangolte, courtesy of The Kitchen Center***

Lofts

Loft theatres started cropping up in the 1960s, when experimental modern dancers were looking for alternative performing spaces to the traditional proscenium stage. Most of them are located in Soho, the area south of Houston Street in lower Manhattan which used to be the main garment-manufacturing district of New York. Attracted by the large, unpartitioned interior spaces, high ceilings, huge windows, skylights, and low rents, growing numbers of artists, musicians, and dancers began moving into industrial lofts. They converted the spaces into living quarters and studios, where they rehearsed, gave classes, and performed.

Performing in lofts enabled choreographers to produce their own concerts inexpensively. It gave them the artistic freedom to do what they wished, and to try out new works in a relaxed setting away from the critics and the pressures of a formal "New York season." Kenneth King, Yvonne Rainer, Simone Forti, Twyla Tharp, Robert Wilson, Cliff Keuter, Meredith Monk, Laura Dean, Emily Frankel, Bill Dunas, Rachel Lampert, and Margaret Beals are just some of the established artists whose work got started in lofts and who like to return to that setting from time to time.

But loft concerts are definitely for adventurous dancegoers —people who don't mind roughing it a bit on the chance that they'll see a Tharp or Cunningham in the making, or catch the performance of a lifetime by an artist on his or her home turf. "Betty Ford doesn't come to loft dance performances," quips Michelle Berne, cofounder of the Loftdance Festival.* Many times it's pot luck: You'll see some of the best new work and some of the worst.

For the most part, loft concerts are no-frills affairs, just a straightforward presentation of the choreography. Dancers perform in an open space with no wings and just a bare wall for a backdrop. Costumes are kept simple and lighting is minimal. Little or no stage makeup is worn. But this isn't as untheatrical as it sounds, because the dances are designed to look good in an understated setting. In most lofts, audience seating is limited to fifty to seventy-five people. It may be on bleachers, folding chairs, or pillows on the floor. You may also be asked to remove your shoes to protect the dance floor. The viewers sit close to each other and to the dancers.

Frequently this makes for a better show. The performers

*From "Imagine Strange Events: You'll Find Them Here," by Mark Deitch in ***The New York Times,*** October 2, 1977. Two years ago dancers Michelle Berne and Kevan Cleary got together and founded the Loftdance Festival to focus public attention on the burst of creative activity taking place in Soho lofts. Thus far the festival's primary function has been to publicize concerts, but occasionally it sponsors workshops, such as the one given recently on economic survival for dancers.

are looser and more relaxed. Many dancers prefer the intimacy of a loft theatre to working on a proscenium stage, because they don't have to "sell" the movement across rows and rows of darkness and can perform with more subtlety and nuance. In some respects, the close viewing range is more of a challenge too, since any faltering or tenseness is painfully apparent to the audience. Whereas a proscenium stage frames the dancers and sets them heroically apart, loft performers are seen in a more human light, sweating and breathing heavily at times. There is an exciting give-and-take between audience and dancers that you don't get anywhere else. All contribute to the energy and chemistry of the event.

At these concerts you'll usually find a congenial mixture of devotees, other dancers, and friends of the performers. They are one of the few places in New York where striking up a conversation with your neighbor seems perfectly natural. Often audience and dancers mingle over free coffee or wine after the show. Because many dance lofts are also living spaces, they have a homey atmosphere; there are comfortable stuffed chairs to sit in during intermission, overgrown house plants, and furry pets roaming around before curtain time. The low overhead means low admission prices. Tickets range from free to $4.00 and TDF vouchers are almost always accepted. Since becoming an enclave for artists, Soho has come to be populated with charming restaurants, shops, art galleries, and local bars. But loft theatres are often in out-of-the-way places that can be dangerous at night. If you're alone, try to attend daytime performances; otherwise, bring a friend.

The more active dance lofts are listed below. The Kitchen and Eden's Expressway are among the best established, and can generally be counted on for quality work. For further information on loft events, check the periodicals recommended in Chapter Four; or contact the Loftdance Festival, c/o Soho Performing Artists Association, 72 Wooster Street, New York, New York 10012 (212-260-7337).

Ambrose Arts Foundation
436 Broome Street
New York, New York 10002
(212-966-1704)

Appleby Studio Theatre
579 Broadway
New York, New York 10012
(212-431-8489)

Margaret Beals's Theatre-in-the-Loft
228 West Broadway
New York, New York 10013
(212-431-3869)

Trisha Brown Studio
541 Broadway
New York, New York 10012
(212-925-6031)

Eden's Expressway
537 Broadway
New York, New York 10012
(212-226-8988)

Greene Street Dance Studio
98 Greene Street
New York, New York 10012
(212-966-4731)

Interart Studio
14 West 23rd Street
New York, New York 10010
(212-242-0694)

The Kitchen
484 Broome Street
New York, New York 10012
(212-925-3615)

Performing Garage
33 Wooster Street
New York, New York 10012
(212-966-3651)

Perry Street Theatre
31 Perry Street
New York, New York 10014
(212-255-7190)

Truck and Warehouse Theatre
79 East 4th Street
New York, New York 10012
(212-228-8558)

Westbeth Theatre Center
151 Bank Street
New York, New York 10014
(212-691-2272)

Dance outdoors

CLARK CENTER DANCE FESTIVAL
The Mall, City University of New York
(CUNY) Graduate Center
33 West 42nd Street
New York, New York 10036
(212-246-4818)

Type of dance presented: Modern, jazz, ethnic, and experimental. The Pepsi Bethel Authenic Jazz Dance Theatre, the Matthew Diamond Dance Company, the Asian American Dance Theatre, the Theatre Dance Collection, the Fred Benjamin Dance Company, and Charles Moore Dances and Drums of Africa are some of the companies who have performed in this annual festival, held from late June through August. The New Choreographers concerts, which showcase the work of promising young artists, is a special feature of the series.

What it's like: Choreographer Alvin Ailey was one of the founders of the Clark Center Dance Festival, established twenty years ago under the auspices of the Clark Center Dance School. A good many companies got their start there over the years, including those of Ailey, Meredith Monk, George Faison, Cliff Keuter, and Diane McIntyre. The festival used to be held at the YM-YWCA at 52nd Street and Eighth Avenue, which was the old school headquarters; but in 1974 the building closed down, the school was relocated, and the summer concert series moved to its present site at the Graduate Center Mall. Although, technically speaking, the festival is held outdoors, the performing area is well protected from the elements, so weather is not a problem. The seating capacity is 238, and a platform stage is erected for concerts. No refreshments are served, but there are plenty of good coffee shops and restaurants in the midtown area.

Tickets: Tickets range from $2.50 to $4.50. TDF vouchers are accepted. Students and senior citizens can get the higher priced seats for $2.50. There are no subscriptions; however, there are advance sales and phone reservations.

Getting there: The CUNY Graduate Center is located on 42nd Street between Fifth and Sixth avenues, midway between the Times Square and Grand Central subway stations. It's right across from the Main Branch of the New York Public Library, and is easily accessible by all major subway lines. The Number 104 bus stops nearby.

COOPER-HEWITT MUSEUM

2 East 91st Street
New York, New York 10028
(212-860-6868)

Type of dance presented: Mostly modern. There have been recent appearances by Kenneth King, Dana Reitz, Nancy Lewis and Company, and David Woodberry and Company. Concerts are held on Tuesday evenings in the spring, summer, and fall.

What it's like: The Cooper-Hewitt Museum, the Smithsonian Institution's National Museum of Design, opened in 1976. Located in the stately Andrew Carnegie Mansion on upper Fifth Avenue, it houses one of the world's foremost collections of decorative art, including textiles, jewelry, drawings and prints, metalwork, ceramics, woodwork, wallpaper, glass, porcelain, and furniture. On Tuesday evenings, when the museum is free to the public, dance performances are presented in the garden area, weather permitting. The large garden of the Georgian mansion is lushly planted with wisteria, azaleas, rhododendron, ivy, chestnut and flowering trees. A platform is set up for most performances. Several hundred viewers can be accommodated, both seated and standing. No refreshments are served.

Tickets: Concerts are free. There are no phone reservations.

Getting there: The closest subway stop is at 86th Street on the Lexington Avenue IRT line, local and express trains. The museum is on Fifth Avenue, across the street from Central Park.

DANCEMOBILE

Harlem Cultural Council
1 West 125th Street
New York, New York 10027
(212-860-8640)
Emery Taylor, President
Sandra Fisher, Program Coordinator

Type of dance presented: Professional black and hispanic jazz, modern and ethnic dance companies. Recent performers have included the Alvin Ailey Repertory Ensemble, Ladji Camara Music and Dance Ensemble, Contemporary Chamber Dance Group, Pepsi Bethel Authentic Jazz Dance Company, Rod Rodgers Dance Company, International Afrikan American Ballet, Kariamu and Company, and the Chuck Davis Dance Company.

What it's like: Now entering its thirteenth year, the Dancemobile program is a traveling concert series, sponsored by the Harlem Cultural Council, which takes place during the months of July and August at various outdoor locations throughout the city. Performances are announced in advance in the local newspapers; or you can inquire about the program schedule at the above phone number. Those interested in having the Dancemobile come to their neighborhood should write to the above address. The Harlem Cultural Council also sponsors a year-round indoor concert series which formerly took place at the Harlem Performance Center. Until another permanent home can be found, it is being held at the Symphony Space on 95th Street and Broadway.

Tickets: All concerts are free, with unreserved seating.

LINCOLN CENTER OUT-OF-DOORS FESTIVAL

- Guggenheim Bandshell at Damrosch Park
- Fountain Plaza

Lincoln Center
Broadway at 64th Street
New York, New York 10023
(212-877-1800)

Type of dance presented: Mostly ethnic and modern. Recent performers at the Guggenheim Bandshell include the Pauline Koner Dance Consort, the Fred Benjamin Dance Company, Pearl Primus, and Middle Eastern dancer, Morocco. The Fountain Plaza has featured performances by Saeko Ichinohe and Company, Jean-Leon Destiné's Afro-Haitian Dance Company, the International Afrikan-American Ballet, and the Rod Rodgers Dance Company. This three-week series of dance, music, and drama events takes place, daytime and evenings, during August and September.

What it's like: At summer's end there may be a lull in dance activity inside the Lincoln Center theatres, but outside the fun is just starting. A platform stage is set up in the Bandshell at Damrosch Park, behind the Metropolitan Opera House at 62nd Street between Broadway and Amsterdam Avenues. Though folding chairs accommodate as many as 7600 people, get there early to claim a good seat; it's usually crowded. This goes for performances at Fountain Plaza too, where a temporary stage is also erected in front of the main buildings, and the seating capacity is 5000. The concerts, funded by Exxon, began in 1971. Daytime performances are ideal for children, since the entertainment often includes roving bands of jugglers, mimes, acrobats, and clowns. Refreshments are available at the outdoor cafe alongside Avery Fisher Hall. Street vendors abound, and across the street on Broadway and Columbus Avenue there is a row of delightful sidewalk cafes and restaurants that cater to the theatre crowd.

Tickets: All seats are free, on a first come, first served basis. The program schedule can be picked up in advance at the Lincoln Center information booth inside the Metropolitan

Opera House, as well as the Library of the Performing Arts. Programs are also listed in the entertainment calendars of the major New York newspapers and ***Cue*** magazine.

Getting there: Take the Seventh Avenue local subway to the 66th Street, Lincoln Center, stop; or the Number 104 Broadway bus.

NEW YORK DANCE FESTIVAL

Delacorte Theatre, Central Park
Entrance on Central Park West and 81st Street
New York, New York 10024
(212-535-5630)

Type of dance presented: Modern, ballet, ethnic, jazz, and tap. Recent attractions have included tap virtuosos Honi Coles and the Copasetics; Rebecca Wright of American Ballet Theatre; the Alvin Ailey Repertory Ensemble; Indrani and Sukanya; Dinizulu and His African Dancers, Drummers and Singers; Les Grands Ballet Canadiens; and the modern dance companies of Phyllis Lamhut, Lucinda Childs, Jennifer Muller, Lar Lubovitch, Barbara Roan, James Cunningham, Rachel Lampert, and Dan Wagoner, among others. Twenty-six companies are presented in twelve performances.

What it's like: The ten-day New York Dance Festival has been held in Central Park's open-air Delacorte Theatre every September since 1963. The comfortable 2300-seat theatre is set against a lovely natural backdrop under the stars. It has a sizable thrust stage that brings the dancers close to the audience. We'll never forget a breathtaking performance there of Eliot Feld's ballet, ***Intermezzo.*** A warm night breeze stirred the girls' skirts as they whirled and leaped and waltzed round and round in the arms of their partners. The dancers seemed to be caught and propelled through space by the lush strains of the Brahms piano music played live on stage. That kind of magic could only take place at the Delacorte.

The theatre's sightlines are good, but occasionally noise from passing airplanes drowns out the sound system. The New York Dance Festival's policy is to present diversified programs, and that it does. On a typical night you might see a lyrical ballet followed by a flamenco dance number and then an abstract modern piece set to atonal music.

When in doubt bring a sweater: the weather can turn unpredictably chilly. The show always goes on unless it's pouring out, in which case it is rescheduled. You can buy coffee, soft drinks, and snacks at the concession stand. And there are always several independent vendors selling the usual assortment of hot dogs, pretzels, ice cream, and soft drinks. Ethnic food and health snacks can also be found. But many people prefer to bring their own box supper and a bottle of wine, and pass the time before the show starts picnicking on the grounds. Unfortunately, the park is dangerous at night, so leave the concert with the crowds and stick to the main paths.

Tickets: The New York Dance Festival is free, coproduced by the Technical Assistance Group (TAG) and the New York Shakespeare Festival. Seating is on a first come, first served basis. The ticket line usually starts forming around 5:00 or 5:30 P.M. for the 8:00 show. Tickets are distributed at 6:15 P.M. (1:15 P.M. for matinees), one to a customer. You can't save a seat for someone who isn't waiting in line. If you arrive late you'll probably get in but have to take your chances on getting a good seat. The only way to reserve seats in advance is by making a $15 tax-deductible contribution to the Festival. For further information write to the Sponsor Department, New York Dance Festival, 463 West Street, New York, New York 10014; or call 212-691-3500.

Getting there: The Delacorte Theatre is located at Belvedere Lake in Central Park. Entrances and footpaths at Central Park West and 81st Street or Fifth Avenue and 79th Street lead directly to the theatre, if you follow the signs. To enter through the west side of the park, take the Seventh Avenue IRT local train to 79th Street and walk east to Central Park West. Or you can take the Eighth Avenue IND local train to 81st Street and Central Park West (also the stop for the Museum of Natural History).

An off-season look at Central Park's Delacorte Theatre.
Frank Gimpaya

Dance on Broadway

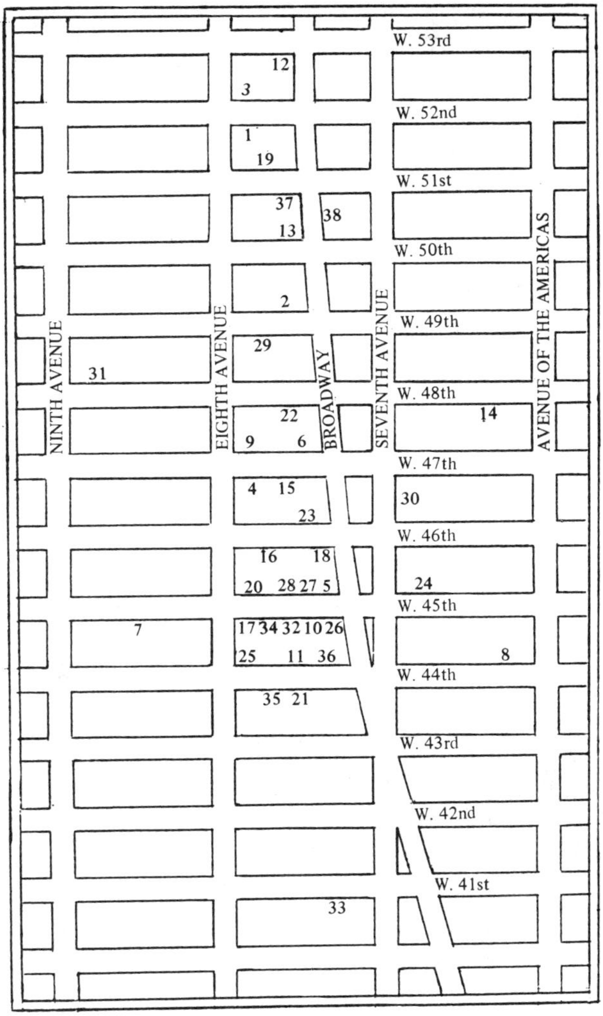

The Broadway theatres. *map courtesy of the I Love New York Campaign*

1. **ALVIN THEATRE**
   250 West 52nd Street
   New York, New York 10019
   212-757-8646
2. **AMBASSADOR THEATRE**
   215 West 49th Street
   New York, New York 10019
   212-265-1855
3. **ANTA THEATRE**
   245 West 52nd Street
   New York, New York 10019
   212-246-6270

4. **BROOKS ATKINSON THEATRE**
256 West 47th Street
New York, New York 10036
212-245-3430

5. **BIJOU THEATRE**
209 West 45th Street
New York, New York 10036
212-221-8500

6. **ETHEL BARRYMORE THEATRE**
243 West 47th Street
New York, New York 10036
212-246-0390

7. **MARTIN BECK THEATRE**
302 West 45th Street
New York, New York 10036
212-246-6363

8. **BELASCO THEATRE**
111 West 44th Street
New York, New York 10036
212-354-4490

9. **BILTMORE THEATRE**
261 West 47th Street
New York, New York 10036
212-867-7000

10. **BOOTH THEATRE**
222 West 45th Street
New York, New York 10036
212-246-5969

11. **BROADHURST THEATRE**
235 West 44th Street
New York, New York 10036
212-246-6699

12. **BROADWAY THEATRE**
Broadway at 53rd Street
New York, New York 10019
212-247-7992

13. **CIRCLE IN THE SQUARE THEATRE**
1633 Broadway (at 50th Street)
New York, New York 10019
212-581-0720

14. **CORT THEATRE**
138 West 48th Street
New York, New York 10036
212-489-6392

15. **EDISON THEATRE**
240 West 47th Street
New York, New York 10036
212-757-7164

16. **46TH STREET THEATRE**
226 West 46th Street
New York, New York 10036
212-246-4271

17. **JOHN GOLDEN THEATRE**
252 West 45th Street
New York, New York 10036
212-246-6740

18. **HELEN HAYES THEATRE**
210 West 46th Street
New York, New York 10036
212-246-6380

19. **MARK HELLINGER THEATRE**
51st Street and Broadway
New York, New York 10019
212-757-7050

20. **IMPERIAL THEATRE**
249 West 45th Street
New York, New York 10036
212-265-2412

21. **LITTLE THEATRE**
240 West 44th Street
New York, New York 10036
212-221-6425

22. **LONGACRE THEATRE**
220 West 48th Street
New York, New York 10036
212-246-5639

23. **LUNT-FONTANNE THEATRE**
205 West 46th Street
New York, New York 10036
212-586-5555

24. **LYCEUM THEATRE**
149 West 45th Street
New York, New York 10036
212-582-3897

25. **MAJESTIC THEATRE**
247 West 44th Street
New York, New York 10036
212-246-0730

26. **MINSKOFF THEATRE**
200 West 45th Street
New York, New York 10036
212-869-0550

27. **MOROSCO THEATRE**
217 West 45th Street
New York, New York 10036
212-246-6230

28. **MUSIC BOX THEATRE**
239 West 45th Street
New York, New York 10036
212-246-4636

29. **EUGENE O'NEILL THEATRE**
230 West 49th Street
New York, New York 10020
212-246-0220

Patrons pouring out of the Ambassador Theatre after a show.
Frank Gimpaya

30. PALACE THEATRE
1564 Broadway
New York, New York 10036
212-757-2626

31. THE PLAYHOUSE THEATRE
359 West 48th Street
New York, New York 10036
212-541-9820

32. PLYMOUTH THEATRE
236 West 45th Street
New York, New York 10036
212-246-9156

33. BILLY ROSE THEATRE
208 West 41st Street
New York, New York 10036
212-391-3999

34. ROYALE THEATRE
242 West 45th Street
New York, New York 10036
212-245-5760

35. ST. JAMES THEATRE
246 West 44th Street
New York, New York 10036
212-398-0280

36. SHUBERT THEATRE
225 West 44th Street
New York, New York 10036
212-246-5990

37. URIS THEATRE
51st Street, west of Broadway
New York, New York 10019
212-586-6510

38. WINTER GARDEN
1634 Broadway (at 50th Street)
New York, New York 10019
212-245-4878

Stretching your dance dollars

With so much good dance to see, you may find that your eyes are bigger than your pocketbook. Don't despair. Many New York theatres provide student rush tickets on the night of the performance, special discounts for senior citizens, or reduced rates to series subscribers (these are noted in the preceding theatre listings). If you're game, you can also try buying inexpensive standing room tickets on the chance of finding some empty seats in better locations later. But by far and away the greatest boon to bargain-hunters is the Theatre Development Fund (TDF) – 1501 Broadway, New York, New York 10036; 212-221-0018 – which sponsors various ticket discount programs for many theatre, music, and dance productions in the city.

TDF's audience mailing list and ticket voucher programs: If you are a student, teacher, retiree, union member, clergyman, American serviceman, member of a community youth group or performing arts professional, you are eligible for these two programs. You may also qualify by organizing a party of ten or more people who wish to attend TDF-subsidized events. By filling out a simple application form you can get on TDF's mailing list, which offers the opportunity to attend first-rate Broadway, off-Broadway, dance and music performances at a substantial savings. TDF ticket vouchers enable dance buffs to see many professional modern, ethnic, and ballet companies for only a dollar. For this you'll need to fill out a separate Dance Voucher order form. Here's how it works: You buy the vouchers from TDF at $1.00 each, and these are accepted by participating dance companies at theatre box offices as payment for admission (some add a $1 or $2 surcharge, although TDF discourages this). The companies then redeem the vouchers from TDF for $2.50 each—over twice the amount you paid for them. About 300 groups take part in the ticket voucher program, and TDF supplies subscribers with a monthly calendar of their concert offerings.

TKTS trailers: The Theatre Development Fund also operates two cut-rate ticket outlets called TKTS, where you can get half-price seats for many Broadway and off-Broadway shows, as well as opera and some dance concerts, on the day of the performance (not long ago we got a terrific pair of box seats to a hit show for $17.00!).

The Times Square Theatre Center is in the heart of the theatre district at Broadway and 47th Street. It is open daily from 3:00 to 8:00 P.M. and Wednesday, Saturday, and Sunday from 12:00 to 2:00 P.M. for matinee performances.

The Times Square TKTS trailer at the height of the summer tourist season. ***Frank Gimpaya***

New York's Favorite Landmark
HORN & HARDART
Automat
Famous for delicious food at old-fashioned prices!
42nd ST-8th AVE. at 33rd ST.
tkts
ONE WAY
ONE WAY
BUS STOP
NO STANDING
entrance
exit
exit
exit
exit

The Lower Manhattan Theatre Center is near Wall Street at 100 William Street and is open weekdays only, from 11:30 to 5:30 P.M. The Lower Manhattan TKTS trailer generally has shorter lines and a better selection of tickets than the one on Broadway. But don't let the long lines at 47th Street scare you. They usually move fast and there is a surprisingly good choice of current shows. Many of the people waiting on line are avid theatregoers who are more than happy to offer friendly advice on what to see, if you're having trouble making up your mind. But before queuing up, check the slate of shows at the entrance of the booth to see if there are seats available for the performance of your choice, and think of alternatives in case they are sold out by the time your turn is up. The pickings are best on weekdays.

2

Where to Study Dance in New York

Directory of dance schools
How to use the directory
School profiles
Quick-reference indices

Independent teachers

College dance: Full-time degree programs and continuing-education classes

Other classes of interest
Body conditioning
Movement studies and improvisation
Gymnastics

Every conceivable form of theatrical dance training is available in New York—ballet, modern, jazz, tap, ethnic, and experimental. Classes that are rare almost everywhere else are commonplace in the dance capital of the world, from adult-beginner and exercise classes for amateurs, to children's dance classes and men's classes, to excellent professional training and performing opportunites at company-affiliated schools. There are dozens of special short-term courses given during school vacations for visiting dancers and teachers. Besides technique, you can take up dance composition or history, learn basic anatomy, or even get voice and acting instruction at some New York studios. Even a beginner can study with famous personalities such as Melissa Hayden and Merce Cunningham. Because so many professional dancers are based here, class fees are slightly lower than the average for the rest of the country, and most city schools are open on weekends and all but the major holidays.

The size, location, and ambience of New York dance schools vary considerably too: from the imposing-looking Harkness Ballet and Martha Graham schools, which are lodged in Eastside townhouses; to the coolly professional atmosphere of places like the American Ballet Theatre School and the School of American Ballet; to the homey environment of small schools like the New York School of Ballet and the Dance Circle; to the dank, worn studios of Phil Black and Don Farnworth in the Times Square theatre district, and the refurbished Soho lofts which house the latest generation of modern dancers. While it may be overwhelming at times, it is just this option to pick and choose that is one of the prime advantages of studying dance in New York. If one school or teacher doesn't suit you, you can always try another and another, until you find the perfect niche for yourself.

But private schools are only one source of dance instruction (though admittedly the most prevalent). In New York you can also study with many fine independent teachers who rent studio space and teach on their own; or at one of the several metropolitan-area colleges that offer full-time degree programs and continuing-education classes in dance; or you can choose from a full complement of dance-related classes—in everything from dance notation to therapeutic exercise and gymnastics—which are sponsored by various dance organizations, private gyms, studios, and YMCAs.

Shop around. They're all here for the browsing.

Directory of dance schools

How to use the directory

This catalog of dance schools has been organized so that readers who know what they are looking for can find it quickly and those who don't can thumb through and make informed choices. The listings are arranged alphabetically but are also cross-indexed in the ***quick-reference indices*** (on page 173) under these categories:

adult beginner classes
children's classes
men's classes
intensive or short-term courses
teachers

Another time-saving device is the listing at the top of each school entry, called ***Techniques offered.*** This lets readers see at a glance which movement techniques are taught at any given school: ballet, modern dance, jazz, tap, ethnic, disco, dance exercise, and so on. More will be said about this later.

Except in rare instances where data were not available or the school did not provide the service in question, each school profile in the directory contains the following information:

Basic essentials:
address, phone number, date established, director/s:
A dance school's founding date is often (but not always) a good indication of its stability. Schools that have been around for five years or more are likely to have a well-established faculty and curriculum. The very fact that they have survived with a steady following in a competitive city like New York probably also indicates that they are doing something right. Some schools—mostly the large ones—have more than one director: the artistic director, who is usually also the founder, and the administrative director or business manager. Inquiries about class schedules, fees, and scholarships should be directed to the latter.

Techniques offered:
The types of dance techniques taught at the school are listed here. Also included under this heading are dance-exercise or body-conditioning classes and stretch and placement classes (classes in which there is concentrated work on improving flexibility and postural alignment). However, classes that are not directly related to dance technique—such as composition classes, repertory or performance workshops, and voice and dramatic training—are listed under the category of ***special courses and instruction.***

Facilities:
Some dance schools have more than one studio or classroom; this enables them to offer several classes concurrently and thus, a more varied schedule. Extra studios often mean that students have more space in which to warm up before class or to practice afterwards. All the schools we profiled

have dressing rooms and bathrooms; some have showers, which may be a necessity for dancers who are not going straight home after class.

Student enrollment:
These figures are intended to give readers a general impression of the size and makeup of the student population at the school. Aside from supplying estimates of the total student enrollment and average class size, school administrators were asked to assess the predominant age and technical ability of their students. This was done because, although many schools offer a wide range of classes, they tend to specialize in teaching certain kinds of dancers. For instance, the American Ballet Theatre School offers ballet classes for adult beginners and advanced beginners, but reports that most of its students are ages ten to seventeen and at the intermediate level. The Alvin Ailey American Dance Center also offers adult-beginner classes in addition to classes for children and aspiring professionals; yet it reports that most of its students are in the eighteen to twenty-five-year age bracket and at the beginning and advanced-beginning levels. The ***age*** and ***level*** breakdown of the student enrollment should give you a rough idea of what types of dancers tend to study at the school, and therefore, some indication of where the primary interests and strengths of the faculty lie.

Entrance requirements:
Although there are no entrance requirements to speak of at most American dance schools, some New York schools have minimum-age restrictions. Other schools, such as the Marjorie Mussman Studio and the Nancy Meehan School, will not accept dancers below the intermediate level; and still others, such as the Merce Cunningham Studio, require that all new students start out in elementary classes regardless of their previous training in other techniques. The School of American Ballet is one of a handful of schools that admit students by audition only.

Classes:
The first listing under this category is similar to that of ***techniques offered,*** but it also specifies the levels at which the classes are taught—beginning, intermediate, or advanced. Ballet classes in pointe work, adagio, variations, and character dance are also noted here.

Classes for people who have never been in a dance class before are called either basic, elementary, fundamental, introductory, or pre-beginner classes. There, everyone starts off at the ***very*** beginning and is given a thorough explanation of the exercises, which are demonstrated slowly and carefully. Similarly, children's pre-ballet or pre-school movement classes offer an introduction to dance in which youngsters learn the rudiments of technique, basic dance terminology, and classroom etiquette, combined perhaps with group play and improvisational games. Beginners' classes are different from pre-beginner classes in that they usually include a mixture of students with varying degrees of prior dance experience.

Some dance schools offer classes at intermediary levels, such as advanced beginner and intermediate-advanced; you may also see slow beginner and fast beginner or slow intermediate and fast intermediate classes. Be aware, though, that standards vary from school to school and that, for example, an advanced beginner class at one studio may be a solid intermediate class at another, or occasionally one school's intermediate class may be the equivalent of an advanced class somewhere else.

For your convenience, underneath the general listing of technique classes available, we have noted the following special classes:

Adult beginner classes, a relatively recent development on the dance scene, are especially designed for the many new students, in their early twenties or older, who are taking up dance for the first time. Most adult beginners are amateur dancers, but a few professionals start out this late too. Because of the rising popularity of recreational dancing, most dance schools these days hold adult beginner classes of some sort in the evenings and on weekends. As in pre-beginner classes (which these are), all students start out at the same level—so no one need feel out of place. The class progresses together, and lessons are geared to mature bodies and minds; technique is developed slowly and carefully. And another thing—many dance instructors seem to enjoy teaching adult beginner classes; they're generally more relaxed and better humored than they are in advanced classes.

Children's classes are adapted to the special needs of growing bodies and minds. This tailoring is particularly important, since adult technique classes are inappropriate for most youngsters. Fortunately, children's classes are widely available. Dance schools usually offer them on Saturdays or after school hours during the week.

Teenager's classes, although scarce, are available at a few dance schools.

Men's classes are almost always offered in ballet, at the intermediate or advanced level, when the specialized skills needed for male classical dancing are developed and perfected. For the most part men's ballet classes focus on masculine movement qualities and work on highly athletic steps such as ***tours en l'air,*** multiple beats and turns, and big jumps and leaps. A few of the larger ballet schools provide beginner classes for boys.

Special courses and instruction:
Included here are:

Intensive or short-term courses that are given in their entirety and are especially designed for dancers who want to sample a technique or school in a limited amount of time. They are usually held during school vacations (summer and Christmas are popular times) so that teachers, out-ot-town dancers, and others who might not otherwise be able to can attend. Examples are the annual four-week June course at the Martha Graham School and the six-week summer course at the School of American Ballet. Teacher-training courses are noted here too.

Special courses and workshops which are not part of the school's regular curriculum but are offered periodically. Examples are Merce Cunningham's Christmas course in technique and composition and Raoul Gelabert's fall course in anatomy for the dancer.

Nontechnique classes, such as dance improvisation and composition; repertory or routines classes; or acting, music, and voice training. Examples are the classes in singing and acting given at the American Dance Machine Training Facility and Eleo Pomare's choreographer's workshop at the Vital Arts Center.

Private classes and coaching, which are arranged by appointment with individual teachers. Some schools restrict this form of special instruction to advanced students and professional dancers.

Accompaniment:
Music is so essential to dancing that good music alone is almost worth the price of a dance lesson. The type of musical accompaniment provided for classes is noted here—whether it is live or recorded, and what kind: piano, percussion, or voice. Several New York schools—such as the Alvin Ailey American Dance Center, the Merce Cunningham Studio, and Studio Revene—pride themselves in offering excellent live accompaniment.

Holidays:
Vacation dates are listed from January to December. If no weekend closings are specified, classes are given on both Saturdays and Sundays. Since dance school holidays are sometimes determined at the last minute, you should call ahead to confirm them.

Fees
Some dance schools charge a "one time only" or annual registration fee in addition to tuition. At most schools you can pay by the single class, or at least take a trial lesson. Or you can buy a series of classes—generally ten or more—at a discount. Series cards or classes bought by the term almost always have a time limit; that is, you have to use them up within a specified number of weeks after the date of purchase. At many schools, class fees are further discounted on a sliding scale, according to the number of lessons taken per week. Some studios also offer reduced rates to professionals who are members of unions such as AGMA, Actor's Equity, and AGVA.

Children's dance classes are frequently shorter* and

*Forty-five minutes, as opposed to the standard hour-and-a-half adult's class.

therefore less expensive than adults' classes, and some schools charge different fees for different classes. For example, at Jo Jo's Dance Factory, which is primarily a jazz school, jazz and tap lessons cost $5.50 each while ballet classes cost $4.50. Private classes or coaching fees are sometimes negotiable, but most fall within the range of $25 to $35 per hour. Special or intensive courses are also priced separately. Payment terms vary from school to school; some ask that you pay the entire tuition in advance while others require only a deposit. Dance schools usually accept personal checks.

Scholarships:
Three kinds of financial assistance are commonly available: full scholarships, which provide free tuition; partial scholarships, which pay for half the tuition costs; and work scholarships, in which students get free classes for helping out with various chores, such as manning the front desk, sweeping up the studio, or assisting at classes. Most dance scholarships are awarded by audition, or at small schools, after the faculty has seen the student in classes long enough

A men's ballet class at the old Alvin Ailey studio on East 59th Street.
Frank Gimpaya

to judge his or her potential. Aside from talent and financial need, many ballet schools have age requirements for scholarship students.

Company affiliations:
Company-affiliated schools are the training grounds for professional dance companies (see the listings of New York-based companies in Chapter Three) and tend to have a more serious atmosphere than the others, with more demanding teachers. For an aspiring career dancer they have the added allure of being a possible source of employment, since new company members are chosen from the ranks of the school's students. But there are other benefits too: classes are less apt to be academic. They are frequently taught by past or present company dancers or by the artistic director himself. Performance values are stressed, and chances are the choreography will be better than average because movement combinations are often taken from the concert repertory.

Also mentioned under this heading are student or apprentice companies and other performing opportunities, such as school recitals and performance workshops.

Principal faculty:
Since there is a rapid turnover of faculty at most New York dance schools, we have included in this listing only the teachers who have been on staff for a minimum of two years.

Summary statement:
Each school was asked to prepare a brief statement summarizing its teaching philosophy, goals, and specialties, as well as what the school felt it had to offer that perhaps others did not. The replies published here were supplied either by the directors or their authorized representatives. We hope that these statements will help to flesh out the school profiles by giving you a feeling for the schools and allowing you to read between the lines of the otherwise rather businesslike listings.

All the information in the directory was obtained from the schools themselves through questionnaires and interviews, and except for some minor editing, it is presented the way it was received. Some school representatives were more informative or articulate than others, and therefore, some entries are more complete.

Abbreviations:
The following shorthand is used in the student enrollment, class-level, and fee entries:

fund = fundamentals
beg = beginning
int = intermediate
adv = advanced
pro = professional
teens = teenagers

School profiles

ALVIN AILEY AMERICAN DANCE CENTER

1515 Broadway (45th Street)
New York, New York 10036
(212-997-1980)

Techniques offered: MODERN, BALLET, JAZZ, ETHNIC (AFRO-CARIBBEAN)

Established: 1970

Director: Reginald K. Ingram

Associate director: Tom Stevens

Artistic directors: Alvin Ailey and Pearl Lang

Scholarship director: Delores Brown

Facilities: 4 studios; dressing rooms; bathrooms; showers

Student enrollment: total: 5100; average class: 40-45
Age: most 18-25; next 25-33; next 10-17; next over 33
Level: most beg and adv beg; next int; next adv

Entrance requirements: none for adults; children 7-14 interviewed and placed in appropriate class

Classes: MODERN (Horton): fund, beg, adv beg, int, adv; MODERN (Graham): fund, beg, adv beg, int, adv; BALLET: basics, beg, adv beg, int-adv, adv, pointe adagio; JAZZ: basics, beg, int, int-adv; ETHNIC (Dunham): fund
Adult beg: see fund and basics classes above
Children: Sat. only; beg and adv beg levels in MODERN, BALLET, and JAZZ
Men: BALLET

Special courses/instruction: Dance Workshop open to all students, announced in advance; on a variety of subjects, including musical-comedy dance, modern dance repertory, lecture/film series on black dance artists.

Accompaniment: live piano and percussion

Holidays: national holidays, Martin Luther King's birthday; fall, spring, and summer breaks; Sundays

Fees: $10 annual registration fee (includes one free class); $5/class; $45/10 classes; $75/20 classes; $35/10 classes, pro rate; time limit on all series cards

Scholarships: full: approximately 100; work: approximately 20, depending on needs of school; for students ages 14-24, chosen by audition each fall and spring, and reviewed for renewal three times a year

Students warm up in a Horton technique class at the Alvin Ailey American Dance Center. ***Frank Gimpaya***

Company affiliations: The Alvin Ailey American Dance Theatre; The Pearl Lang Dance Company; The Alvin Ailey Repertory Ensemble, an apprentice group of fourteen scholarship students, directed by Sylvia Waters, who tour nationally and are paid a weekly stipend as well as an honorarium for performances; and The American Dance Center Workshop, twenty-five scholarship students who perform in public schools, parks, hospitals, and other institutionalized settings, under the direction of Kevin Rotardier.

Principal faculty: Pepsi Bethel (jazz), Delores Brown (ballet), Robert Christopher (ballet), Barbara Cole (ballet), Nat Horne (jazz), Denise Jefferson (Graham), Pearl Lang (Graham), Genia Melikova (ballet), Milton Myers (Horton), Marjorie Perces (Horton), Joan Peters (Dunham), Patricia Thomas (Graham), and Bertram Ross (Graham) ***Children's faculty:*** Pepsi Bethel, William Figueroa, Lucinda Ransom, and Tom Stevens

Summary statement: "The school is under the artistic direction of Mr. Alvin Ailey, who has long been committed to the proliferation of dancers and dance audiences. Our main goal is to produce high-caliber dancers to perform on the concert stage. We have two very active student companies which both provide a performing arena for our more talented students and take dance to new audiences. Recently we have gained a large following of adult beginners in our evening fundamentals and basics classes. Our Saturday Children's Program has a separate faculty and includes an open house for parents in June. We are especially proud of the excellent musicians who accompany our classes. They are all artists in their own right."

Authors' note: The Ailey School's spanking new facilities at the Minskoff Theatre Building (use the 45th Street arcade entrance below the Minskoff Theatre marquee) are a bit colder and more bureaucratically run than its former studio on East 59th Street. At present class registration procedures are confusing: some so-called "open" classes are filled with scholarship students and become closed to the general public an hour or so before they're scheduled to begin. In all likelihood the current popularity of the Ailey school and its expert faculty will continue—if not increase—at its new headquarters. Therefore it is a good idea for students to call ahead to make certain that the classes they wish to take are still open.

Since in some ways the Ailey staff are still getting used to their new surroundings and school policy is still in a state of flux, the situation may improve in the future. Perhaps separate classes will be created for scholarship students, leaving the open classes free for general attendance. The Alvin Ailey American Dance Center does have a good track record and has been unusually progressive in the past. Its associate director, Tom Stevens, began as a scholarship student in 1971.

AMERICAN BALLET CENTER
(The Joffrey School)
434 Avenue of the Americas (at 10th Street)
New York, New York 10011
(212-254-8520)

Techniques offered:	BALLET, TAP
Established:	1957
Executive administrator:	Edith D'Addario
Artistic director:	Robert Joffrey
Associate director:	Gerald Arpino
Facilities:	3 studios; dressing rooms; bathrooms; showers
Student enrollment:	total: 900; average class: 25 Age: most 18-25; next 10-17; next 25-33 Level: most int; next adv; next beg; next adv beg
Entrance requirements:	audition for placement at proper class level
Classes:	BALLET: basic, beg, beg-int, int, adv int, adv, pointe, character; TAP: beg ***Adult beg***: BALLET: see basic and beg classes above; TAP: see beg class above ***Children*** (under 14): BALLET: pre-ballet, beg, int, adv ***Men***: BALLET: men's class
Special courses/instruction:	Summer Intensive Course with guest teachers, for out-of-town students, 8 weeks in July and August; Teacher's course
Accompaniment:	piano
Holidays:	Easter, Christmas; two-week June break, August break; weekends
Fees:	$4/class; $32/10 classes; $30/10 classes, pro rate; other discounts given depending on number of classes taken per week
Scholarships:	Full, partial, and work-study are available for girls ages 14-19 and boys ages 14-20; must have slender body and proper proportions for classical ballet; chosen by audition, according to ability and potential for joining the Joffrey Ballet Company or the Joffrey II Company; scholarships are given for summer course as well as year-round study.
Company affiliations:	Joffrey Ballet Company; Joffrey II Company (an apprentice company comprised of scholarship students; the group tours and dancers are paid for performances).
Principal faculty:	Gerald Arpino, Meredith Baylis, Sally Bliss, Robert Joffrey, Dorothy Lister, Sidney Lowenthal, Francoise Martinet, Basil Thompson, and guest teachers from the Joffrey Ballet Company
Summary statement:	"The school aims primarily to train and develop young dancers; the teaching philosophy is that of the great masters of ballet—which is a well-rounded classical and character technique. The school does train students at every level, however. It includes children's classes up to the profes-

sional level, as well as classes for adult beginners who are interested in learning the technique of ballet for the sole purpose of understanding the art."

Authors' note: Every member of the faculty at this school has impressive professional credentials. Not only are choreographers Robert Joffrey and Gerald Arpino on hand to teach some of the advanced classes, there are also, for example, former Ballet Russe soloist Meredith Baylis; Basil Thompson, who danced with American Ballet Theatre and the Sadler's Wells Ballet; and Sally Bliss, who performed with American Ballet Theatre, Joffrey Ballet, and the National Ballet of Canada, and who currently directs the Joffrey II apprentice company.

AMERICAN BALLET THEATRE SCHOOL

3 West 61st Street
New York, New York 10023
(212-JU6-3355)

Techniques offered: BALLET

Established: 1952

Registrar: Peter Ramsey

Director: Leon Danielian

Facilities: 6 studios; dressing rooms; bathrooms; showers

Student enrollment: total: 1500; average class: 30 (more in summer)
Age: most 10-17; next 18-25; next 25-33; next over 33
Level: most int; next adv; next adv beg; next beg

Entrance requirements: none for the Open Division; audition for the Scholarship Division

Open Classes: BALLET: int, adv int, adv, pro, pointe

Adult beg: BALLET: adult beg and adv beg classes
Children (ages 9 and up): BALLET: graded beg classes; when children reach int level, they join the regular classes at the school
Teens: BALLET: pre-intermediate classes for teens with some ballet training who are not yet ready to go into intermediate-level classes

Special courses/instruction: Summer Intensive Course, 6 weeks in July and August

Accompaniment: piano

Holidays: Christmas-New Year's, Washington's birthday, Easter weekend, Memorial Day weekend, summer break, Sundays

Fees: $5/class; $4/class, pro rate; $18/4 classes, 1 per week; $35/8 classes, 2 per week; $48/12 classes, 3 per week; other discount series available for 4 or more classes per week; $30/10 classes, pro rate (must be taken in 8 weeks)

Scholarships: Full scholarships are available for girls from 13-17 and boys from 13-18; all dancers must be proper weight for their size, and girls should be under 5'7"; offered for summer course as well as year-round study. Scholarships are reviewed at the start of the fall, spring, and summer terms; summer scholarship auditions are held in New York and several major cities throughout the U.S. (inquire at the school for further information).

Company affiliations: American Ballet Theatre; Ballet Repertory Company (a 20-member junior company under the direction of Richard Englund; dancers tour and are paid for performances)

Principal faculty: Nansi Clement, Leon Danielian, Michael Maule, Olga Merinowa, Valentina Pereyaslavec, Patricia Wilde, and guest teachers from American Ballet Theatre

Summary statement: "The ABT School runs two separate divisions, each with its own classes. The Open Division covers the teaching of dancers on all levels—beginning, intermediate, advanced, and professional—who wish to have a career as a dancer or a knowledge of dance for careers as teacher, choreographer, dance critic, or dance historian. The Scholarship Division is a more intense course of training for young dancers of above average caliber with potential to become members of ABT."

Authors' note: Most of ABT's teaching staff are former company dancers. Patricia Wilde was a celebrated ballerina with the New York City Ballet.

AMERICAN CHAMBER BALLET CENTER

231 West 54th Street
New York, New York 10019
(212-974-9504)

Techniques offered: BALLET, JAZZ, TAP

Established: 1974

Director: Trutti Gasparinetti

Facilities: 1 studio; dressing rooms; bathrooms

Student enrollment: total: 150; average class: 14
Age: most 18-25; next over 25; next 12-17
Level: most beg and int; next adv int

Entrance requirements: no students under 12

Classes: BALLET: adv beg, int-adv, pointe; JAZZ: int, adv; TAP: beg

Special courses/instruction: Private classes: Coaching (with choreography if requested)

Accompaniment: piano, tapes, records, drums

Holidays: Easter, July 4, one week in August, Christmas; Sundays

Fees: $3.50/class, ballet; $4.50/class, jazz; $3.75/class, tap; $30/10 classes, tap and ballet; $35/10 classes, jazz; $15/hour, private classes; $20/hour, private pointe classes

Scholarships: Company members with union card may take free classes as a warmup before rehearsals.

Company affiliations: Ballet Interim Workshop Company (civic-type ballet company)

Principal faculty: Trutti Gasparinetti (ballet), Betsy Haug (jazz), Alicia Lovely (ballet)

Summary statement: "The Director, Trutti Gasparinetti, has performed professionally since 1953 in summer stock, night clubs, industrials, television, and stage shows at the Roxy, City Center, and Equity Library theatres. Twice a week, in addition to her standard-length classes, she teaches a two-hour ballet class that combines beg with int level students, and in which all the exercises begin on the left side for a more even technique. Ms. Gasparinetti has set up Ballet Interim as a Workshop company for students who are ready to perform but have no place to go to get their "stage legs," and for professional dancers who are between engagements. The company is also the realized home of Ms. Gasparinetti's accumulated experiences and talents of the past 28 years."

Authors' note: Trutti Gasparinetti taught at both the Alvin Ailey American Dance Center and the Ballet Arts School before establishing her own studio. Betsy Haug teaches a fast, loose jazz style that builds on momentum. Her classes are a favorite among Broadway dancers, and it's a treat to watch her advanced students. When Haug, who is a nightclub performer and choreographer, is out of town, Danny Buraczewski takes over her classes.

AMERICAN DANCE MACHINE TRAINING FACILITY

Harkness House for Ballet Arts
4 East 75th Street (3rd Floor)
New York, New York 10021
(212-879-5750)

Techniques offered: THEATRE DANCE, BALLET, JAZZ

Established: 1977

Director: Lee Theodore

Facilities: 4 studios; dressing rooms; bathrooms; showers

Student enrollment: total: 250; average class: 17
Age: most 18-25; next 10-17 and 33 and over, in equal proportions; next 25-33
Level: most int; next adv beg; next adv; next beg

Entrance requirements: none

Classes: THEATRE DANCE: int-adv (each class begins with what is essentially a jazz warmup. Students then learn various musical-comedy choreographic styles, with each day devoted to a different era—Mondays, the 1920s; Tuesdays, the 1930s; Wednesdays, the 1940s; Thursdays, the 1950s; and Fridays, the 1960s); BALLET: int-adv; JAZZ: adult beg; REPERTORY THEATRE DANCE: current works and new reconstructions from the American Dance Machine repertory, for advanced students only

Adult beg: see adult beg jazz class above
Children (ages 6 and up): LYRIC THEATRE DANCE: ballet classes for children, graded by age
Teens: THEATRE DANCE class for teenagers

Special courses/instruction: Singing/vocal technique; Acting, speech, and movement class (combines scene studies with work on acting techniques and movement for actors); Summer course at American University in Washington, D.C. (taught by American Dance Machine staff at the university's Academy for the Performing Arts); Coaching (for dancers preparing for auditions or shows, by appointment)

Accompaniment: piano (for ballet), percussion (for theatre dance and jazz)

Holidays: major national holidays; Sundays; class schedule curtailed in summer

Fees: $5/annual registration fee; $4/class, $35/10 classes; pro rate (for union members): $3/class, $30/10 classes; coaching fees are negotiable

Scholarships: Limited work scholarships are available to promising students, who are usually selected by audition in the fall.

Company affiliations: American Dance Machine, an Equity repertory company that preserves, reconstructs, and performs major choreography from the American musical theatre; most of these are show stoppers from hit Broadway musicals in which members of the company dance, sing, and act. There are no student apprentices, but dancers are often chosen from the best advanced students in the repertory class.

Principal faculty: Nenette Charisse (int-adv ballet), Nancy Chismar (theatre dance), Phyllis Goldman (children's ballet), Judy Magee (acting, speech, and movement class), Buzz Miller (repertory), Jim Raitt (singing), Lee Theodore (theatre dance)

Summary statement: "The American Dance Machine Training Facility was founded in 1977 by teacher, choreographer, and veteran Broadway performer Lee Theodore. As a dancer, she has been featured in numerous Broadway shows, but is probably best remembered for having created the role of "Anybody's" in the original stage version of ***West Side Story.*** The purpose of the school is to train young dancers in the history and technique of the important choreographic styles associated with American musical-comedy dance. It is one of the few places in the country where serious students can get all-around training in preparation for musical theatre careers—including vocal and acting instruction. Among our teaching staff are such top-notch professionals as Theodore; the legendary Nenette Charisse, who trained José Limón, Jerome Robbins, Valerie Bettis, and Gwen Verdon; Buzz Miller, a featured dancer in dozens of Broadway musicals and films who has worked with most of the major Broadway choreographers; as well as dancers from the company."

Authors' note: Although the American Dance Machine is located in the Harkness House for Ballet Arts and shares some facilities with the Harkness Ballet School, its classes are run completely independently.

MARY ANTHONY DANCE STUDIO
736 Broadway (7th Street)
New York, New York 10003
(212-OR4-8191)

Techniques offered: MODERN, BALLET

Established: 1954

Director: Mary Anthony

Facilities: 1 studio; dressing rooms; bathroom

Student enrollment: total: 150; average class: 15
Age: most 18-25; next 25-33; next 10-17; next 33-over
Level: most int; next adv; next beg; next adv beg

Entrance requirements: none, but the school places students at appropriate class level

Classes: MODERN: elem, beg, beg-int, int, adv; BALLET: int (for modern dancers)
Adult beg: see elementary modern class above

Special courses/instruction: Repertory for intermediate and advanced dancers, offered fall, winter, and summer; Creative Workshop in Acting, Improvisation, and Composition; Private classes

Accompaniment: piano, percussion

Holidays: national holidays; Sundays

Fees: \$5/2 trial classes; \$4.50/class; \$3.50/class, pro rate; \$30/8 classes; \$42/12 classes; \$50/20 classes (there is a one-month time limit on all series cards); \$10 half-hour, private classes

Scholarships: Work scholarships are available for students who have studied at the studio six months or more (exceptions made for outstanding talents).

Company affiliations: Mary Anthony Dance Theatre

Principal faculty: Mary Anthony (modern), Wendy Barker (ballet), Gwendolyn Bye (beg modern), Daniel Maloney (modern), Ross Parkes (modern and repertory)

Summary statement: "Our philosophy is geared to performance, whether for theatre or life itself. A unique aspect of the training here is the Creative Workshop, which is a course in acting, improvisation, and composition—leading to studio performances. In the past, our repertory students have also given studio performances."

Authors' note: Mary Antony studied with Hanya Holm (a protégé of German expressionist Mary Wigman), later performing in the Holm company, as well as on Broadway and with Anna Sokolow's troupe. Anthony's own work has a strong dramatic thrust, and her classroom teaching also stresses dramatic expression. Ross Parkes was a principal dancer with Martha Graham for many years.

ASAKAWALKER DANCE STUDIO
385 Broadway (below Canal Street)
4th Floor
New York, New York 10013
(212-925-4599)

Techniques offered:	MODERN
Established:	1977
Directors:	Takako Asakawa and David Hatch Walker
Facilities:	1 studio; dressing rooms; bathrooms; showers
Student enrollment:	total: 100; average class: 15 Age: most 18-25; next 25-33 and 10-17 in equal proportions; next 33-over Level: most int; next adv; next adv beg; next beg
Entrance requirements:	none
Classes:	MODERN (Graham): elementary-beg, int-adv
Accompaniment:	piano, percussion
Holidays:	major national holidays; Sundays
Fees:	$4/class, $35/10 classes
Scholarships:	Full and work scholarships are available to promising students who have the potential to join the company.
Company affiliations:	Asakawalker Dance Company
Principal faculty:	Takako Asakawa (int-adv), Amy Edelstein (elementary-beg), Paula Galleron (int-adv, elementary-beg), Andre Lengye (int-adv, elementary-beg), David Hatch Walker (int-adv). All teachers are members of the company.
Summary statement:	"Takako Asakawa and David Hatch Walker, former principals with the Martha Graham Company, have created a company and school to develop the professional dancer into an articulate performing artist and to provide the beginning dancer with an enjoyable and professional introduction to dance. Both Miss Asakawa and Mr. Walker have years of extensive teaching experience in colleges and universities throughout the United States, as well as in Europe and the Orient. Their work reflects an ongoing evolution and modification of basic principles developed in modern dance—contraction and release, spiral, fall and recovery, use of the breath, and the motivation of movement from the energy centers of the body. Floor work, standing exercises, and movement through space provide a well-rounded and integrated study of movement and its possibilities as expression in dance. The studio is large, with an excellent floor."

BALLET CLASSIQUE
321 East 73rd Street
New York, New York 10021
(212-PL3-2310)

Techniques offered: BALLET

Established: 1972

Director: Patricia M. Wattley (A.R.A.D.)

Facilities: 1 studio, bathrooms

Student enrollment: total: 50; average class: 8 (maximum 10)
Age: most under 25 and over 33; least 25-33
Level: most beg; next adv; next int; next adv beg

Entrance requirements: personal interview and trial class before assignment to proper class level; no children under 4½; students in the advanced class must be able to do classwork

Classes: (all follow Royal Academy of Dancing syllabus): BALLET: beg, int, adv-pro
Adult beg: BALLET: adult beg and int classes
Children: BALLET: babies' class (for ages 4½ to 5 yrs), and five levels of graded children's classes from beg to int-adv

Special courses/instruction: Master classes by guest teachers; Private classes; Coaching

Accompaniment: piano, tapes for adult beg and int classes

Holidays: spring, summer, and Christmas recess; weekends

Fees: $4.50/class; $45/10 classes; $35/10 classes, pro rate; $165/33 weeks, 1 class per week; $7.50/hour, semiprivate coaching for R.A.D. exams; $20/hour, private classes

Scholarships: Full and partial are available, depending on student's ability and financial need.

Company affiliations: none

Principal faculty: Jane Vann (adult beg and children's classes), Patricia M. Wattley (all other classes)

Summary statement: The R.A.D. syllabi are standard courses of study for ballet which were established in 1935 by the Royal Academy of Dancing to raise the quality of ballet instruction in England and the British Commonwealth. There are, however, R.A.D. certified teachers like Patricia Wattley in the United States. "At Ballet Classique," says Miss Wattley, "the children's syllabus has five grades for once-a-week students ages 6 to 12, and was created by the Royal Academy's current president, Dame Margot Fonteyn. The major (or advanced) syllabus ranges from elementary to advanced levels. Aside from teaching the English method, we have a special approach to children in that they are placed in classes according to ability, not age. As part of the training they study interpretive dance, music, and national and historical dances. Classes are small, and each dancer is given individual attention. Every spring a R.A.D. examiner from England comes to observe classes and evaluate our teachers based on how well the students are doing."

BALLET SCHOOL OF LINCOLN SQUARE

246 West 80th Street
2nd Floor
New York, New York 10024
(212-595-8359)

Techniques offered: BALLET, MIME, JAZZ

Established: 1975

Director: Barbara Walczak

Facilities: 2 studios; dressing rooms; bathrooms

Student enrollment: total: 100; average class: 15
Age: most 10-17; next 18-25
Level: most adv beg; next beg, int, and adv in equal pro portions

Entrance requirements: The school is for children and young adults between th ages of 6 and 20, but adults' classes are taught by independ ent teachers who rent studio space (see classes below).

Classes: (for children and young adults): BALLET: pre-ballet I, pre ballet II, beg I (basic beg), beg (for more advanced begin ners), int, adv, pointe; variations; some partnering is include in the advanced technique class; MIME (combined levels)

Adult beg: An adult beginner ballet class (taught by Ann Moser) and an intermediate jazz class (taught by Veleri Camille) are also offered independently of the school' curriculum.

Special courses/instruction: Summer course (for intermediate and advanced students consisting of daily technique classes); Private classes; Coach ing

Accompaniment: piano or recorded music

Holidays: public school holidays; summer vacation in August; Sun days

Fees: $4/class; $30/10 classes; lower monthly and term rates ar available according to the number of classes taken per week

Scholarships: Full and work scholarships are available, based on the stu dent's ability and financial needs.

Company affiliations: none, but student workshop performances are held twice year

Principal faculty: Zahava Gratz (mime), Donna McEntee (children's pre-balle and beg ballet), Robert Maiorano (int and adv ballet), Bar bara Walczak (int and adv ballet, pointe, variations)

Summary statement: "We attempt to give our students disciplined and thoroug classical ballet training with as much personal attention a possible and an emphasis on correct body placement and in dividual problems. Since dance is also a theatrical art form we give studio performances, mainly so that our student can grow as performers as well as in technique. Our olde students are taught ballets from current repertories and ar encouraged to perfect the technique and particular qualit necessary for each role. Whether or not they aspire to pe forming careers, we try to teach them how to work intelligently and with love and respect for the dance. We also try to help place older students in the schools of professional companies when they are ready. Barbara Walczak, the director of the school, received her principal training from Phylis Marmein, Igor Schwezoff, and the School of American Ballet under the directorship of George Balanchine. At age sixteen she joined the New York City Ballet, remaining with the company for five seasons and later touring with the Alicia Alonso Ballet Company and Andre Eglevsky's Ballet Divertissements. Faculty member Robert Maiorano is also from the New York City Ballet. The studio space itself was lovingly renovated by volunteers, right down to the laying of the new oak dance floors. When classes are not in session, the facilities are rented out for dance-related activities and rehearsals."

COLLETTE BARRY AND SUSAN KLEIN SCHOOL OF DANCE

226 West 56th Street
New York, New York 10019
(212-757-2288)

Techniques offered: BALLET, STRETCH AND PLACEMENT

Established: 1974

Directors: Collette Barry and Susan Klein

Facilities: 1 studio; dressing rooms; bathrooms

Student enrollment: Age: most 18-25; next 25-33; next 33-over; next 10-17
Level: most int; next adv beg; next beg; next adv

Entrance requirements: none

Classes: BALLET: beg, int; STRETCH AND PLACEMENT
Adult beg: see beg ballet and stretch and placement classes above

Special courses/instruction: Guest workshops by dance therapists and movement analysts; Coaching

Accompaniment: piano

Holidays: national holidays; Sundays

Fees: $3.25/class; $32.50/10 classes

Scholarships: Work scholarships are available; dancers are chosen according to school's needs and student's availability.

Company affiliations: none

Principal faculty: Collette Barry (ballet), Susan Klein (stretch and placement)

Summary statement: "The primary goal of the school is to train dancers. We do intensive body alignment work on a personal basis. Alignment and placement are taught as a dynamic state of being rather than as static rules imposed on the body. The student is taken through various stages of development: (1)

body awareness through breathing and fundamental exercises; (2) the concept of weight and leverage; (3) 'finding one's legs'; (4) the flow of the spine; (5) the articulation of the shoulder girdle, arms, and hands; (6) carriage of the head; (7) the ballet vocabulary. The school is greatly involved with rehabilitation work. We approach a localized injury as a symptom of a total body problem and deal with it in a total body way."

Authors' note: Collette Barry has also taught at the Don Farnworth Studio and Clark Center in New York, as well as at Connecticut College. Classes at this studio are very much in a state of flux. Only the permanent ones are listed here; but from time to time there are classes given in various modern techniques (i.e., Limón and Hawkins) and improvisation. The stretch and placement lessons concentrate on exercises to improve posture and to center and stretch the body without tension.

VALERIE BETTIS DANCE STUDIO

22 West 15th Street
New York, New York 10011
(212-691-8790)

Techniques offered: MODERN, BALLET, JAZZ, STRETCH

Established: 1963

Director: Valerie Bettis

Facilities: 4 studios, dressing rooms, bathrooms

Student enrollment: total: over 200; average class: 8-15
Age: most 10-17; next 18-25; next 25-33; next 33-over
Level: most beg; next adv; next adv beg; next int

Entrance requirements: none

Classes: MODERN: beg, int, adv; BALLET: beg, int, adv; JAZZ: technique and improvisation; STRETCH

Adult beg: see beg classes above
Children: JAZZ: technique and improvisation for children 8-13 years old; MODERN: technique and improvisation for children and teenagers (ages 3 and up)

Special courses/instruction: Twelve-week technique and improvisation course for actors and dancers (Saturdays only); Four-week June course in modern dance technique and improvisation (for intermediate-level students); Private classes; Coaching

Accompaniment: tapes, records, percussion

Holidays: national holidays; Sundays

Fees: $3.50 registration fee; $3.50/class, 1 per week; $3/class, 2 per week; pro rates available; $48/12 sessions, Saturday Workshop (see above)

Scholarships: Full and partial available, granted according to student's potential and financial need

Company affiliations: Valerie Bettis Dance Theatre Company, some members of which are chosen from the actors' and dancers' workshop; combines music, drama, and dance

Principal faculty: Valerie Bettis, Bonnie Estes, Carole Ann Lewis (all teach modern dance and ballet); Caroline Ryburn (jazz); and guest teachers

Summary statement: "We stress individual attention to students, with an emphasis on professional goals as well as a thorough understanding of the amateur's needs. In the same way, we feel the children's classes are also very special, and introduce creativity in all the allied arts. Valerie Bettis is equally well known as a performer, choreographer, and director. A native of Texas, her New York training was taken with Hanya Holm. She was a member of Miss Holm's company for three years, after which she made her debut as a choreographer. Miss Bettis' best-known concert works are ***As I Lay Dying,*** for her own company; ***A Streetcar Named Desire,*** for American Ballet Theatre; and ***The Desperate Heart,*** a solo for herself. Her Broadway credits include ***Two On The Aisle*** and ***Beggar's Holiday.*** In addition, she has choreographed for and appeared on film and television.

LA ROCQUE BEY SCHOOL OF DANCE THEATRE

169 West 133rd Street
New York, New York 10030
(212-926-0188)

Techniques offered: AFRO-CARIBBEAN, AFRO-JAZZ, EXERCISE, DISCO

Established: 1960

Director: La Rocque Bey

Facilities: 2 studios; dressing rooms; bathrooms

Student enrollment: total: 300; average class: 30
Age: most 10-17; next 18-33; next 33-over
Level: most beg; next adv beg and int; next adv

Entrance requirements: none

Classes: AFRO-CARIBBEAN: combined levels; AFRO-JAZZ: combined levels; BODY TONING AND REDUCING; DISCO DANCE

Adult beg: see Afro-Caribbean, Afro-jazz, exercise, and disco classes above
Children (ages 3-12): AFRO-CARIBBEAN and AFRO-JAZZ (Saturdays only)
Teens: AFRO-CARIBBEAN and AFRO-JAZZ

Special courses/instruction: Drum classes; Private classes

Accompaniment: drums, bells

Holidays: national holidays; Sundays

Fees: $5/registration fee; $3/class; $12/month, 1 class per week; $60/term (20 weeks), 1 class per week; other rates for other series

Scholarships: Full scholarships available

Company affiliations: The La Rocque Bey Dancers and Drummers; the Afro-American Youth Club; students also participate in the school's annual spring concert, held last year at the Symphony Space theatre

Principal faculty: La Rocque Bey (dance), Paul Harris (drum), Arthur Maddox (drum), William McPherson (drum), Debbie Wilson (dance), Anthony Wooden (dance)

Summary statement: "The La Rocque Bey School of Dance Theatre is dedicated to serving the privileged and the underprivileged in the New York metropolitan area and surrounding communities. The majority of the school's efforts are directed toward the performing arts such as dance, music, and drama. However, there are also classes in African languages, karate, and reducing. Through these cultural experiences students have the opportunity to develop into performing artists by participating in classes and workshops. The workshops consist of an adult group, a teenage group, and a tiny tot group. Each group is searching for its specified talents and developing them by studying some of the old approved ideas and trying out new ones. This is accomplished by performing in the classrooms, listening to lectures on cultural achievement, and exchanging ideas among themselves. The La Rocque Bey School of Dance Theatre also credits itself with having two professional performing groups: the La Rocque Bey Dancers and Drummers (an adult group), and the Afro-American Youth Club (a teenage group). Both companies have appeared extensively throughout the East Coast, Midwest, and Canada."

PHIL BLACK DANCE STUDIO

1630 Broadway (51/52nd Street)
New York, New York 10019
(212-CI7-2675)

Techniques offered: JAZZ, TAP, BALLET

Established: 1961

Director: Phil Black

Facilities: 2 studios; dressing rooms; bathrooms

Student enrollment: total: 400; average class: 20
Age: most 18-25; next 10-17; next 25-33; next 33-over
Level: most beg; next adv beg; next int; next adv

Entrance requirements: none

Classes: JAZZ: beg, adv beg, int, adv; TAP: beg, adv beg, int, adv; BALLET: beg-int

Frank Gimpaya

PHIL BLACK
DANCE STUDIO
ON DONUTS
PIZZA
PIZZA

Children and teens (Saturdays only): TAP: beg, adv beg; JAZZ: beg

Special courses/instruction: Performing workshops: Private classes

Accompaniment: records and congo drum

Holidays: national holidays; Sundays

Fees: $3.50/class; $3/class, pro rate; $25/10 classes; $50/hour, private classes and choreography

Scholarships: none

Company affiliations: none

Principal faculty: Phil Black (jazz, tap), Robin Black (ballet), Dennis Dennehey (jazz), Jean Giordano (tap), Betty Thomas (tap), Herb Wilson (jazz)

Summary statement: "The School's reputation speaks for itself. Students come to study from Canada, Europe, and all parts of America. We specialize in teaching a variety of jazz styles such as African Rock, Modern Jazz, Blues, and Broadway styles. We strive for strength, control, and perfection. Phil Black worked sixteen years on Broadway and has choreographed for Broadway and television. Among his students are Goldie Hawn, Joey Heatherton, George Segal, Vivian Reed, and Eddie Mecca."

Authors' note: Phil Black's classes are all business. He doesn't coddle his students—not even the small fry he teaches from the cast of ***Annie.*** But they always come back for more. Show business dancers find that Black's classes help them keep up with the latest jazz styles. It's a good idea to warm up on your own before taking one, though, because they move fast from the moment they begin.

ALONSO CASTRO DANCE THEATRE

5 West 20th Street
New York, New York 10011
(212-992-4403)

Techniques offered: MODERN, BALLET, SPANISH DANCE

Established: 1971

Director: Alonso Castro

Facilities: 3 studios; dressing rooms; bathrooms; showers

Student enrollment: total: 60; classes limited to 20
Age: most 18-25; next 25-33; next 33-over
Level: most beg and adv beg; next int; next adv

Entrance requirements: minimum age, 15; all students start as beginners and progress through the class levels

Classes: MODERN: beg, adv beg, adv int; BALLET: basic, beg, int, adv; SPANISH DANCE

Adult beg; see basic ballet class above

Special courses/instruction: Ten-week summer workshop (June 19-August); Coaching

Accompaniment: piano, drums, records

Holidays: legal holidays; Sundays

Fees: $4/class; $35/10 classes (there is a time limit)

Scholarships: Full, part, and work-study scholarships are available.

Company affiliations: Alonso Castro Dance Theatre

Principal faculty: Alonso Castro (modern, ballet), Maria Nora (Spanish), Douglas Turnbaugh (ballet)

Summary statement: "The school emphasizes relaxation (principles of yoga), awareness of one's own body as an instrument, and developing the student's personality and individuality as a dancer. Students are given a chance to participate in performances with the Alonso Castro Dance Theatre. Before founding his own company, Alonso Castro performed classical Spanish dance. He also appeared with the Irene Fokine Ballet Company and the Edith Stephen Dance Connection."

CHAMBER DANCE GROUP
226 West 56th Street
3rd Floor
New York, New York 10019
(212-925-5375)

Techniques offered: BALLET, MODERN, JAZZ TAP

Established: 1977

Director: Nannette Bearden

Facilities: 2 studios; dressing rooms; bathrooms; showers

Student enrollment: total: 50; average class: 12
Age: most 18-25; next 25-33; next 10-17
Level: most int; next adv; next beg

Entrance requirements: none

Classes: BALLET: beg, int, adv, adagio, stretch; JAZZ TAP
Adult beg: BALLET: basics class
Children: BALLET: children's classes
Teens: 2-hour BALLET-MODERN DANCE WORKSHOP

Special courses/instruction: Teacher's training course (July and August); Private classes; Coaching

Accompaniment: piano, records

Holidays: Easter, summer break, Christmas; Sundays

Fees: $3.50/class; $30/10 classes; $22.50/10 classes, pro rate; $10/private class; up to $25/coaching

Scholarships: Partial scholarships are available.

Company affiliations: The Contemporary Chamber Dance Group

Principal faculty: Monica Diaz (ballet), Sonya Dobrovinska (ballet, teenagers' workshop, teacher's training course), Marvin Gordon (ballet), Marian Horosko (ballet, stretch), Jeffrey James (jazz tap), Keith Lee (ballet)

A jazz class at the Chamber Dance Group.
Ron Reagan

Summary statement: "The Chamber Dance Group's philosophy is to dev… awareness of the importance of dance and its relatio… to the total personality of the individual. Secondly, we… y to give youngsters, as well as adults, an environment of creative expression and an outlet for individual growth; and to bring to the community at large an arts program that will revitalize the neighborhood and serve as a resource center for other arts groups. We plan to give Sunday studio concerts and courses in dance appreciation, as well as organize monthly visits to various dance performances."

CLARK CENTER FOR THE PERFORMING ARTS
939 Eighth Avenue (57th Street)
New York, New York 10019
(212-246-4818)

Techniques offered: MODERN, JAZZ, AFRO-ETHNIC, TAP, BALLET, EXERCISE

Established: 1959

Director: Louise Roberts

Facilities: 2 studios; dressing rooms; bathrooms; showers

Student enrollment: average class: 35-45
Age: most 18-25; next 25-33; next 33-over; next 10-17
Level: most adv beg; next int; next beg; next adv

Entrance requirements: none

Classes: MODERN (Horton): beg, int; MODERN (Limón): int, int-adv; JAZZ: beg, adv beg, int; AFRO-ETHNIC (Dunham): beg, int; AFRO-ETHNIC (Brazilian): mixed class for all levels; TAP: beg, adv beg, int; BALLET: beg, int; ADULT EXERCISE

Adult beg: see beg modern, jazz, Afro-ethnic, tap, and ballet classes above

Children: BALLET and TAP classes (Saturdays only)

Special courses/instruction: Special summer courses (vary each year)

Accompaniment: piano, percussion

Holidays: national holidays; Sundays; no Saturday classes in July and August

Fees: $5/year, registration fee; $3/class, adults; $2/class, children; $2.50/class, pro rate for union members; $27.50/10 classes; $50/20 classes, 2 per week

Scholarships: Work-study scholarships are available for students preparing for a performing or teaching career who are free to attend program of classes designed by the school; students are chosen by audition, according to potential and financial need.

Company affiliations: Pepsi Bethel Authentic Jazz Dance Theatre; Fred Benjamin Dance Company; Charles Moore Dances and Drums of Africa; Clark Center also presents an annual summer dance festival at the City University of New York Graduate Center Mall on 42nd Street, which includes a New Choreographers Series of works by promising young artists produced gratis.

Principal faculty: Jill Albert (modern), Fred Benjamin (jazz), Pepsi Bethel (jazz), Shelley Frankel (jazz), Eleanor Harris (tap), Romana Krysanowska (ballet), Richard Levi (modern), Loremil (Brazilian), Judy Lasko (Limón), Lenore Latimer (Limón), Charles Moore (Dunham), Marjorie Perces (Horton), Lucinda Ransom (ballet), Tina Steinway (modern)

Summary statement: "The main thrust of our program is in modern, jazz, and ethnic dance forms. Because we believe in providing students with a well-rounded dance education, we also teach some ballet classes. We feel our low tuition fees, friendly atmosphere, and high artistic standards make it possible for all kinds of dance students to study here—for professional training, avocation, and recreation. Clark Center was the first home of Alvin Ailey's American Dance Theatre. Besides Mr. Ailey, among the choreographers whose creative lives have been launched, assisted, or enhanced by Clark Center are George Faison, Fred Benjamin, Art Bauman, Kei Takei, Diane McIntyre, Bill Dunas, and Eleo Pomare."

Authors' note: What the worn, cramped studios at Clark Center lack in ambience they more than make up for in the quality and diversity of classes. The teaching staff is among the finest around for modern, jazz, and Afro-ethnic dance. To give you an idea: Pepsi Bethel began his career as one of Whitey's Lindy Hoppers at the famed Savoy Ballroom in Harlem. After attending Adelphi University and appearing in a number of Broadway musicals, he formed his own company, the Pepsi Bethel Authentic Jazz Dance Theatre. Bethel is a small, wiry man who moves and talks fast; you have to be in shape for even his beginner classes, which progress at a brisk clip and are attended by a good many professionals. Fred Benjamin has also danced on Broadway. He has performed with Talley Beatty's company and currently directs his own troupe. As a teacher he says he specializes "in preparing dancers for auditions and showing them how to perform and sell choreography." Shelley Frankel performed with Donald McKayle; Lenore Latimer, a former member of the José Limón Dance Company, has taught at Connecticut College and Bard College. Marge Perces, who danced with the late Lester Horton, also teaches Horton technique at the Alvin Ailey school. Charles Moore is a past member of the Alvin Ailey American Dance Theatre and the Donald McKayle Dance Company. His concert group, Charles Moore Dances and Drums of Africa, is well known to New York audiences. Lucinda Ransom also performed with Alvin Ailey.

At a recent celebration of the Center's twentieth anniversary, director Louise Roberts announced plans to move the school to the 444-448 buildings on West 42nd Street's Theatre Row. Clark Center's new home, which should be ready for occupancy by June 1980, will include four new studios and a 250-seat theatre especially designed for dance.

CAROL CONWAY SCHOOL OF DANCE

35 Bond Street (same as East 3rd Street)
New York, New York 10012
(212-674-8034)

Techniques offered: MODERN

Established: 1975

Director: Carol Conway

Facilities: 1 studio; dressing rooms; bathroom

Student enrollment: total: 65; average class: 15
Age: most 18-25; next 25-33; next 33-over; next 12-17
Level: most int; next adv; next adv beg; next beg

Entrance requirements: minimum age, 12

Classes: MODERN: elem, int, adv
Adult beg: see elem modern class above

Special courses/instruction: Summer workshop; Private classes (by arrangement)

Accompaniment: none or percussion

Holidays: New Year's Day, Memorial Day, July 4, Labor Day, Thanksgiving Day, Christmas Day; Sundays

Fees: \$5/first single class; \$4/class; \$35/10 classes, 1 per week; \$30/10 classes, 2 or more per week

Scholarships: for apprentices to the company only

Company affiliations: Carol Conway Dance Company

Principal faculty: Will Ansorge, Carol Conway

Summary statement: "The modern dance classes taught at the school are designed to train a dancer to be able to move with the greatest possible range, power, and speed of attack. Integration at the center of the body and development of a strong, flexible spine make possible a broad range of movement through contraction, spiral, and arch. Through integration at the center a dancer is also able to lengthen the muscles of the legs and so achieve greater range in movement through space and in extension work. Training in correct transfer of body weight and development of the ability to move with a controlled flow of energy enables a dancer to avoid injury and so enjoy a longer career. On a regular basis throughout the year, the production and performing facilities of our loft studio are made available free of charge to new choreographers, so that they may show their dances."

Authors' note: Carol Conway studied and performed with Erick Hawkins for a number of years, and his anatomically based, free-flowing technique is very much a part of Conway's teaching approach. She is an interestingly long and gazelle-like dancer, whose classes are good for adult beginners and dancers who have been working with too much tension. Will Ansorge is a member of Conway's company and has also studied with Hawkins.

MERCE CUNNINGHAM DANCE STUDIO

Westbeth Artists Complex
463 West Street
New York, New York 10014
(212-691-9751)

Techniques offered: MODERN

Established: 1959

Artistic director: Merce Cunningham

Administrator: David Vaughan

Facilities: 2 studios; dressing rooms; bathrooms, showers

Student enrollment: total: 250; average class: upper levels, 35 and over; lower levels, 15
Age: most 18-25; next 25-33; next 33-over; next 10-17
Level: most int; next adv beg; next adv; next beg

Entrance requirements: New students with less than 2 years previous training must take the fundamentals class; those with 2 years previous training must take the elementary class; advancement is at the instructor's discretion; no latecomers to class.

Classes: MODERN (Cunningham): fundamentals, elem, elem-int (Saturdays only), int, adv (by invitation only—company classes taught by Merce Cunningham)

Adult beg: see fundamentals class above

Special courses/instruction: Christmas course in technique and dance composition; Summer workshops in technique, composition, and repertory; Video dance workshops

Accompaniment: piano

Holidays: New Year's Day, Memorial Day, Labor Day, Thanksgiving Day, Christmas Day; Sundays

Fees: $15/one-time registration fee; $4/class, trial class only; $31/10 classes (must be taken within 5 weeks)

Scholarships: Full: 5 boys, 4 girls (varies); chosen according to professional dance potential, talent, and financial need; reviewed quarterly

Company affiliations: Merce Cunningham and Dance Company

Principal faculty: Ruth Barnes, Merce Cunningham, Barbara Ensley, Meg Harper, Albert Reid, Valda Setterfield, Marya Ursin, and members of the company

Summary statement: "The technique is aimed toward training a student to be a professional dancer, with special emphasis on the technical requirements and the contemporary ideas of music and visual collaboration that are involved in the work of Merce Cunningham and Dance Company."

Authors' note: Cunningham likes to make unannounced teaching appearances in the elementary and intermediate classes. It's a rare treat—he's a wonderful teacher.

DANCE CENTER – 92ND STREET YM-YWHA
1395 Lexington Avenue
New York, New York 10028
(212-427-6000, ext 721)

Techniques offered: MODERN, BALLET, TAP

Established: about 1942

Director: Sharon Luckman

Assistant director: Hillary Gal

Facilities: 3 studios; dressing rooms, bathrooms; showers

Student enrollment: total: 425; average class: 10-15
Age: most 18-25; next 25-33; next 33-over; next 10-17
Level: most beg; next adv beg; next int; next adv

Entrance requirements: none

Classes: MODERN (Limón): int-adv; MODERN (Redlich): int-adv
Adult beg: (mornings and evenings): MODERN: introduction, beg, int; BALLET: beg, int; TAP: beg
Children (ages 3-17): graded classes in pre-dance and rhythmic play, modern dance, and ballet

Special courses/instruction: Workshops with guest teachers and companies are planned; Teacher training workshop in children's instruction; Workshop for dance accompanists

Accompaniment: piano, percussion

Holidays: all legal holidays and Jewish holidays; weekends

Fees: $3.50/class, Redlich and Limón classes only; all other classes paid on a semester basis, with different rates for different classes; discount for children taking two courses per semester

Scholarships: Partial for children, and work scholarships for serious dance students training for careers

Company affiliations: Don Redlich Dance Company

Principal faculty: Nancy Bielski (ballet), Bruce Block (modern), Kim Cahill (tap), Robyn Cutler (Limón), Hillary Gal (modern), Ellen Kogan (modern, ballet), Sharon Luckman (modern), Idelle Packer (modern), Fran Parker (modern), Don Redlich and members of his company (modern), Kathy Robens (modern), Don Washington, Jr. (jazz)

Summary statement: "We have a graded dance program for students ages three years and up, geared to both professionally oriented and recreational dancers. The emphasis is on modern dance as a means to artistic expression and personal growth. Our children's program includes dance technique along with structured improvisation and composition."

Authors' note: The 92nd Street "Y" is a landmark of modern dance history. Martha Graham, Doris Humphrey, José Limón, and Pearl Lang, among others, launched their work there. Currently the Don Redlich Dance Company is in residence.

DANCE CIRCLE
763 Eighth Avenue (46/47th Street)
New York, New York 10036
(212-541-7986)

Techniques offered:	BALLET
Established:	1969
Director:	Alfredo Corvino
Facilities:	2 studios; dressing rooms; bathrooms
Student enrollment:	total: 80-100; average class: 18 Age: most 18-25; next 25-33; next 10-17 and 33-over Level: about equal proportions of all levels
Entrance requirements:	none
Classes:	BALLET: elem, sub-int, int, adv, pointe, adagio, characte ***Adult beg***: BALLET: basic class ***Men***: BALLET: men's class (for regular students)
Special courses/instruction:	Coaching (for roles)
Accompaniment:	piano
Holidays:	New Year's, Easter, 2 weeks at the end of summer, Christmas; Sundays
Fees:	$3.50/class; $30/10 classes; $25/hour, coaching for nonprofessionals; $15/hour. coaching for professionals
Scholarships:	available for students with potential
Company affiliations:	Dance Circle Company (a classical repertory company made up of scholarship students at the school)
Principal faculty:	Andra Corvino, Alfredo Corvino, Ernesta Corvino, Richard Lile
Summary statement:	"We offer six grades of ballet technique, and stress enjoyment. Dance without enjoyment is worthless. Even those who will not become professionals should understand the nuances of dancing. The Dance Circle Company performs in the New York City area."
Authors' note:	This is a small, friendly, family-run studio. Alfredo Corvino performed with the Kurt Jooss Ballet and the Ballet Russe de Monte Carlo. A kindly and dedicated teacher, he is much respected and beloved by New York's professional dancers. His detailed explanations and analytic approach to training are particularly helpful to modern and jazz dancers who want to strengthen their technique.

THE DANCE CONNECTION
55 Bethune Street #630A
New York, New York 10014
(212-989-2250)

Techniques offered:	MODERN

Established: 1969

Director: Edith Stephen

Facilities: 1 studio; dressing rooms; bathrooms; showers

Student enrollment: total: 75; average class: 10-12
Age: most 18-25; next 25-33; next 33-over; next 10-17
Level: most adv beg; next int; next adv; next beg

Entrance requirements: none

Classes: MODERN: beg, int, adv; MODERN CHOREOGRAPHY AND IMPROVISATION: int, adv
Adult beg: see beg class above
Children: creative modern dance for ages 6-13

Special courses/instruction: "Art of Performing" workshop (for intermediate and advanced dancers); Private classes; Coaching

Accompaniment: records, drums

Holidays: national holidays; Sundays

Fees: $4/adult's class; $3.50/children's class; $35/10 classes; $10/hour, private class

Scholarships: Full, partial, and work-study available; chosen according to serious interest and consistency; reviewed biannually

Company affiliations: Edith Stephen Dance Connection

Principal faculty: Edith Stephen and members of the company

Summary statement: "Classes at the Dance Connection join all the various aspects of dance—technique, improvisation, choreography, and the art of performing. We try to give the student a centering experience the purposes of which are: to emerge with control of the whole body; to broaden the range of movement so that the dancer can work in any technique, knowing that his/her body has been developed for strength, alignment, flexibility, and relaxation; to tap the inner creative sources and have the courage to express them; to learn the elements of choreography and find out what his/her special contribution is; and finally to be able to perform, learning that dance is bigger than life and yet finding the most natural way of expressing this. What is unique about the school is that we still limit the classes to twelve people. All get individual attention and private consultation so we can find out their weaknesses and strengths, and see that they develop and improve."

DANCE MEWS
43 East 19th Street
New York, New York 10003
(212-982-7299)

Techniques offered: MODERN-BALLET

Established: 1976

Director: Satoru Shimazaki

Facilities: 1 studio; dressing rooms; bathrooms

Student enrollment: total: 75; average class: 12
Age: most 18-25; next 25-33
Level: most int; next adv; next adv beg

Entrance requirements: none

Classes: MODERN-BALLET: beg-int

Accompaniment: piano

Holidays: national holidays; weekends

Fees: $3.50/class; $30/10 classes

Scholarships: Full and work scholarships are available; students must audition successfully, but more important, want to become serious dancers and artists.

Company affiliations: Satoru Shimazaki and Dancers

Principal faculty: Satoru Shimazaki

Summary statement: "The technique is derived from a strong balletic base and various modern techniques. The emphasis is on centering, strength, and linear movement. Clear positions and bodily control are to be maintained and developed. The dancer must learn to concentrate in order to see himself and others in space."

THE DANCE MOVEMENT

218 West 72nd Street
New York, New York 10023
and
231 East 51st Street
New York, New York 10022
(212-724-5645)

Techniques offered: BALLET, EXERCISE

Established: 1974

Business manager: Sherry Hinkle

Director: Gail Kachadurian

Facilities: 3 studios; dressing rooms; bathrooms; showers

Student enrollment: total: 250; average class: 15
Age: most 25-33; next 33-over; next 18-25; next 10-17
Level: equal proportions of all levels

Entrance requirements: none

Classes*: BALLET: beg, adv beg, int, adv, pointe, variations; BALLET EXERCISE

Adult beg: see beg ballet and exercise class above
Children: BALLET: pre-ballet (ages 4-6), children's I (ages 7-9), children's II (ages 10-12)

Special courses/instruction: Choreographers' workshop, a weekly class in which faculty members choreograph dances on intermediate and advanced students; the works are sometimes performed at student recitals; Private classes

Accompaniment: recorded music

Holidays: New Year's, last two weeks in August, Thanksgiving weekend, Christmas; Sundays

Fees: adults must register for 6-week terms: $25/6 classes, 1 per week; $46/12 classes, 2 per week; $62/18 classes, 3 per week; rates continue to decrease according to the number of classes taken per week; $85/18-week semester for children, 1 class per week; $25/hour, private classes

Scholarships: none

Company affiliations: The Dance Movement

Principal faculty: Roberta Altman, Dale Brown, Jack Hertzog, Gail Kachadurian, Robbie Kaplan, Pam Mundy, Stephanie Sorine; and guest teachers, including Bruce Wells of the Connecticut Ballet and formerly of the New York City Ballet

Summary statement: "This school is unique in the way it teaches ballet. Our concept is individualized, noncompetitive, pleasurable learning on a serious and professional level. That really isn't a contradiction. We are not for the most part training professional dancers. Our students come because they love ballet and want to understand it better; they want to know how it feels to dance, to perform. Or they come because they want to understand their own bodies better; for health and grace. And many of them come for all those things. Director Gail Kachadurian was a ten-year member of the New York City Ballet and also has a B.S. from New York University in dance therapy. Our teachers are completely professional. They have danced with some of the best companies in the world: the New York City Ballet, the Paris Opera Ballet, the Pennsylvania Ballet. They are young and they still dance. So they can still demonstrate correctly and beautifully. We also have a Ballet Exercise division for people who want to concertrate more on firming and slimming and less on dancing. Our studio facilities are large, clean, and beautiful. We have the best floors, mirrors, and lighting available."

*Please note that some classes are held only at the West Side studio and some only at the East Side location. Be sure to check.

Larry Rhodes' advanced/professional ballet class at DancerSchool.
Otto M. Berk

DANCERSCHOOL

450 Avenue of the Americas (10/11th Street)
New York, New York 10011
(212-260-8367)

Techniques offered: BALLET, JAZZ, EXERCISE, GYMNASTICS

Established: 1977

Administrative director: Taffy Wendelken

Artistic director: Dennis Wayne

Facilities: 3 studios; dressing rooms; bathrooms; showers

Student enrollment: total: 350; average class: 15-25
Age: most 18-25; next 25-33; next 10-17; next 33-over
Level: most int; next adv; next beg; next adv beg

Entrance requirements: none

Classes: BALLET: beg, int-adv, adv-pro; JAZZ: beg-int; SPECIAL EXERCISE

Adult beg: BALLET: adult beg, beg-int; see also special exercise class above

Children (ages 5-13): INTRODUCTION TO DANCE (Saturdays only); BALLET: beg I, beg II, int I (Saturdays only); GYMNASTICS

Men: a men's ballet class is planned for the near future

Special courses/instruction: A summer intensive course to include advanced ballet technique, pointe, adagio, a men's ballet class, and modern dance classes is planned for the near future.

Accompaniment: piano and tapes

Holidays: national holidays; Sundays

Fees: $4/class; $4.50/adult beg ballet; $35/10 classes, ballet; $20/5 classes, ballet; $35/10 exercise classes; other rates for other classes and other discount series available; children's tuition is paid by the semester

Scholarships: Full and work for advanced students

Company affiliations: Dennis Wayne's Dancers, a ballet and modern dance repertory company

Principal faculty: Dick Bonelle (exercise), Tom Cooperman (jazz), Esfir Goldenshtein (gymnastics), Mary Keough (adult beg and int ballet, children's classes), Michelle Marceau (jazz), Haynes Owens (int-adv ballet), Richard Ploch (adult ballet), Lawrence Rhodes (adv-pro ballet)

Summary statement: "DancerSchool and its studios physically reflect a new concept in dance training by providing abundant light, air flow, and places to relax and rest designed to complement and refresh the body. The requirement of the dancer's art—gaining complete control of his or her body—is an arduous one. Recognizing this, the school and its environment, while providing the necessary training equipment and following a thorough and demanding curriculum, also emphasize the body's role and its needs for comfort, ease, and spontaneity. The technical training given is of the highest quality, and the faculty reflects this search for excellence. Offering a wide variety of dance classes including ballet, modern, jazz, adagio, and special exercise at all levels, the aim of the school is to develop dancers according to their own needs and not by any one 'technique.' "

Authors' note: With backing from actress Joanne Woodward, Dennis Wayne founded the Dancers company and school after a bright career as a featured dancer with the Joffrey Ballet and American Ballet Theatre. Like most new schools, this one has had the usual turnover of teachers and classes during its first two years of existence, but it seems to be operating on a more even keel now. The present faculty is impressive. Larry Rhodes has been a principal with the Joffrey Ballet, the Harkness Ballet, the Eliot Feld Ballet, and the Netherlands Dance Theatre and is currently with Dancers. Haynes Owens has also performed with the Joffrey and has built up an enthusiastic student following (he has a droll sense of humor that people love). Tom Cooperman is a Broadway dancer currently appearing with the American Dance Machine company. Esfir Goldenshtein, the children's gymnastics teacher, is a Master of Sports from Russia.

DANCE THEATRE OF HARLEM

466 West 152nd Street
New York, New York 10031
(212-690-2800)

Techniques offered: BALLET, TAP, ETHNIC, MODERN, EXERCISE

Established: 1969

Directors: Arthur Mitchell and Karel Shook

Facilities: 3 studios; dressing rooms; bathrooms; showers

Student enrollment: total: 1100; average class: 26
Age: most 10-17; next 18-25; next 25-33; next 33-over
Level: most beg; next adv beg; next int; next adv

Entrance requirements: no children admitted under 8 years old; children must take a minimum of 3 classes per week

Classes: BALLET: beg, int, adv, pointe, adagio; ETHNIC: open to students of all levels; TAP: beg, int, adv; MODERN (Graham): int; ADULT EXERCISE CLASS (Saturdays)
Adult beg: see beg classes above
Children: BALLET: all levels and pointe; TAP: all levels; ETHNIC: all levels
Men: BALLET

Special courses/instruction: Repertory workshop (advanced students only); Movement for singers; Vocal technique; Costume design and sewing

Accompaniment: piano, percussion

Holidays: national holidays, Martin Luther King's birthday; Sundays

Fees: *adults*: (ages 18 and up): \$10/annual registration fee; \$5/class; \$30/10 classes; other series for Sept-June term
children: tuition ranges from \$180-\$324 for Sept-June term, depending on level of advancement

Scholarships: Full, partial, and work scholarships are available; students are chosen according to talent, physical proportions, and financial need; full scholarships are offered to children in "Artist-in-School" program by arrangement with their public schools.

Company affiliations: Dance Theatre of Harlem; apprentices to the company are chosen from scholarship students and get full tuition paid, as well as a \$75-per-week stipend.

Principal faculty: Mary Barbour (costume design), Vicki Fedine (ballet), Mary Hinkson (modern), Tanaquil LeClercq (ballet), Arthur Mitchell (ballet), Melvin Purnell (ethnic), Karel Shook (ballet), Victoria Simon (ballet), Carol Sumner (ballet), Ann Tyus (tap), Zelda Wynn (costume design)

Summary statement: "The Dance Theatre of Harlem is dedicated to making the finest training available in all the disciplines we offer at a price that can be afforded by those who might otherwise be deprived. It might be said that all students at DTH are on scholarship, since our fees are very low and subsidized to allow everyone to be able to study. We are also involved in making the performing arts available to a wide audience—to those who have hitherto never been in a theatre other than to see a movie. Another one of our specialties is teaching children. Whether or not students go into professional dance, the discipline gained from classical training improves the quality of their everyday lives. All the skills taught at DTH are geared to foster a sense of achievement."

Authors' note: Director Arthur Mitchell was the first black dancer ever to perform with the New York City Ballet. From there he went on to form the first nationally recognized black classical ballet company and school.

MADAME DARVASH BALLET STUDIO

1845 Broadway (62nd Street)
3rd Floor
New York, New York 10023
(212-265-5608)

Techniques offered: BALLET

Established: 1975

Director: Gabriella Taub-Darvash

Facilities: 1 studio; dressing rooms; bathrooms; showers

Student enrollment: total: 200; average class: 25-30
Age: most 18-25; next 10-17; next 25-33
Level: most adv; next int; next adv beg and beg

Entrance requirements: none

Classes: BALLET: adult beg, int-adv, adv, pro, pas de deux, variations
Adult beg: see adult beg ballet class above

Special courses/instruction: Summer course in character dance; Coaching (for professionals)

Accompaniment: piano

Holidays: Christmas, Thanksgiving, New Year's; Sundays

Fees: $4/class, $35/10 classes; pro rate: $3.50/class, $30/10 classes

Scholarships: none

Company affiliations: none

Principal faculty: Madame Gabriella Taub-Darvash (adv, pro, int-adv, beg); Jody Fugate (int-adv, beg); K. Guzikova (character); Nora Kovach (int-adv), Donald Mahler (pas de deux); Rosanna Seravalli (int-adv, adv, beg)

Summary statement: "The training at this school is strictly Kirov-oriented. Madame Darvash is a magna cum laude graduate from the Lunarcharsky Choreographic Institute in Moscow. She completed her balletic studies at the Kirov School in Leningrad. Nora Kovach is also a Kirov product, having had private classes from Agrippina Vaganova for one year during her training there. At our school there is a personal approach to each student's problems, body type, and cultural level."

DAVIS DANCE CENTER

100 West 23rd Street
New York, New York 10011
(212-255-8005)

Techniques offered: JAZZ, TAP, MODERN, BALLET

Established: 1975

Director: Joe Davis

Facilities: 1 studio; dressing rooms; bathrooms

Student enrollment: total: 100; average class: 8
Age: most 18-25; next 25-33; next 33-over; next 10-17
Level: most adv beg; next beg; next int; next adv

Entrance requirements: none

Classes: FUNDAMENTALS OF TECHNIQUE (for students with little or no previous training); JAZZ: basics I and II, int, adv int; TAP: basics I and II, int; MODERN: elem, int; BALLET: adult beg

Adult beg: see fundamentals of technique, jazz basics, tap basics, elementary modern dance, and adult beg ballet classes above

Special courses/instruction: Coaching

Accompaniment: piano, percussion, records

Holidays: national holidays; Sundays

Fees: $4/class; $3.50/class, pro rate; $35/10 classes; $30/10 classes, pro rate; $30/10 classes, 4 per week

Scholarships: Work scholarships are available for students with financial need and the desire to learn.

Company affiliations: none

Principal faculty: Joe Davis (tap, fundamentals of technique), Oldyna Dynowska (ballet), Jean Hilzinger (jazz), Saeko Ichinohe (modern), Robert Lane (jazz), Gail Pearson (jazz), Frank Pietri (jazz)

Summary statement: "Through my school, I hope to provide a center where top-quality dance training is offered by a faculty truly concerned with the individual development of each student, under conditions of maximum support for both teacher and student. For this reason, classes are limited in size, with graded levels to assure steady and proper growth. In addition, I want a school where not only performing dancers, but singers, actors, and potential choreographers or teachers can feel comfortable—their needs understood and met, their goals and the part dance plays in them, respected. The Davis Dance Center offers a unique specialty: a comprehensive tap dance technique that utilizes the technique developed in other major dance forms (ballet, jazz, and modern). In other words, we teach a tap technique that not only focuses on rhythm but uses the whole body moving in space."

DOWNTOWN DANCE STUDIOS and DOWNTOWN COMMUNITY DANCE WORKSHOP*

189 Lexington Avenue (31/32nd Street)
New York, New York 10016
(212-683-1967)

Techniques offered: BALLET, MODERN, JAZZ, SPANISH DANCE, EXERCISE

Established: 1970

Executive director: Robert Shuster

Artistic director: Paschal Guzman

Facilities: 2 studios; dressing rooms; bathrooms

*The Downtown Community Dance Workshop is the name of the children's program at the Downtown Dance Studios.

Student enrollment: total: 150; average class: 10
Age: most 10-17; next 18-25; next 25-33; next 33-over
Level: most beg; next adv beg; next int; next adv

Entrance requirements: minimum age, 4; children must be registered by parent

Classes: BALLET: fundamentals, beg, adv beg, int; MODERN JAZZ: int; SPANISH DANCE: beg, int; FLAMENCO: adv; BALLET EXERCISE

Adult beg: see ballet fundamentals and exercise class above
Children (ages 4-14): graded classes are available in BALLET, including pointe, according to child's age and experience; SPANISH DANCE

Special courses/instruction: Four-week summer workshop for children (ages 6 and up); Private classes

Accompaniment: tape, records, piano, guitar

Holidays: national holidays; summer breaks in the first week of July and at the end of August; Sundays

Fees: $5/class; $3.50/class, pro rate; $30/10 classes; $25/10 classes, pro rate; $25/ballet fundamentals course (8 classes); $15/month, children's workshop (2 classes per week); $25/2 classes per week, summer workshop; $40/3 classes per week, summer workshop; $15/hour, private classes

Scholarships: Full and partial available for workshop children who attend classes regularly and participate in performances

Company affiliations: Paschal Guzman/Downtown Ballet Company; Mercedes Lois Spanish Dance Company

Principal faculty: Machiko Cho (ballet, modern), Sima Damestoy (ballet), Paschal Guzman (ballet), Charles Haack (ballet), Socorra Jones (exercise), Shelagh Kruger (exercise), Mercedes Lois (Spanish), Beth Rosenbluth (ballet), Gail Waterman (ballet, modern jazz)

Summary statement: "The Children's Workshop is designed to provide youngsters in our community, especially those of Hispanic tradition, with an introduction to dance and an awareness of their cultural heritage. We believe that the professional discipline of dance—especially ballet—body control, better work habits, and an expanded interest in all the arts create healthier persons. Classes are aimed at teaching basic body movement and the relationship of the body to the space in which its moves, whether alone or in coordination with others. Rhythmic exercises lead to group movements in patterns and then into choreographed combinations using Hispanic and other ethnic dance steps and music. Pride in and knowledge of our cultural heritage evolve from these experiences. Each group is taught at the level of the age and experience of its children. Older children come twice a week for a full one-and-a-half-hour session. Smaller children take pre-ballet for a single, shorter period each week. Workshop performances at public schools and elsewhere give all the children—performers and audience—artistic experience not otherwise obtainable. Classes at the Downtown Dance Studios are open to all students."

Authors' note: Paschal Guzman has performed with the Harkness Ballet, the Pennsylvania Ballet, and the National Ballet in Washington, D.C. Mercedes Lois formerly taught at the Harkness Ballet School.

LOUIS FALCO STUDIO

131 West 24th Street
New York, New York 10011
(212-691-9933)

Techniques offered: MODERN

Established: 1975

Directors: Louis Falco and Juan Antonio

Facilities: 1 studio; dressing rooms; bathrooms

Student enrollment: total: 250; average class: 30-40
Age: most 18-25; next 25-33; next 10-17; next 33-over
Level: most int, next adv

Entrance requirements: At present there are no classes below the intermediate level; dancers must audition for workshops.

Classes: MODERN: int, adv

Special courses/instruction: Repertory class; Improvisation workshops

Accompaniment: percussion

Holidays: national holidays; weekends

Fees: $4/class; $30/10 classes (with time limit)

Scholarships: work-study; chosen by audition and according to financial need

Company affiliations: Louis Falco Dance Company

Principal faculty: Juan Antonio and members of the Falco company

Summary statement: "We emphasize the joy of moving; breath; fall and rebound in movement; the challenge of technique—of having it and throwing it away."

Authors' note: For many years Louis Falco was a featured dancer with José Limón, and he and his company of superdancers teach a Limón-based technique. The movement is beautiful to watch and exhilarating to do—but you have to be in shape and know what you're doing. Most classes are fast-paced and energetic, with lots of use of momentum.

FARNWORTH AND HAUER SCHOOL OF DANCE

1697 Broadway (54/55th Street)
New York, New York 10019
(212-581-0599)

Techniques offered: BALLET, JAZZ, TAP, ACROBATICS

Established: 1966

Administrative director: Robert Hauer

Artistic directors: Don Farnworth and Charles Kelley

Facilities: 3 studios; dressing rooms; bathrooms

Student enrollment: total: 600; average class: 20-25
Age: most 18-25; next 10-17 and 25-33; next 33-over
Level: most int; next beg, adv beg and adv in equal proportions

Entrance requirements: none

Classes: BALLET: beg, int, adv int, adv; JAZZ: pre-beg, beg, beg-int, int-adv; TAP: beg, adv beg, int-adv, ACROBATICS: all levels

Adult beg: see pre-beg jazz class and beg ballet and tap classes above

Special courses/instruction: Six-week summer course for ballet teachers (from mid-July to end of August); Private classes

Accompaniment: piano, records, drums

Holidays: Memorial Day weekend, July 4, Labor Day week, Christmas to New Year's week; Sundays

Fees: $5/class; $4/class, pro rate for union members; $21/6 classes; $18/6 classes, pro rate; all series cards expire in 2 months; $40/hour, private classes

Scholarships: Full and work-study scholarships are available, primarily for intermediate-level students; recipients must take a minimum of 15 classes per week.

Company affiliations: Young America Dance Company (performs in public schools)

Principal faculty: Robert Atwood (ballet), Philip Cook (tap), Don Farnworth (ballet), Charles Kelley (jazz, tap, acrobatics), P.J. Tomc (jazz)

Summary statement: "Don Farnworth is best known for his unique, anatomically based method of teaching ballet technique, designed to improve posture, movement, and confidence in students who do not have the perfect body to start with. Students at the school are not encouraged to strive futilely for instant perfection; instead, they learn how to learn. They begin by finding out what their physical abilities really are and accepting themselves at their own level. Then students can realistically build a firm, secure foundation for expressive movement, and replace attitudes of fear, dejection, or defiance with self-confidence gained by strength and achievement. Youngsters learn that authority need not be threatening or condescending. Teachers at the school are warm, friendly people (not autocratic ballet masters)."

Authors' note: Don Farnworth is a positive-thinking man who devised his method of ballet training in the process of rehabilitating himself from polio. The idea is to improve movement range through correct body placement and by becoming sensitized to what the body is doing at all times. Farnworth teaches students to feel when they are straining and to learn to let go of excess tension in the muscles. He has helped a great many dancers recover from injuries, and they swear by him. (Several members of the Paul Taylor Dance Company, for example, attend his classes when they're in town.) Before his long association with the Farnworth studio, Charles Kelley used to teach at the Harkness Ballet School and the old June Taylor school in New York. Kelley doesn't go in for lengthy explanations, but sparks fly when he dances. In his tap classes, one learns style and vocabulary, more than mechanics. Philip Cook's slow and thorough teaching style is good for beginning tap students.

FOKINE BALLET SCHOOL

340 East 79th Street
New York, New York 10021
(212-TR6-4855)

Techniques offered: BALLET

Established: 1936

Director: Christine Fokine

Facilities: 1 studio; dressing rooms; bathrooms

Student enrollment: total: 260; average class: 15
Age: most 6-17; next 18-25; next 25-33; next 33-over
Level: equal proportions of all levels

Entrance requirements: none

Classes: BALLET: beg, beg-int, int, adv, pointe
Adult beg: see beg ballet class above
Children (ages 6 and up): BALLET: beg, int, adv, pointe (for girls ages 12 and older)

Special courses/instruction: Choreography for teachers; Coaching

Accompaniment: piano

Holidays: May 25-September 30; December 23-January 2; weekends

Fees: $5/class; $47.50/10 classes; $160/season, children's classes, 1 per week

Scholarships: none

Company affiliations: none

Principal faculty: Christine Fokine, Joyce Herring, Francis Patrelle

Summary statement: "We offer excellent training based on the Fokine Method. Personal attention is also stressed. Christine Fokine became a member of the Original Ballet Russe de Monte Carlo when she was sixteen years old and toured with them in Europe. Returning to this country, she joined the Metropolitan Opera Ballet and was also soloist for many seasons with the Fokine Ballet Company. She received her training in America with Michel Fokine, Anatole Vilzak, and Alexandra Fedorova. In Europe she studied with Princess Mathilde Kchessinska and Lubov Tchernicheva. Miss Fokine has taught ballet for forty-one years, during which time her main interest has been the training of children and young dancers. Both Francis Patrelle and Joyce Herring were previously associated with the Juilliard School."

Authors' note: The Fokine Ballet School was founded by Michel Fokine, the great Russian dancer and choreographer whose reforms ushered in the age of modern ballet. Fokine insisted that dancers use their entire bodies when they moved and that, rather than being purely decorative, ballet choreography should stem from dramatic action and characterization. His ballets are still performed all over the world, among them, "Les Sylphides," "Petrouchka," and the haunting solo he created for Anna Pavlova, "The Dying Swan."

FORELLA STUDIO

168 West 48th Street
3rd Floor
New York, New York 10036
(212-489-6390)

Techniques offered: JAZZ, BALLET

Established: 1972

Director: Ronn Forella

Facilities: 2 studios; dressing rooms; bathroom

Student enrollment: total: 250; average class: 15-20
Age: most 18-25; next 25-33; next 14-17; next 33-over
Level: most int; next adv beg; next beg; next adv

Entrance requirements: minimum age, 14

Classes: JAZZ: introduction, beg I, beg II, int, adv; BALLET: beg
Adult beg: see introduction to jazz class above

Special courses/instruction: Private classes: Coaching

Accompaniment: records, tambourine

Holidays: July 4, Labor Day, Thanksgiving, Christmas through New Year's Day; Sundays

Fees: $4.50/class; $35/10 classes (must be taken within six weeks); $30/hour, private classes or coaching

Scholarships: work-study available for dedicated students

Company affiliations: Second Century Dance Theatre

Principal faculty: Anna Maria Fanizzi (ballet), Ronn Forella (jazz), Michael Kubala (jazz), John Mederos (jazz)

Summary statement: "The school is designed to bring about an intelligent awareness of the body to dancers, through training with vitality and dedication. Enormous satisfaction for the novice as well as the professionally oriented dancer can be gained here! The jazz training utilizes ballectic body placement—straight spine and square hips—so the dancer can stand up securely and the legs and feet can stretch and be developed fully."

Authors' note: Ronn Forella has choreographed for films, Broadway musicals, television, and industrial shows, as well as for his own company, the Second Century Dance Theatre. His school, which is located in the heart of New York's theatre district, is heavily attended by Broadway dancers.

GELABERT STUDIOS
255 West 86th Street
New York, New York 10024
(212-TR4-7188)

Techniques offered: BALLET, REMEDIAL EXERCISE, MODERN, JAZZ

Established: 1958

Director: Raoul Gelabert, Ph.T., M.S.

Facilities: 2 studios; gymnasium; dressing rooms; bathrooms; showers

Student enrollment: total: 125; average class: 12-15
About equal proportions of all ages and levels

Entrance requirements: minimum of 2 classes per week for adults

Classes: BALLET: beg, int, adv, pointe; MODERN (Limón): beg, int; JAZZ: beg-int; BODY MOVEMENT: open to all levels (Gelabert's special remedial exercises to strengthen and stretch various parts of the body; for dancers and nondancers).

Adult beg: BALLET: adult beg class; see also body movement class above

Children: CREATIVE DANCE (for ages 3-6); BALLET (for ages 7 and up): beg and int classes

Special courses/instruction: Anatomy course (2 nights per week, held every fall); Intensive three-week June seminar in anatomy and kinesiology for the dancer; Private consultations

Accompaniment: percussion, records, tapes, piano

Holidays: national holidays, 5 weeks in summer, Christmas and Easter breaks; Sundays

Fees: $5.50/class in ballet; $6/class in modern dance or body movement; $47/10 ballet classes, 2 per week; $51/10 modern or body movement classes, 2 per week; $4.50/class in children's creative movement; $20/5 creative movement classes; $26/5 children's ballet classes, 1 per week; $50/10 children's ballet classes, 2 per week; $30-50/private consultations, depending on length of time

Scholarships: Partial scholarships available for children ages 9-11 with a minimum of one year previous training in ballet

Company affiliations: none

Principal faculty: Lois Chiarello (creative dance for children), Ann Clark (Limón), Raoul Gelabert (ballet, body movement, private consultations, anatomy and kinesiology seminars), Pamela Schwartz (body movement classes)

Summary statement: "Mr. Gelabert is a pioneer in the field of kinesiotherapy: the prevention of injuries and rehabilitation of the dancer's body to function properly. He believes the well-trained dancer must know the body's structure and movements. An awareness and understanding of the kinesthetic function of the dancer's body makes it possible to correct a particular position or movement that may be causing stress. The stress that eventually becomes a strain, and later an injury, can be avoided by correct execution, which relieves tension in the affected area of the body. The classes are carefully limited in number to fulfill the individual's needs and accomplish the following purposes: pointing out vulnerable areas of the body most affected by the demands of technique; analyzing the student's type of physique in regard to proportion, alignment, shape of legs, elasticity, or tightness, in order to develop better understanding of the individual body mechanism; conditioning the body to gain strength and flexibility for the improvement of dance technique, through the Gelabert exercises in the body movement class and carefully directed instruction in ballet technique."

Authors' note: Raoul Gelabert was trained in classical ballet technique (he was a student of Olga Preobrajenska and Bronislava Nijinska in Paris) as well as physical therapy and kinesiology. He has written a two-volume book, ***Raoul Gelabert's Anatomy for the Dancer***, which fully describes his views on injury prevention and illustrates his specially designed corrective exercises. He also writes periodic articles for ***Dancemagazine.*** Gelabert's classes are not what you would call dancy; but they have helped dancers who are recovering from injuries and who have physical problems or conditions that need remedial work.

THE MARTHA GRAHAM SCHOOL
316 East 63rd Street
New York, New York 10021
(212-TE8-5886)

Techniques offered: MODERN

Established: 1926

Administrative director: Linda Hodes

Artistic director: Martha Graham

Facilities: 3 studios; dressing rooms; bathrooms; showers

Student enrollment: total: 250; average class: 25
Age: most 18-25; next 25-33; next 10-17; next 33-over
Level: most beg; next adv beg; next int; next adv

Entrance requirements: minimum age, 8; placement in classes and advancement by faculty permission only

Classes: MODERN (Graham): fundamentals I and II, elem, int, adv-pro

Adult beg: see fundamentals classes above
Children: Saturday children's classes in Graham technique
Teens: classes for teens in Graham technique meet twice a week

Special courses/instruction: Intensive courses in Graham technique (given 1 week, Easter; 4 weeks, June; 2 weeks, Christmas; 2 weeks, January); Repertory course for advanced students only, meets periodically during the year and is often used to screen new members for the Graham company.

Accompaniment: piano

Holidays: New Year's Day, July 4, Labor Day, Thanksgiving, Christmas; Sundays

Fees: $15/one-time registration fee; $5/trial class; $3-$5/class, depending on number taken per week; other rates for intensive courses; pro rates for union members

Scholarships: Full scholarships are available for advanced students with potential for joining the company; dancers are chosen by audition each September.

Company affiliations: The Martha Graham Dance Company

Principal faculty: (all former or current members of the Graham company): Armgard Von Bardeleben, Chris Dakin, Jane Dudley (guest), Diane Grey, Linda Hodes, Judy Hogan, Pearl Lang (guest), Susan McLain, Kenny Pearl, Tim Wengard.

Summary statement: "The Martha Graham School is the only school in the country where, for the length of time required to master a craft and perfect a talent, the serious dance student may learn the Martha Graham technique. Believing that dance is an elemental way of expressing life, the school offers individuals the best and strictest training in the art whether or not it is their aim to become professional dancers. Graham technique has been a mainstay in the training of the serious modern dancer. Most of the major choreographers of contemporary dance in America have been students of Martha Graham or members of her company. These include Alvin Ailey, Patricia Birch, John Butler, Merce Cunningham, Erick Hawkins, Pearl Lang, Sophie Maslow, Anna Sokolow, Paul Taylor, Glen Tetley. As the Artistic Director, Martha Graham is actively involved in her school when she is not on tour with the Martha Graham Company."

HARKNESS BALLET SCHOOL

Harkness House for Ballet Arts
4 East 75th Street
New York, New York 10021
(212-794-0200)

Techniques offered: BALLET, JAZZ/DISCO, DANCE EXERCISE

Established: 1965

Director: Theodore Bartwink

Facilities: 5 studios; dressing rooms; bathrooms; showers

Student enrollment: total: 200; average class: 35
Age: most 18-25; next 10-17; next 25-33
Level: most int; next adv beg; next adv; next beg

Entrance requirements: none for children and open adults' classes; audition required for students in the Scholarship Trainee Program (they have their own classes)

Classes: BALLET: basic beg, beg, int, adv, beg pointe, pas de deux; JAZZ/DISCO: beg; DANCE EXERCISE

Adult beg: see basic beg ballet, beg jazz/disco, and dance exercise classes above

Children (ages 5 and up): BALLET: pre-ballet and beg ballet for children with no previous training, and five other levels of children's ballet classes graded according to age and experience

Men: BALLET: men's technique class

Special courses/instruction: A five-week intensive summer course which is given in July and August and is open to a limited enrollment of intermediate and advanced students and includes 5 hours of classes, 5 days per week (to reserve a space in the course, a $50 non-refundable deposit must be made in advance); Coaching

Accompaniment: piano or tape-recorded music

Holidays: July 4, summer, Thanksgiving through Christmas break; Sundays

Fees: $4/class, $35/10 classes (no time limit); children's tuition is paid by the term (September-May) and ranges from $175 to $400, depending on the student's age and number of classes taken per week; $300/5-week summer intensive course

Scholarships: Full scholarships for 20 boys and 20 girls are awarded each September and January to students who audition sucessfully and have financial need; a limited number of scholarships are also offered for the summer intensive course.

Company affiliations: none

Principal faculty: Nancy Bielski (beg and int ballet, children), Nenette Charisse (adv ballet), Renita Exter (beg and int ballet, children), Anne Hebard (beg and int ballet, children), Larry Kingery (beg ballet, jazz/disco, dance exercise), John Prinz (int ballet, men's class), Elena Tchernishova (adv ballet)

The main studio at the Harkness Ballet School. ***Frank Gimpaya***

Summary statement: "The Harkness Ballet School prides itself in its scholarship program—in the preparation and molding of serious career-minded ballet students for acceptance in professional ballet companies. We endeavor in our children's program to influence young children either in the choice of ballet as a professional career or in the appreciation of it as an art form. In the Open Program we provide classes for the intermediate and advanced professional, as well as a program for adult beginners, to enhance their physical wellbeing and encourage an interest in and appreciation of the art. In our opinion, the Harkness School differs from others in that our teachers are superior and teaching technique and methods are strictly adhered to."

Authors' note: Probably the most resplendent dance facility in New York, the Harkness House for Ballet Arts is located in a nineteenth-century townhouse on upper Fifth Avenue. It was the former residence of International Business Machines executive Thomas Watson, and the interior is replete with marble floors, crystal chandeliers, plush draperies, and original paintings. Both the Harkness House and the ballet school (which was the official school of the now defunct Harkness Ballet company) are the philanthropic projects of the American composer and balletomane, Rebekah Harkness. When Mrs. Harkness bought the building in 1965, it was renovated to meet the needs of young ballet students, and it presently contains five studios, ample dressing rooms, an extensive dance and performing arts library, a listening library, audio-visual facilities, and a canteen. The school's instructional staff includes Nancy Bielski, who studied at the Royal Ballet School in London and has performed with the Harkness company and the Boston Ballet; Nanette Charisse, who trained Gwen Verdon, Donald Saddler, Nora Kaye, and Helen Gallagher, among others; former Kirov Ballet soloist, Elena Tchernishova, and John Prinz, formerly of the New York City Ballet and American Ballet Theatre.

HARLEM DANCE STUDIO

144 West 121st Street
New York, New York 10027
(212-662-2057)

Techniques offered: MODERN, BALLET

Established: 1971

Directors: Carolyn Adams and Julie Adams Strandberg

Facilities: 1 studio; dressing rooms; bathrooms; showers

Student enrollment: total: 100; average class: 12
Age: most 4-12; next 13-17; next 18-25; next 25-33
Level: most adv beg; next beg; next int; next adv

Entrance requirements: minimum age, 4

Classes: MODERN: beg, int, adv; BALLET: beg, int, adv
Adult beg: see beg modern dance and ballet classes above
Children: Saturday CHILDREN'S MOVEMENT CLASS (for ages 4-6; includes basic modern dance movement and a short, elementary ballet barre)
Teens: MODERN: beg

Special courses/instruction: Advanced course in modern dance, given during summer and Christmas vacation; Coaching, for serious students

Accompaniment: piano, records

Holidays: national holidays; Sundays

Fees: adults and teens: $2.50/class, $18/10 classes; children: $2/class, $15/10 classes, sibling rate (for families with more than one child enrolled in classes)

Scholarships: available according to the student's potential, consistent attendance, and financial need

Company affiliations: Patchwork (a student performing group)

Principal faculty: Carolyn Adams, Diane Casey, Michele Shulterbrandt, Julie Adams Strandberg (all teach both modern dance and ballet); and guest faculty

Summary statement: "Carolyn Adams, a featured member of the Paul Taylor Dance Company since 1965, and her sister Julie Adams

Strandberg, director of the dance department at Brown University and vice-chairman of the Rhode Island Council on the Arts, codirect the Harlem Dance Studio and its student company, Patchwork. Both projects are located in a restored 1886 brownstone in central Harlem. Patchwork presents lecture-demonstrations and performances at New York City public school assemblies, churches, and institutions. In addition to sponsoring the school and company, the Harlem Dance Foundation has plans to further serve the needs of artists in its community by offering a performing arts library, rehearsal space, art gallery, and ultimately, theatre and film facilities."

ERICK HAWKINS SCHOOL OF DANCE
78 Fifth Avenue (13/14th Street)
New York, New York 10011
(212-255-6698)

Techniques offered: MODERN

Established: 1952

Director: Erick Hawkins

Facilities: 1 studio; dressing rooms; bathrooms

Student enrollment: total: 350; average class: 15
Age: most 18-25; next 25-33; next 33-over
Level: most adv beg; next beg; next int; next adv

Entrance requirements: no children

Classes: MODERN (Hawkins): fundamentals, beg elementary, adv elementary, int, adv (enrollment by invitation only)
Adult beg: see fundamentals class above

Special courses/instruction: Technique and composition course, given Christmas and June*; Coaching

Accompaniment: none

Holidays: Sundays

Fees: $30/10 classes (5-week time limit); $50/10 classes, no time limit; $15/3-class series for out-of-town students; other fees for Christmas and June courses

Scholarships: none

Company affiliations: Erick Hawkins Dance Company

Principal faculty: Lucia Dlugoszewski (composition), Erick Hawkins, Rand Howard, Cynthia Reynolds, Cori Terry, Cathy Ward. All except Dlugoszewski teach technique classes.

*Local housing accommodations are sometimes arranged for out-of-town students taking these special courses. Check with the school for details.

Summary statement: "The aim of the training at the Erick Hawkins School of Dance is to develop a general theory of 'modern dance' technique that is adequate for our time and exemplifies our scientific knowledge of the body's correct functioning. The goal is a complete technical training with no split between technique and esthetics (what you want to say theatrically and your skill in saying it)—again, for our time. Which is why the 'modern dance' came into existence. Erick Hawkins' approach to technique is to recognize that nonWestern peoples never denied their sensuous and inwardly intuited body experiencing. This way joins and complements our best scientific knowledge. It reinforces the most fruitful psychological, spiritual, and esthetic aims of beautiful dance art."

Authors' note: Erick Hawkins has developed a major modern dance technique that is fluid, tension-free, and healthful because it is based on the body's anatomical structure. It not only provides an excellent foundation for serious dance study, but a point of view which ultimately leads the way to more centered, sensuous, stress-free living. Classes taught by Hawkins himself are philosophically as well as technically illuminating.

MELISSA HAYDEN STUDIO

1845 Broadway (60/61st Street)
New York, New York 10023
(212-582-7929)

Techniques offered: BALLET

Established: 1977

Director: Melissa Hayden

Facilities: 1 studio; dressing rooms; bathrooms

Student enrollment: total: 500; average class: 35
Age: most 18-25; next 25-33; next 10-17; next 33-over
Level: most adv; next int; next adv beg; next beg

Entrance requirements: none

Classes: BALLET: beg level 1 (absolute adult beg), beg level 2 (basic-adv beg); beg level 3 (more experienced adults), adv int, adv-pro; pointe/ variations; pas de deux

Adult beg: see three levels of adult beg ballet classes above
Men: BALLET: men's technique and variations class

Special courses/instruction: none

Accompaniment: piano

Holidays: Christmas and New Year's Day

Fees: $4/class, $2/barre only, $35/10 classes (if you just take the barre, it counts as a half-class on the series card); pro rate: $3.50/class, $30/10 classes

Scholarships: Full scholarships are available to 5 boys and 5 girls with talent and financial need; reviewed twice a year.

Company affiliations: none

Principal faculty: Alfonso Catá, Melissa Hayden, Wilhelm Burmann

Summary statement: "This school offers the sum total of the considerable knowledge, experience, and training of its faculty, thus helping to bridge the gap between the advanced student and professional dancer, and to enhance the knowledge and potential of the professional dancer who studies here. Melissa Hayden is of course well known to New York audiences as a former ballerina with the New York City Ballet for whom George Balanchine created many important roles. Wilhelm Burmann began his performing career in his native Germany with the Stuttgart Ballet, under the direction of the late John Cranko. He was a principal dancer with the Frankfurt Opera Ballet and the Geneva Ballet, as well as a soloist with the New York City Ballet, the Pennsylvania Ballet, and the New Jersey Ballet. Alfonso Catá has also performed with several major companies, including Roland Petit's Ballet de Paris, the Stuttgart Ballet, the Joffrey Ballet, the New York City Ballet, and the Pennsylvania Ballet. Catá has choreographed over twenty works for the repertoires of the Geneva Ballet and the Frankfurt Opera Ballet."

Authors' note: The still beautiful Melissa Hayden has a down-to-earth yet delightfully eccentric teaching style. Her classes have humor and charm and are filled with that elegant Balanchine movement that is a joy to do. Hayden gives a slow, thorough, and intelligent barre; in the center work, the emphasis is on dancing and musicality.

HENRY STREET SETTLEMENT DANCE SCHOOL

466 Grand Street
New York, New York 10002
(212-766-9338)

Techniques offered: MODERN, ETHNIC, TAP, JAZZ, EXERCISE, BALLET

Established: 1946

Director: Frank Ashley

Facilities: 4 studios; dressing rooms; bathrooms; showers

Student enrollment: total: 250; average class: 12
Age: most 4-10; next 11-17; next 18-25; next 25-33; next 33-over
Level: most beg and adv beg; next int; next adv

Entrance requirements: audition for advanced classes

Classes: MODERN: adult beg, int, adv; ETHNIC: adult beg, int; TAP: beg-int; ADULTS' EXERCISE CLASS; DIRECTOR'S WORKSHOP (JAZZ): a weekly advanced jazz class for adults, and one for children, taught by Frank Ashley; enrollment is by invitation only.

Adult beg: see adult beg modern dance and ethnic classes and adult's exercise class above

Children: MODERN: pre-modern (for ages 4-5), beg modern (for ages 6-8), beg modern (for ages 9 and up), int (for ages 9 and up); BALLET (ages 9 and up): beg, int; ETHNIC (ages 7 and up): beg, int, adv; TAP (ages 5 and up): beg, int

Teens: MODERN: beg

Accompaniment: tapes, percussion

Holidays: national holidays; month of August; Sundays

Fees: All classes are given once a week, and tuition ranges from $30-$51 for a 30-week course; $2.50/class, pro rate; financial assistance for up to half of the tuition cost is available for Lower East Side residents.

Scholarships: available according to student's potential and financial need

Company affiliations: Frank Ashley Dance Company (an interracial modern dance company)

Principal faculty: Frank Ashley (adv modern and jazz classes), Sherry Chorney (exercise), Aisha Kahlil (ethnic), Gary Mackay (tap), Bernard Riddick (modern), Sylvia Rincon (modern, ballet), Carol Simpson (modern, ballet)

Summary statement: "The school program for youngsters is geared to the special needs of the Lower East Side community. The advanced classes are geared to the needs of the dance company, and in the adult beginner classes the enjoyment of movement is stressed. Frank Ashley, the director of the dance program since 1976, was born in Kingston, Jamaica, where he received his early dance training. After coming to New York Mr. Ashley studied at the Martha Graham School and subsequently performed with the companies of Graham, Pearl Lang, Yuriko, and Eleo Pomare, and as guest artist with the Repertory Dance Theatre of Trinidad. He has also appeared on Broadway and national television. Mr. Ashley has recently been awarded a choreography fellowship by the National Endowment for the Arts."

A senior class concert at the High School of Performing Arts.
courtesy of the dance department, High School of Performing Arts

HIGH SCHOOL OF PERFORMING ARTS, DANCE DEPARTMENT*

A division of Fiorello H. LaGuardia High School of Music and the Arts
120 West 46th Street
New York, New York 10036
(212-247-6082)

Techniques offered: MODERN, BALLET, THEATRE, DANCE

Established: 1948

Chairman: Lydia Joel

Student enrollment: total: 200; average class: 25-27

Entrance requirements: Students of this free public high school are accepted for entrance in the ninth or tenth grade only and must apply in the fall of the previous year. They must be New York City residents and have graduated satisfactorily from junior high or an eight-year elementary school. Auditions for new students are held each year in January (the school takes fifty-five out of about a thousand applicants) and consist of brief classes in modern dance and ballet plus the presentation by the auditioner of a three-minute solo dance of his or her choice. Candidates are judged primarily on body proportion, coordination, musicality, ability to follow the class, energy, and flexibility. No prior dance training is required for ninth grade applicants, but tenth graders are expected to have intermediate-level technique.

Classes: MODERN: beg, int, adv; BALLET: beg, int, adv, pointe, variations, adagio; THEATRE DANCE (includes traditional folk dance, Russian character dance, Indian, Spanish and other ethnic forms, historic dance, jazz, and tap). Although all students must take both ballet and modern dance, by their sophomore year they major in one and minor in the other.

Special courses/instruction: Music for dancers; Drama for dancers; Dance history; Dance Survey (an introduction to dance terminology, nutrition, and anatomy)

Accompaniment: piano for most classes

Holidays: public school holidays

Fees: all classes are free

Company affiliations: none, but students do have other performing opportunities. Juniors and seniors perform at school assemblies, and each graduating class gives a senior concert, which is often attended by the New York press.

Principal faculty: David Christel (modern), Lawrence Eddington (ballet), Penny Frank (modern), Lydia Joel (dance history), Sarah Malament (music), Bella Malinka (ballet, historic dance, character dance), Matteo (ethnic), Suzanne Walker (jazz), Stefanie Zimmerman (ballet), and guest teachers

*The dance department is one of three separate programs in the High School of Performing Arts; the other two are drama and music.

Summary statement: "The dance department of the High School of Performing Arts owes its spectacular record of achievement to the rich talents of its students and the excellent training of its professional faculty. We offer individual attention to the would-be performer, demanding in return concentration and discipline, the tools of artistic freedom. A student at the High School of Performing Arts must be deeply motivated, capable of absorbing the wealth of materials offered, and able to enjoy working hard. School starts at 8:20 A.M. and ends at 3:00 P.M. There is a half-day of college preparatory academic study and a half-day of studio classes. Upper-class students have after-school rehearsals, and additional outside study at professional dance studios may be recommended. Eliot Feld, Arthur Mitchell, Dennis Wayne, Eartha Kitt, Dudley Williams, Louis Falco, Brunilda Ruiz, Rosemary Dunlevy, and Christian Holder are just a few of our graduates."

Authors' note: Dance-department chairman Lydia Joel performed with Hanya Holm and for many years was the editor-in-chief of *Dancemagazine.*

NAT HORNE MUSICAL THEATRE SCHOOL

440 West 42nd Street
New York, New York 10036
(212-736-7128)

Techniques offered: JAZZ, BALLET, MODERN, FENCING, VOICE, ACTING

Established: 1975

Executive director: Albert Reyes

Artistic directors: Nat Horne and Edward Brown

Administrative director: Virginia Brown

Facilities: 3 studios; dressing rooms; bathrooms; showers

Student enrollment: total: 250; average class: 30
Age: most 18-25; next 25-33; next 10-17; next 33-over
Level: most beg; next adv beg; next int; next adv

Entrance requirements: none

Classes: JAZZ: basics, beg, int, adv; BALLET: basics, beg-int; MODERN (Horton): beg, int; MUSICAL THEATRE WORKSHOP (for scholarship students and company members only): combined work on musical-theatre skills such as dancing, singing, and acting, and studio performances

Adult beg: see jazz basics and ballet basics classes above
Children: BALLET: beg (Saturdays only)

Special courses/instruction: Voice (given in three-month sessions; admission by interview only; includes basics of stage singing and sight reading); Fencing for beginners

Accompaniment: recorded music and live piano

Holidays: Thanksgiving and Christmas

Fees: $5/annual registration fee; $3.50/class; $30/10 classes; $78/13-week session in voice training; pro discounts for union members

Scholarships: 12 full, 30 partial, and 30 work scholarships are available to students interested in pursuing professional performing careers; acceptance is by audition in singing, dancing, and acting.

Company affiliations: Nat Horne Musical Theatre Company (six dancers who perform Horne's choreography, which is a blend of jazz with modern dance and ballet); Musical Theatre Workshop (see *classes* above)

Principal faculty: James Darling (fencing), David Dusing (voice), Nat Horne (jazz), Agnes Johnson (modern), Otto Maximilian (acting), Yaeko Sasaki (ballet)

Summary statement: "The school is geared to train performers for the commercial stage, especially musical theatre. Dancing, singing, and acting are required as students advance. Members of the Nat Horne Musical Theatre Company are required to be well versed in all three disciplines. Our faculty includes Nat Horne, a veteran of sixteen Broadway shows, choreographer, and principal jazz dance instructor at the Alvin Ailey American Dance Center; Yaeko Sasaki, dancer, choreographer, and a Juilliard scholarship graduate who has performed as a soloist with Alexandra Danilova and was founder and director of a ballet school in Tokyo, Japan; voice instructor David Dusing, who has performed with Harry Belafonte, John Raitt, and the Robert DeCormier Singers; modern dancer Agnes Johnson, a former member of the Alvin Ailey American Dance Theatre and the casts of several Broadway musicals; and James Darling, a former intercollegiate fencing champion from Cal State, who has staged fencing scenes for several theatrical productions."

Authors' note: Founder Nat Horne is well respected as a dedicated and dynamic jazz dance teacher.

DAVID HOWARD SCHOOL OF BALLET

36 West 62nd Street
New York, New York 10023
(212-757-9877)

Techniques offered: BALLET

Established: 1977

Director: David Howard

Facilities: 1 studio; dressing rooms; bathrooms; showers

Student enrollment: average class: 40
Age: most 18-25; next 25-33; next 33-over; next 10-17
Level: most adv; next int; next beg and adv beg in equal proportions

Entrance requirements: students must be working up to the level of the classes they are taking

Classes: BALLET: adult beg, adv beg, basic int, int, adv-pro; pointe; pas de deux

Adult beg: see adult beg ballet class above

Special courses/instruction: Five-week introductory course for adult beginners; Dance history course (with guest lecturers and demonstrations by well-known ballet dancers; offered three times a year); Private classes: Coaching

Accompaniment: piano

Holidays: national holidays

Fees: $4/class, $35/10 classes; $2.50/class, pas de deux and pointe; $40/5-week adult beg course; $50/dance history course; fees for private classes and coaching are negotiable

Scholarships: Work scholarships are available for 5 boys and 5 girls who are talented and interested in living in New York City; tuition is sometimes reduced for students with potential.

Company affiliations: none at present, but may be added in the future

Principal faculty: David Howard (adv-pro, int, and adult beg); Douglas Wassell (int, adult beg)

Summary statement: "The School has a strictly classical ballet program, and the classes follow a traditional training concept with a kinesthetic approach concentrating on the flow of movement. Classes are offered to students and professionals, but each class is geared to the level of its dancers. The intermediate and advanced classes are two hours in length, with a fifty-minute barre (and in David Howard's classes, a brief session of therapeutic floor exercises) before the center begins."

Authors' note: David Howard was a soloist with the Royal Ballet in England and the National Ballet of Canada. He was the director of the Harkness Ballet School, where he also taught for several years, and is current president of the National Association for Regional Ballet. In addition, Howard has produced a number of teaching record albums on ballet and is writing a book on his classical dance theories, which is scheduled for publication sometime this year. Douglas Wassell has performed with Les Grand Ballets Canadiens and has taught at the Harkness Ballet School and New York University. This conveniently located and handsome school is popular to the point of being overcrowded, especially during evening and Saturday classes. Among Howard's students are Gelsey Kirkland, Patricia McBride, Leslie Browne, and several other members of American Ballet Theatre and the New York City Ballet. Both Howard and Wassell (who is younger and slightly less formal) know how to get a point across or lighten up a class with a bit of good-natured humor. Both give slow, methodical barres. Howard is not only good at challenging advanced dancers but is wonderful with his adult beginners.

INTERNATIONAL DANCE SCHOOL

Studio 819, Carnegie Hall
881 Seventh Avenue (56th Street)
New York, New York 10019
(212-CI7-6056/974-9490)

Techniques offered: BALLET, JAZZ, TAP, ETHNIC, DISCO, MODERN, STRETCH

Established: 1956

School administrator: Anton Germano

Artistic director: Fedor Lensky

Facilities: 3 studios; dressing rooms; bathrooms

Student enrollment: total: 1000 ; average class: 15-20
Age: most 25-33; next 33-over; next 18-25; next 10-17
Level: most adv beg; next beg; next int; next adv

Entrance requirements: none

Classes: BALLET: basic beg, fast beg, int, adv, pointe, turn (combined levels, work on ballet turns); JAZZ: basic beg, fast beg, int, adv; TAP: basic beg, fast beg, slow int, int, adv, adv routines; ETHNIC (Spanish): basic beg (work with castanets only), beg (combine basic steps with use of castanets), int; ETHNIC (Middle Eastern): basic beg, adv beg; ETHNIC (Far Eastern): beg; DISCO DANCE: basic beg, int; MODERN (combined Graham and Limón technique, with some yoga warmup exercises): basic beg; STRETCH: combined levels

Adult beg: see basic beg ballet, jazz, tap, ethnic, disco, and modern dance classes above

Special courses/instruction: Coaching

Accompaniment: piano, drum

Holidays: major national holidays; Sundays

Fees: $4-$4.50/class; $40/10 classes (3-month time limit); pro rate: $35/10 classes (1-year time limit for union members who are advanced dancers, and 1-month time limit for union members at the beginner's level); other rates for other series; coaching rates vary

Scholarships: none

Company affiliations: none

Principal faculty: Gene Aguirre (disco, jazz), Oceola Bragg (ballet), Mary Jane Brown (tap), Miss Dalel (Middle Eastern), Carlos Fernandez (Spanish), Blanche Felsher (ballet), Marvin Gordon (ballet), Dianne Hakek (ballet, turn), Bill Herter (modern, stretch), Lillian Heitzman (jazz), Carol Hess (tap), Janis Kasni (disco), Mr. Kirik (Far Eastern), Fedor Lensky (ballet), John Mederios (jazz), Miss Phaedra (Middle Eastern), Al Sambogna (jazz), George Tomal (ballet), Frank Wagner (jazz), Harry Woolever (jazz)

Summary statement: "The school that offers the best training for any theatrical dance form to anybody in the friendliest environment is the International Dance School."

Authors' note: Fedor Lensky, artistic director and founder of this long-standing school, performed with the Paris Opera Ballet and the Kurt Jooss Ballet in Germany.

FINIS JHUNG BALLET
2182 Broadway (78th Street)
New York, New York 10024
(212-877-4740)

Techniques offered: BALLET, EXERCISE

Established: 1976

Director: Finis Jhung

Facilities: 1 studio; dressing rooms; bathrooms

Student enrollment: average class: 50

Entrance requirements: none

Classes: BALLET: beg, int, adv; SPECIAL EXERCISE
Adult beg: BALLET: adult's basic, adv beg; see also exercise class above

Accompaniment: piano

Holidays: legal holidays; Sundays

Fees: $4/class; $35/10 classes

Scholarships: none

Company affiliations: none

Principal faculty: Steven Adcock (exercise), Finis Jhung (ballet), Liane Plane (ballet)

Summary statement: (from Finis Jhung): "I try to teach students the way I wish I had been taught. I believe that everyone—regardless of age or body type—can learn to do things in ballet if they are shown good body placement and the proper method. And that is what we do here."

Authors' note: Jhung was critically acclaimed for his brilliant jumping and allegro work as a principal dancer with the Harkness Ballet; he is also a former soloist with the San Francisco Ballet. Liane Plane performed with American Ballet Theatre and appeared in the original Broadway cast of ***West Side Story.*** Steven Adcock was an instructor with the Nikolaus Exercise Centers before coming to teach at the Jhung studio. Due to a throat ailment, Jhung uses a microphone to amplify his voice when he teaches.

JO JO'S DANCE FACTORY
1721 Broadway (56th Street)
New York, New York 10019
(212-586-2940)

Techniques offered: JAZZ, TAP, BALLET, DISCO, BODY CONDITIONING

Established: 1970

Director: Jo Jo Smith

Co-directors: Anna Grayson and Sue Samuels

Facilities: 2 studios; dressing rooms; bathrooms; showers

Student enrollment: total: 500; average class: 20
Age: most 18-25; next 25-33; next 33-over; next 10-17
Level: most int; next adv beg; next beg; next adv

Entrance requirements: none

Classes: JAZZ: beg, int, adv-pro; TAP: new beg, beg, int, adv; BALLET: beg-int; DISCO; BODY CONDITIONING (adults' exercise class)

Adult beg: see beg jazz, new beg tap, and body conditioning classes above

Children (ages 4-8): combined ballet, jazz, and modern dance class

Special courses/instruction: Private classes: Coaching

Accompaniment: drums, records

Holidays: New Year's Day, Christmas; Sundays

Fees: $15/annual registration fee; jazz and tap: $5.50/class, $40/10 classes; ballet: $4.50/class, $40/10 classes; disco: $8.50/class, $40/5 classes, $60/5 classes for couples; pro discount: 50¢ off single class fee and $5 off series cards

Scholarships: Full scholarships available to students with talent and financial need

Company affiliations: Jo Jo Smith and Company

Principal faculty: Joel Bergman (tap), Kelly Carroll (jazz), Debbie Joyce (jazz), Don Paradise (ballet), Ken Samuels (jazz), Sue Samuels (ballet, jazz), Jo Jo Smith (jazz)

Summary statement: "Jo Jo Smith's style as a dancer and choreographer is famous throughout Europe and South America, where he has performed extensively. Besides his Broadway, television, and concert credits, he is known and widely acclaimed as a teacher. His classes are composed primarily of students who themselves are professionals or teachers. A list of Jo Jo's pupils over the years reads like a Who's Who in show business and includes such performers as Barbra Streisand, Joey Heatherton, Julie Newmar, and Julie Budd. His mother, Anna Grayson, once danced with Katherine Dunham and now codirects the Dance Factory. The basic emphasis in the training is on a strong technique and a good healthy body. Without these two attributes one will have a very difficult time with Jo Jo's style. Since the work is so exacting, one needs to have a tremendous amount of discipline. The primary goal of the school is to produce well-rounded dancers through proper training, nutrition, and no smoking. We have recently opened a health food-juice bar on the premises."

Authors' note: Jo Jo Smith was trained by the late Syvilla Forte and choreographers Katherine Dunham and Talley Beatty. He is an exceptional dancer and musician and a patient teacher.

SALVADOR JUAREZ SCHOOL OF BALLET

939 Eighth Avenue (57th Street)
Studio 305A
New York, New York 10019
(212-974-9437)

Techniques offered: BALLET, JAZZ

Established: 1967

Director: Salvador Juarez

Facilities: 1 studio; dressing rooms; bathrooms; showers

Student enrollment: total: 400; average class: 15
Age: most 18-33; next 10-17 and 33-over in roughly equal proportions
Level: most adv beg through adv; next beg

Entrance requirements: none

Classes: BALLET: basic beg, beg, beg-int, int-adv, toe, pirouette class; JAZZ: int
Adult beg: see basic ballet class above

Special courses/instruction: Private classes; Coaching

Accompaniment: piano, records

Holidays: national holidays; Sundays (June to August only)

Fees: $4/class; $35/10 classes; $20/hour, private class or coaching

Scholarships: Work scholarships are available to regular students, according to their financial need and the requirements of the studio; no audition is necessary.

Company affiliations: none

Principal faculty: All classes are taught by Salvador Juarez or an assistant.

Summary statement: "My training program is a composite of various techniques and exercises, with emphasis on the Russian technique. I have created a barre based on my experiences as a ballet student and as a professional dancer with the following companies: The Alicia Alonso Ballet Company, the Ballet Russe de Monte Carlo, The Mexico City Ballet, and the Ballet Concierto de Mexico. I give a slow, extensive barre with concentration on proper placement, accurate technique, and the development of endurance. The latter part of the class is devoted to balance work in the center, long adagios, pirouette practice, and allegro combinations. My goal is to turn out a strong, well-developed dancer who understands what he or she is doing both physically and mentally."

HAVA KOHAV THEATRE/DANCE FOUNDATION

2390 Broadway (88/89th Street)
New York, New York 10024
(212-877-1667)

Techniques offered: MODERN

Established: 1974

Director: Hava Kohav

Facilities: 1 studio; dressing rooms; bathrooms

Student enrollment: total: 60; average class: 8
Age: most 7-25; next 25-33; next 33-over
Level: most beg and adv beg; next int and adv, in roughly equal proportions

Entrance requirements: none

Classes: MODERN MOVEMENT: beg, int, adv

Adult beg: see beg modern movement class above
Children (ages 7-12): SATURDAY CHILDREN'S THEATRE WORKSHOP (combines movement, improvisation, and fantasy play)

Special courses/instruction: Private classes

Accompaniment: percussion

Holidays: legal holidays, summer break; Sundays

Fees: $5/class, $23/5 classes (3-week time limit), $43/10 classes (10-week time limit); $54/12-week term, children's workshop; $20/hour, private classes

Scholarships: A work scholarship is available, awarded according to student's talent and financial need.

Company affiliations: Hava Kohav Theatre/Dance Company

Principal faculty: Gale Freeman (children's classes), Hava Kohav (modern movement)

Summary statement: (from Hava Kohav): "In the classes I teach, I aim to reach the person, working to mobilize, free, and stimulate the areas from which spontaneity springs; to stretch, limber, and build upwardly; to find and strengthen one's center, balance, concentration, and ability to function on several levels at the same time. I try to teach students to listen to their own timing, to develop and sensitize their inner musicality; and to help them acquire flexibility of mind, as well as physical stamina, endurance, and the simple joy and exhilaration of moving in space."

Authors' note: Israeli-born Hava Kohav is a Juilliard graduate who has directed her own dance company for several years. Her teaching credits include nine years at the dance department of the 92nd Street YM-YWHA, eleven years on the faculty of the music department of the 92nd Street "Y," and four years teaching at her former studio on 56th Street. Gale Freeman, who teaches the children's workshop, has a B.A. in theatre from Temple University and has previously taught at the Henry Street Settlement House.

THE GLORIA KOSOWSKI CHILDREN'S DANCE THEATRE*

130 West 17th Street
New York, New York 10011
(212-242-0984)

Techniques offered: MODERN, ACROBATICS, ADULTS' EXERCISE

Established: 1976

School administrator: Will Ferry

Facilities: 1 studio; dressing rooms; bathrooms

Student enrollment: total: 35; average class: 5
Age: most students 6-17; also some adult exercise students
Level: most beg and adv beg

Entrance requirements: All classes except adults' exercise are for children ages 6-17

Classes: All classes are one hour long except for dramatics, which is a two-hour class.
Adult beg: ADULTS' EXERCISE CLASS
Children and teens: MODERN DANCE: primary (ages 6-8), beg-int (ages 9-12), int-adv (ages 9-12), teens (ages 13-17); ACROBATICS: I (ages 6-12) and II (ages 12-17); DRAMATICS: I (ages 6-11) and II (ages 12-17)

Accompaniment: piano or percussion

Holidays: major national holidays, summer break; Sundays

Fees: $5/registration fee; $3.50/class, children and adults; $24/8 classes, adults; term rates are also available for children's classes.

Scholarships: Full scholarships are available for children who are sincerely interested in dance and financially unable to pay tuition.

Company affiliations: none, but students give workshop performances and informal demonstrations during the year

Principal faculty: Elizabeth Himelstein (dramatics), Paula Mason (beg and beg-int modern), Phyllis Sanfilippo (int-adv and teens' modern, adults' exercise), Randy Stein (acrobatics)

Summary statement: "The Gloria Kosowski Children's Dance Theatre is a nonprofessional school for children. We are dedicated to the emotional and creative development of our students in a warm and friendly environment of dance, drama, and acrobatics. Our class sizes are limited in order for our teachers to give greater personal attention to each student. Any child interested in our program is welcome, and we do our utmost to make this financially possible. We also have an adult exercise class which meets Tuesday and Thursday evenings. In addition, our studio is available for rental as a rehearsal and performance space.

*Gloria Kosowski, the young University of Utah graduate who founded this school, was tragically killed during a robbery of her loft in 1978. Friends, associates, students, and local business people have pitched in to continue her work and raise funds to provide free tuition for many children.

"Our modern dance classes include instruction in technique, which prepares the body for basic movement by working on exercises which develop strength, stretch, coordination, and flow of movement; improvisation, which allows students to dance in an unrehearsed and spontaneous way; and composition, or the creation of dances in which students are encouraged to choose their own music, lighting, and costumes. Drama classes encompass discoveries in sensory awareness, movement, theatre games, improvisation, storytelling, and puppetry. Acrobatics deals in the physical development of correct body alignment, muscle tone, and coordination through basic tumbling and balancing techniques. Students are taught in accordance with their abilities and always with safety in mind.

"Our teachers are chosen on the basis of both their artistic ability and their enthusiasms for working with children. Elizabeth Himelstein was company manager of the Children's Theatre of the Open Eye and is presently teaching speech at the Neighborhood Playhouse in New York. Paula Mason has taught modern dance, improvisation, and composition at Bryn Mawr College for the past eighteen years. Phyllis Sanfilippo holds a bachelor's degree in physical education from the State University of New York at Cortland and has done graduate work in dance at the University of Wisconsin at Madison. She continues her professional studies with Zena Rommett in New York. Randy Stein holds a bachelor's degree in dance from Indiana University and has performed two seasons with the Big Apple Circus as an acrobatic clown."

HENRY LE TANG PROFESSIONAL SCHOOL OF DANCE

1717 Broadway (54/55th Street)
New York, New York 10019
(212-245-9213)

Techniques offered: TAP, JAZZ

Established: 1937

Director: Henry Le Tang

Facilities: 4 studios; dressing rooms; bathrooms

Student enrollment: total: 300; average class: 8
Age: most 18-33; next 10-17 and 33-over in equal proportions
Level: most beg; next adv beg through adv

Entrance requirements: none

Classes: TAP: beg, int, adv; JAZZ: adult beg, beg, int, adv
Adult beg: see beg tap and adult beg jazz classes above
Children (ages 7 and up): beg tap classes offered on Saturdays

Special courses/instruction: Private classes; Coaching

Accompaniment: piano

Holidays: New Year's, Christmas; Sundays; weekends in summer

Fees: tap: $6/class, $45/10 classes; jazz: $4/class, $40/10 classes; $40/10 tap classes, pro rate; coaching: $20/hour, beg and $25/hour, int

Scholarships: none

Company affiliations: The Le Tang Dancers

Principal faculty: Frank Hatchett (jazz), Ellie Le Tang (tap, jazz), Henry Le Tang (tap)

Summary statement: "Henry Le Tang, director of The Henry Le Tang Professional School of Dance for four decades, has coached, counseled, and choreographed for some of the most renowned stars of the entertainment industry. Former students and those whose careers have been influenced by Mr. Le Tang include: Betty Hutton, Eleanor Powell, Lena Horne, Peter Gennaro, Milton Berle, Sugar Ray Robinson, Bill "Bojangles" Robinson, Bette Midler, and Lee Marvin. He has choreographed reviews and nightclub acts for Flip Wilson, Lola Falana, Ben Vereen, and Joe Frazier. We give individual attention to students in class. Our sole purpose is to turn out the kind of good performers we used to have years ago. We do not lie or take money on false pretenses. This is important to us."

Authors' note: Henry Le Tang also choreographed the Broadway show ***Eubie***. In his tap classes the emphasis is on learning routines rather than an analysis of technique or mechanics. Le Tang's beginning tap class is attended by more advanced dancers and is therefore not recommended for absolute beginners.

VALENTINA LITVINOFF STUDIO OF DANCE

149 Bleecker Street (between Thompson Street and LaGuardia Place
New York, New York 10012
(212-AL5-7562)

Techniques offered: MODERN

Established: 1963

Director: Valentina Litvinoff

Facilities: 1 studio; dressing rooms; bathrooms; showers

Student enrollment: total: 50; average class: 10
Age: most 25-33; next 33-over; next 18-25
Level: most int, next beg; next adv; next adv beg

Entrance requirements: none

Classes: MODERN (includes technique, improvisation, and dance composition): beg, int, adv

Adult beg: see beg modern class above

Valentina Litvinoff with her students. ***Susan Katz***

Special courses/instruction: Intensive courses (occasionally offered during Christmas vacation and in June; call for information); Lectures on human body movement and various aspects of dance; Private classes

Accompaniment: recorded music, percussion, and occasionally piano

Holidays: major national holidays; sometimes a two-month summer break; Sundays

Fees: $6/class; $80/16-week semester, 1 class per week; $144/16-week semester, 2 classes per week; $3/class for students taking 3 or more lessons per week, with tuition payable by the month; $25/hour, private classes

Scholarships: Full and partial scholarships are available.

Company affiliations: none

Principal faculty: All classes are taught by Valentina Litvinoff, with occasional assistance by an advanced student.

Summary statement: "Valentina Litvinoff trained with Martha Graham, Louis Horst, and Doris Humphrey and performed with the Humphrey-Weidman company. She has also directed her own dance troupe, as well as choreographed for theatre, including a critically acclaimed production of ***The Trojan Women.*** Miss Litvinoff has made extensive studies of the Alexander Technique and Lulu Sweigard's theory of ideokinesis—both of which employ the use of mental imagery to promote more healthful and efficient movement and improve body alignment. She also incorporates elements of ethnic dance and various principles of yoga and T'ai Chi Ch'uan in her classes. She has written a book on her movement philosophy entitled ***The Use of Stanislavsky Within Modern Dance*** and has authored several articles for ***Dance Scope, The Journal of Aesthetics and Art Criticism***, and ***The Drama Review.*** In Litvinoff's classes each student works at his or her own level, and even the beginner dances right away. Conditioning exercises are immediately combined with dance movement, so that the pupil gets the feeling of dancing right away. There is no separation between technique and dancing."

LOUIS-NIKOLAIS DANCE THEATRE LAB

33 East 18th Street
New York, New York 10003
(212-777-1120)

Techniques offered: MODERN

Established: 1948

Directors: Murray Louis and Alwin Nikolais

Facilities: 3 studios; dressing rooms; bathrooms

Student enrollment: total: 100
Age: most 18-25 and 25-33 in roughly equal proportions
Level: most int and adv, in equal proportions; next beg

Entrance requirements: no students below high-school age; regular class attendance

Classes: MODERN DANCE TECHNIQUE: beg, int, adv; THEORY (improvisation class); DANCE COMPOSITION. All daytime students must take the full curriculum, which consists of a daily technique class followed by a lesson in theory (given 4 days per week) or composition (given 1 day per week).

Adult beg: adult beg classes, consisting of 2- and 3-hour sessions which combine technique and improvisation, are held two evenings per week and on Saturdays.

Special courses/instruction: Special intensive Christmas and June courses (these include technique, theory, and composition and are given from 10 A.M. to 2 P.M. daily)

Accompaniment: percussion

Holidays: national holidays, July 1 to September 29; Sundays

Fees: $7/annual registration fee; all classes are paid on a semester (October to January and January to May) or special-course basis; semester rates for daytime students: $330/5 days per week, $290/4 days per week; other rates for evening and Saturday adult beg classes

Scholarships: Work scholarships are available to a limited number of students who are chosen according to their individual needs and capabilities; they are rarely given to new students.

Company affiliations: The Murray Louis Dance Company; The Nikolais Dance Theatre

Principal faculty: Michael Ballard, Beverly Blossom, Claudia Gitelman, Arlene Laub, Lynn Levine, Murray Louis, Alwin Nikolais, Gerald Otte, Gerald Pearson, Sara Pearson, Robert Small, Joan Woodbury, and guest instructor, Hanya Holm

Summary statement: "The Louis-Nikolais Dance Theatre Lab is the vital continuation of an internationally significant dance education program which originated in 1948 at the Henry Street Playhouse. The school is the source of dancers for the companies of Murray Louis and Alwin Nikolais, as well as teachers of contemporary dance. Approved by the United States Department of State under its Visitors' Exchange Program, its student body is international in composition. The Louis-Nikolais Dance Theatre Lab has provided uniquely trained teachers to schools and colleges throughout the country. It serves as an experimental laboratory where exploration of the art of dance is pursued by members of both companies, guest choreographers, and its own students."

Authors' note: Alwin Nikolais is a former student of Hanya Holm, a disciple of the German expressionist school of modern dance, which was characterized by strong gymnastic training and the associate study of music, rhythm, and dance composition. Murray Louis was Nikolais's protégé and for many years a leading dancer in his company.

LUIGI'S JAZZ CENTRE
36 West 62nd Street
New York, New York 10023
(212-247-1995)

Techniques offered: JAZZ

Established: 1957

Director: Luigi

Facilities: 2 studios; dressing rooms; bathrooms; showers

Student enrollment: total and average class enrollments vary
Age: most 18-33; next 33-over; next 10-17
Level: roughly equal proportions of all levels

Entrance requirements: none

Classes: JAZZ: introduction, style class (beg technique), beg, int, adv
Adult beg: see jazz introduction class above

Special courses/instruction: Private classes

Accompaniment: records

Holidays: national holidays; Sundays

Fees: $4/class; $40/10 classes; $35/10 classes, pro rate for union members; $25/hour, private class

Scholarships: none

Company affiliations: Luigi's Dance Ensemble

Principal faculty: Luigi, Ric Salinas

Summary statement: "The Luigi technique teaches students to feel movement from the inside—finding the inner control and natural emotion, rather than the outside wasted energy. Our students are mostly adult professionals."

Authors' note: The school and balletic jazz technique of Luigi (he goes by one name only) are internationally known. A former dancer on Broadway and in nightclubs and film, he is still a compelling performer when leading a class, and his good-natured, offbeat personality has won over numerous devotees. All classes begin with a progression of set warmup exercises, which are the backbone of Luigi's movement style.

MANHATTAN SCHOOL OF DANCE
78 Fifth Avenue (16/17th Street)
New York, New York 10011
(212-255-6563)

Techniques offered: BALLET

Established: 1968

Director: Robert U. Ossorio

Facilities: 1 studio; dressing rooms; bathrooms

Student enrollment: total: 160; average class: 15-20
Age: most 18-25; next 25-33; next 10-17; next 33-over
Level: most int; next adv; next beg; next adv beg

Entrance requirements: minimum age is 8; an audition is required for students in the children's and professional classes; children must enroll for the entire year

Classes: BALLET: adult beg, int, pro; pointe: elementary, pro; pas de deux

Adult beg: see adult beg ballet class above
Children: BALLET I (for ages 7-9), BALLET II (for students with two years prior training)
Men: men's professional ballet class

Special courses/instruction: Dance history course (given intermittently)

Accompaniment: piano

Holidays: major national holidays, Easter recess, Summer recess (July and August), Christmas recess; Sundays

Fees: adults: $5/trial class, $35/10 classes; children's ballet I: $300/year (September to June), 2 classes per week; children's ballet II: $450/year (September to June), 3 classes per week

Scholarships: awarded according to student's individual situation and financial need; students are chosen by audition and personal interview

Company affiliations: none

Principal faculty: Margaret Craske, Alice Tempkin Green (history), Loren Hightower, Dorothy Hill, Christopher Lyall, Robert Ossorio, Terry Pines, Sallie Wilson

Summary statement: "The Manhattan School of Dance is a nonprofit organization dedicated to handing on the principles of the Cecchetti Method with a genuine personal relationship between student and teacher; to prepare students, where feasible, for a professional career in dance; and to give others an appreciation and love for the dance while helping their physical wellbeing. The faculty includes Sallie Wilson, principal dancer with the American Ballet Theatre; Dorothy Hill, who has appeared in the works of Ruth Page, Jerome Robbins, Donald Saddler, John Butler, and other prominent choreographers; Loren Hightower, who has performed in concert, film, Broadway, and television productions; Robert Ossorio, who has worked in films with Eugene Loring and Gene Kelly; and Margaret Craske, who danced with the Diaghilev Ballets Russes and the Royal Italian Ballet in London. Ms. Craske studied with the late Enrico Cecchetti and received a certificate from him qualifying her to teach his method. She has also been on the faculty of the Royal Ballet School in London and the Metropolitan Opera Ballet School. Sallie Wilson is one of her former students."

NANCY MEEHAN DANCE COMPANY AND SCHOOL

Westbeth Artist Complex
463 West Street
Room 1201
New York, New York 10014
(212-929-2143)

Techniques offered: MODERN

Established: 1970

Director: Nancy Meehan

Facilities: 1 studio; dressing rooms; bathrooms

Student enrollment: total: 90; average class: 15
Age: most 18-25; next 25-33; next 33-over; next 10-17
Level: most int; next adv beg; next adv; next beg

Entrance requirements: Students must have had at least one year of previous study in modern dance.

Classes: MODERN: beg, int, adv

Special courses/instruction: Private classes

Accompaniment: percussion

Holidays: New Year's, Thanksgiving, Christmas; Sundays

Fees: $5/trial class; $40/10 classes, 1 or 2 per week; $35/10 classes, 3 or more per week

Scholarships: available, depending upon current company needs and student's professional dance potential

Company affiliations: Nancy Meehan Dance Company

Principal faculty: Risa Friedman, Katherine Mapp, Nancy Meehan, Wendy Shifrin

Summary statement: "Our goal is to build a strong technique through centering and released flow of energy rather than tension. We believe that a broad dynamic change can be developed by the use of weight in coordination with momentum to achieve a direct movement attack."

Authors' note: Nancy Meehan was a principal dancer with the Erick Hawkins Dance Company for several years, and her style is Hawkins-derived, though it is physically more vigorous and dynamically more varied. Students attending her early evening classes get an added bonus—magnificent sunsets seen from the studio's western-exposed windows.

MONSALVE DANCE STUDIO

126 Fifth Avenue (17/18th Street), 7th Floor
New York, New York 10011
(212-675-8921)

Techniques offered: BALLET, DANCE EXERCISE

Established: 1974

Director: Jorge Monsalve

Facilities: 1 studio; dressing rooms; bathrooms; showers

Student enrollment: total: 100; average class: 12-15
Age: most 10-17; next 18-33; next 33-over
Level: most beg, adv beg, and adv in equal proportions; next int

Entrance requirements: none

Classes: BALLET: fundamentals, beg, int, adv; DANCE EXERCISE CLASS
Adult beg: see ballet fundamentals and dance exercise class above

Special courses/instruction: Private classes; Coaching

Accompaniment: piano

Holidays: national holidays; Sundays

Fees: $4.50/class; $40/10 classes

Scholarships: Partial scholarships available according to student's age and talent

Company affiliations: Monsalve Dance Nucleus

Principal faculty: All classes are taught by Jorge Monsalve or his assistant, Susanne Wray.

Summary statement: "Chilean-born Jorge Monsalve has appeared in classical roles with the Ballet Classico Nacional de Chile, Otto Werberg's Ballet Theatre, Ballet de Camara de Buenos Aires, and the Ballet Mexico Contemporaneo. He has also performed and toured extensively in South and Central America with his own company. Monsalve choreographed for theatre, musicals, film, and television in Mexico City before coming to New York. He formed the Dance Nucleus company with the purpose of showing his choreography in collaboration with new dancers, musicians, and artists. In his ballet classes Mr. Monsalve teaches a technique based on the Vaganova method, but with a contemporary approach. Emphasis at all levels of training is on correct body movement, placement, and alignment as a foundation for good ballet technique and further progress. Clarity of technique and purity of line are stressed to avoid mannerisms and unnecessary movements."

MORELLI BALLET, INC.
69 West 14th Street
New York, New York 10011
(212-242-1903)

Techniques offered: BALLET, JAZZ

Established: 1968

Director: Wilson Morelli

Facilities: 4 studios; dressing rooms; bathrooms

Student enrollment: total: 800; average class: 25
Age: most 25-33; next 18-25; next 33-over; next 10-17
Level: most adv; next int; next adv beg; next beg

Entrance requirements: no children

Classes: BALLET: basic beg, adv beg, slow int, int, adv; JAZZ: beg, slow int, adv

Adult beg: see basic beg ballet and beg jazz classes above

Special courses/instruction: Coaching; Choreoground workshop (showcase for new choreographers)

Accompaniment: piano, drums

Holidays: national holidays, Christmas; Sundays

Fees: $4/class; $35/10 classes (one-month time limit); $3.50/class, pro rate (for union members)

Scholarships: none

Company affiliations: none

Principal faculty: Andrea Brown (jazz), Jocelyn Lorenz (ballet), Nancy Mikota (ballet), Wilson Morelli (ballet), Lynn Simonson (jazz)

Summary statement: "Morelli Ballet is a professionally oriented school. This is not a school for exercise students or children. Most students who come here are interested in careers. All faculty stress proper body placement to prevent injuries. Wilson Morelli, the director, has performed with the American Ballet Theatre, the Municipal Theatre of Rio de Janeiro, the Ballet de Paris, and with Roland Petit. He has appeared in over fifty film and television productions and has previously taught at the Ballet Russe de Monte Carlo School and the American Ballet Theatre School, among others."

Authors' note: Pixieish Lynn Simonson is an intelligent and energetic teacher. She uses improvisation in class, and creates performance situations for her advanced students (such as having half the class sit out in front and act as an audience while the other half performs a combination). Simonson, who takes an active interest in her students, also organizes her own workshop performances from time to time. Her classes are relaxed and fun. The choreography is Las Vegas style, but she does get dancers to really cut loose and move. Simonson works barefoot—perhaps because the studio floor is slippery—so jazz shoes are not needed.

MARJORIE MUSSMAN STUDIO

78 Fifth Avenue
7th Floor
New York, New York 10011
(212-242-4491)

Techniques offered:	BALLET, MODERN
Established:	1976
Director:	Marjorie Mussman
Facilities:	1 studio; dressing rooms; bathrooms
Student enrollment:	average class:30 Age: most 18-25; next 25-33; next 10-17; next 33-over Level: most int; next adv
Entrance requirements:	intermediate- to professional-level dancers only
Classes:	BALLET: int, adv; MODERN (Graham): int
Special courses/instruction:	Private classes: Coaching
Accompaniment:	piano
Holidays:	1 week in summer, Thanksgiving, Christmas, Sundays; other breaks announced in advance
Fees:	$3.50/class
Scholarships:	work scholarship; for student who is talented, responsible, intelligent, and in financial need
Company affiliations:	none
Principal faculty:	Mary Hinkson (modern), Marjorie Mussman (ballet), and guest teachers
Summary statement:	(from Marjorie Mussman): "In my teaching, I use the correct placement principles developed by Maggie Black to mobilize the body through space and to develop a strong physicality."
Authors' note:	Marjorie Mussman has performed with the Joffrey Ballet, the José Limón Dance Company, and Anna Sokolow's company. Like her mentor, Maggie Black, Mussman has students repeat each exercise at the barre twice, so that they can absorb and apply corrections. The placement is based on the proper positioning of the pelvis and spine over the legs, squaring the hips off, and coordinating body movement so there is a maximum of movement without strain. Mary Hinkson is a veteran teacher and former principal dancer with the Martha Graham Dance Company.

VERA NEMTCHINOVA SCHOOL OF CLASSICAL BALLET

Hotel Ansonia
2nd Floor
73rd Street and Broadway
New York, New York 10023
(212-724-5800)

Techniques offered: BALLET

Established: 1963

Director: Madame Vera Nemtchinova

Facilities: 1 studio; dressing rooms; bathroom

Student enrollment: total: 100; average class: 10
Age: most 10-17; next 33-over; next 25-33; next 18-25
Level: most int; next adv; next adv beg; next beg

Entrance requirements: most children under 7 years old not accepted

Classes: BALLET: beg, int, int-adv, adv-pro, pointe
Adult beg: see beg ballet class above
Children: BALLET: beg (for ages 7 and up), int (for ages 8 and up)

Special courses/instruction: Private classes; Coaching

Accompaniment: piano

Holidays: national holidays; 1 week at the end of summer; Sundays

Fees: $4/class; $35/10 classes (with time limit); lower rates for students taking 3 or more classes per week; pro rate: $3.50/class; $30/10 classes; $20/hour, private classes or coaching

Scholarships: none

Company affiliations: none

Principal faculty: Madame Vera Nemtchinova

Summary statement: "Madame Nemtchinova gives very fine training in pure classical ballet technique. She has a fairly small, private school, and the classes are small enough to allow her to give a great deal of individual correction, which is not always available in the larger 'company' schools. Madame is known for her careful training of beginning children, as well as her disciplined training of dancers at all other levels."

Authors' note: Vera Nemtchinova is a famous "old school" Russian ballerina and teacher who has had a long and illustrious performing career with the Diaghilev Ballets Russes, René Blum's Ballet Russe de Monte Carlo, Colonel de Basil's Original Ballet Russe, and American Ballet Theatre. She was married to the late Anatole Oboukhov, Russian premier danseur and teacher at the School of American Ballet.

NEUBERT BALLET INSTITUTE

Carnegie Hall
Studio 803
881 Seventh Avenue (56th Street)
New York, New York 10019*
(212-MU5-7754)

Techniques offered: BALLET

Established: 1961

Director: Christine Neubert

Facilities: 6 studios; dressing rooms; bathrooms; showers

Student enrollment: average class: 12-15
Age: most 10-25; next 25-33; next 33-over

Entrance requirements: The school has two divisions, an open Educational and Cultural division for which there are no entrance requirements, and a Professional Division for which students must audition; minimum age for pre-ballet students is 3½.

Classes: BALLET: beg, int, adv-pro, pointe, adagio, variations
Children (ages 3½ and up): pre-ballet and graded ballet classes for children
Men: men's ballet class

Special courses/instruction: Special vacation courses given during Easter, summer, and Christmas holidays; Private classes; Coaching

Accompaniment: records, tapes, piano

Holidays: national holidays; Sundays; children's classes follow academic school-year calendar

Fees: $4/trial class; $45/10 classes; $35/10 classes, pro rate; lower rates for students taking several classes per week

Scholarships: Full and work scholarships are available to students who show professional dance potential and financial need; chosen by audition.

Company affiliations: The Neubert Ballet Company; Children's Ballet Theatre

Principal faculty: Sandra Balestracci, Erica Goodman, Stefan Hoff, Julliu Horvath, Mikhail Korogodski, Doyna Moraru-Wechsler, Christine Neubert, Nina Popova, Joanna Ross, Dennis Seetoo, and guest teachers

Summary statement: "Known as one of the leading 'big ballet schools' in New York, the Institute offers seventy-five courses at its Carnegie Hall and Riverdale studios, from pre-ballet for young children to advanced variations and soloist training for professionals. 'Our goal,' says Christine Neubert, noted choreographer and teacher, 'is to maintain a major institution capable of nurturing talent from the earliest phases to the full culmination as a performing artist.' The school's faculty, composed of distinguished principals and soloists from major ballet companies, stresses individual attention and the personal development of each student. High standards

*There is also a branch in Riverdale, New York.

of technique are taught with 'love and understanding.' In addition to the Professional Division, the Neubert Ballet Institute maintains an Open Division for dancers of all ages, which offers ballet classes for adults, beginners, and experienced students. Although separate from the school, the two affiliate companies—the celebrated Children's Ballet Theatre and its senior group, the young adult professional Neubert Ballet Company—play a vital role in developing future performers. Their repertory of original ballets and high level of performance have been hailed by critics as a major contribution to America's cultural and theatrical achievement."

Authors' note: Christine Neubert is the choreographer and director of both the Neubert Ballet Company and the Children's Ballet Theatre. Other faculty include Stefan Hoff, a former soloist with American Ballet Theatre; Nina Popova, a former ballerina with the Ballet Russe and past director of the Houston Ballet; Mikhail Korogodski, who has appeared as a guest artist with the Bolshoi Ballet; and Erica Goodman, a former principal dancer with the Joffrey Ballet.

Youngsters await their teacher at the New Ballet School.
Lois Greenfield

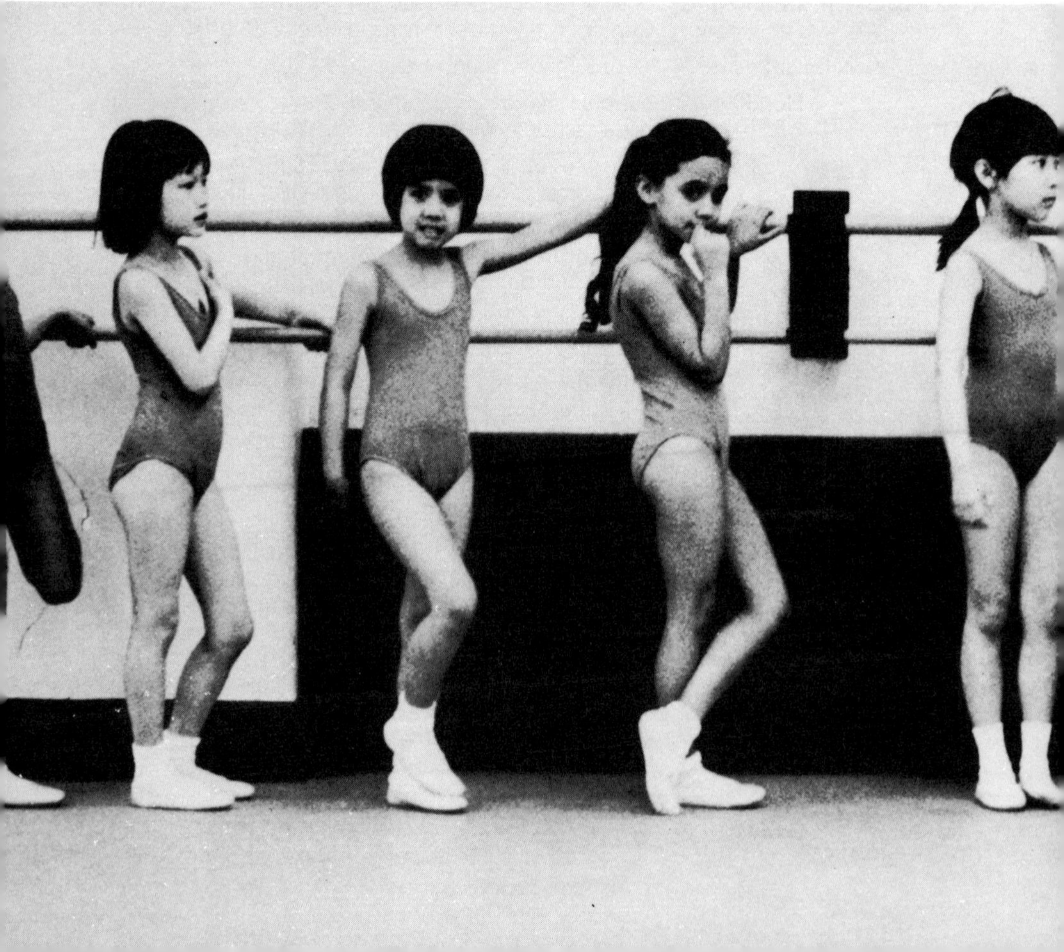

THE NEW BALLET SCHOOL
890 Broadway
New York, New York 10003
(212-777-7710)

Techniques offered:	BALLET
Established:	1978
School administrator:	Georgia Delano
Artistic director:	Eliot Feld
Facilities:	3 studios; dressing rooms; bathrooms; showers
Student enrollment:	total: 194; average class: 18 Age: all are in primary school grades 2 to 5 Level: all are beginners
Entrance requirements:	All students are selected through auditions held in the New York City public schools designated by the seven participating community school districts. Children must be in grades 2 to 5. To inquire about the program or auditions, contact the principals of the following participating schools: Lower East Side (District 1): P.S. 19, 61, 110, and 134; Chinatown (District 2): P.S. 1 and 2; Chelsea (District 2): P.S. 11;

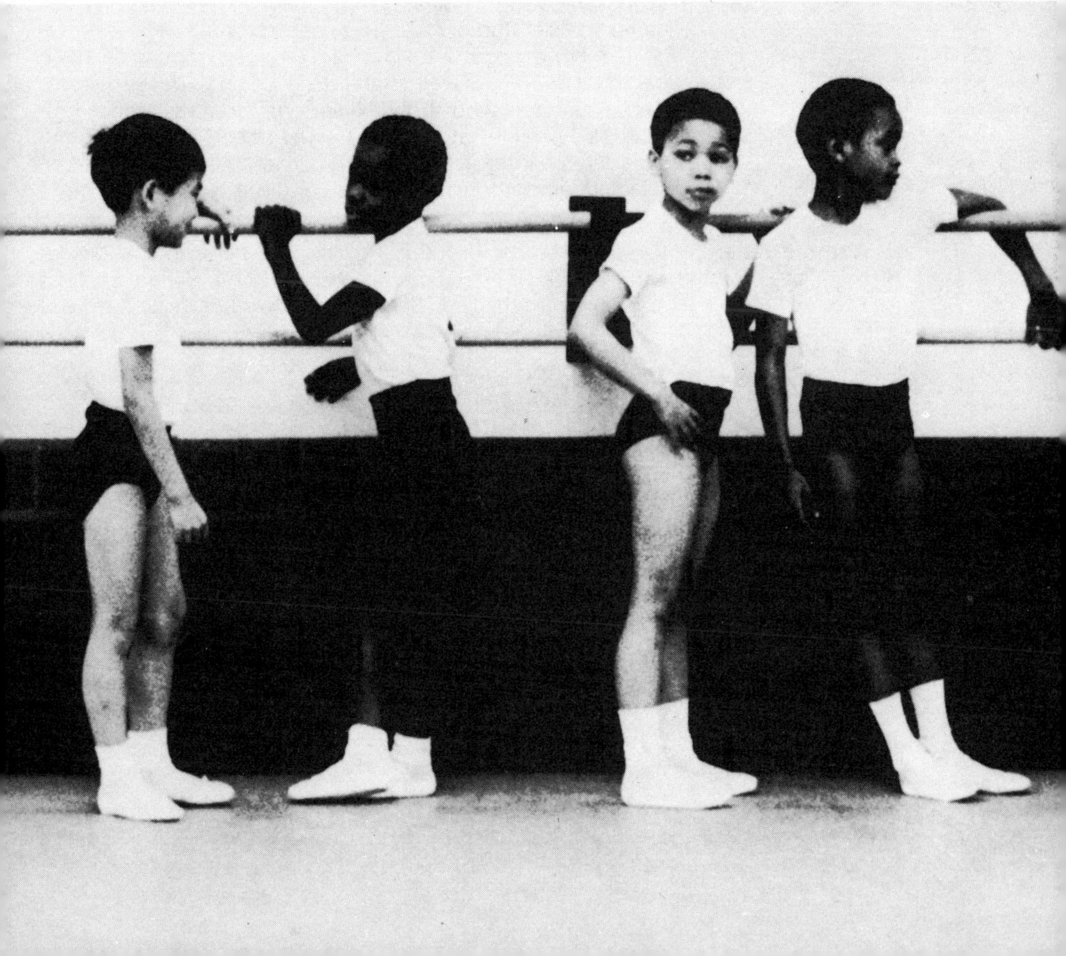

Greenwich Village (District 2): P.S. 41; East Harlem (District 4): East Harlem Block School, P.S. 83, Bilingual Bicultural Mini School, P.S. 121, and P.S. 146; Harlem (District 5): P.S. 92, 123, 129, and 154; Fort Greene, Brooklyn (District 13): P.S. 20, 46, 67, and 307; Park Slope, Brooklyn (District 15): P.S. 39, 107, and 321.

Classes: BALLET FOR CHILDREN: beg

Special courses/instruction: Six-week summer intensive course, for promising students already in the program; classes meet three times a week

Accompaniment: piano

Holidays: program operates from October to June and follows the public school vacation schedule

Fees: all tuition is free

Company affiliations: Eliot Feld Ballet

Principal faculty: Henley Haslam, Brunilda Ruiz

Summary statement: "Since January 1978, in cooperation with the New York City Board of Education, the New Ballet School has been providing free professional ballet training (including practice clothes and shoes) to talented New York City public school children in grades two to five. Students are selected on the basis of their natural facility for movement, flexibility, coordination, musicality, and enthusiasm. The youngsters come to the studio for classes one morning per week, escorted by an adult. Each child receives training in basic ballet technique, as well as an introduction to dance history. Those children who show exceptional progress, concentration, ability, and interest are invited to continue during the summer for intensive study. Each year new students will be selected, and those invited to continue will receive more advanced training."

Authors' note: Faculty member Brunilda Ruiz is a former principal dancer with the Joffrey Ballet and the Harkness Ballet. She has also taught at the High School of Performing Arts.

NEW DANCE GROUP STUDIO

254 West 47th Street
New York, New York 10036
(212-245-9327)

Techniques offered: MODERN, BALLET, JAZZ, ETHNIC (HAITIAN, AFRO-CARIBBEAN)

Established: mid-1930s

Director: Hope Moss

Facilities: 3 studios; dressing rooms; bathrooms

Student enrollment: total: 600; classes limited to 22 dancers
Age: most 18-25; next 25-33; next 33-over
Level: most beg; next adv beg; next int

Entrance requirements: minimum age is 14; class levels are assigned by school

Classes: MODERN: introduction; MODERN (Graham): beg, adv beg, int; MODERN (Horton): beg, adv beg, int; MODERN (Humphrey-Weidman): beg, adv beg; BALLET: introduction, beg, adv beg, int, int-adv, pointe, partnering; JAZZ: introduction, beg, adv beg; HAITIAN AND AFRO-CARIBBEAN: beg, int

Adult beg: see introduction classes in modern dance, ballet, and jazz above

Special courses/instruction: Beginners' modern dance for New York City public school teachers (for in-service credit); Techniques and choreography of Isadora Duncan; Movement and improvisation for dancers, actors, and singers

Accompaniment: piano, drums

Holidays: legal holidays; Rosh Hashana and Yom Kippur; Sundays; Saturday classes are suspended during summer

Fees: $3/registration fee; $3.50/1½-hour class; $3/1-hour class; $27.50/ten 1-hour classes; $33/ten 1½-hour classes; term rates according to number of classes per week; registration fee is credited toward full tuition; pro rates: $20/ten 1-hour classes; $25/ten 1-½ hour classes

Scholarships: Full: 15 adults; partial: 15 high school students; work: 4; chosen by audition and reviewed annually; students must have potential for performing career

Company affiliations: Sophie Maslow Dance Company; Joyce Trisler Danscompany; the Jean-Leon Destiné Haitian-Afro Caribbean Dance Company; the Isadora Duncan Heritage Group

Principal faculty: Cheryl Bell (Horton), Stanley Berke (Graham), Margot Colbert (ballet), Jean-Leon Destiné (Haitian, Afro-Caribbean), Ana Marie Forsythe (Horton); Penny Frank (Graham), Celene Keller (ballet), Julia Levien (Duncan course), Sophie Maslow (Graham), Dorene Richardson (Graham, Humphrey-Weidman); Poli Rogers (jazz).

Summary statement: "The School runs on a tri-semester basis with graded classes. Although we offer a variety of techniques to professionals and nonprofessionals, all classes are taught on a professional level. Our particular aims are to train students for professional careers and also to serve by building knowledgeable dance audiences. Among our ex-scholarship students are: Donald McKayle, Pearl Primus, Jaime Rogers, Eliot Feld, and a great many others who have gone on to establish successful careers."

Authors' note: As its name implies, the New Dance Group Studio was a hotbed of politically conscious modern dancers in the 1930s and 1940s. (Early modern dance was sometimes called "new dance.") This school still offers a particularly wide spectrum of modern dance techniques. It has a distinguished and unusually stable faculty, some of whom have been there for nearly twenty years. Since classes are geared to young adults and adults, most are given in the late afternoon and evening.

NEW YORK ACADEMY OF BALLET

667 Madison Avenue (61st Street)
New York, New York 10021
(212-838-0822)

Techniques offered: BALLET, JAZZ, BODY CONDITIONING

Established: 1958

Director: Florence Lessing

Facilities: 2 studios; dressing rooms; bathrooms; showers

Student enrollment: total: 800; average class: 22
Age: most 18-25; next 25-33; next 10-17; next 33-over
Level: most beg; next int; next adv beg; next adv

Entrance requirements: none

Classes: BALLET: basic, adv beg, int, adv-int, adv, pointe I and II; JAZZ: beg, int, adv; ADULT DANCE-FOR-BODY CONDITIONING CLASSES

Adult beg: see basic ballet, beg jazz, and body conditioning classes above

Children: BALLET: pre-ballet (for ages 5 and 6); for children ages 7-13: beg ballet I and II, int ballet I and II, adv ballet

Special courses/instruction: Private classes

Accompaniment: piano, drum

Holidays: national holidays; Sundays

Fees: adults: $4.50/trial class; $34/8 weeks, 1 class per week; $60/8 weeks, 2 classes per week; children: $145/36-week semester (September to June), 1 class per week; $265/36-week semester (September to June), 2 classes per week; lower rates for students taking several classes per week; $25/hour, private class

Scholarships: Full and partial scholarships are available to advanced and intermediate students; they are awarded on the basis of talent and the school's need for advanced pupils.

Company affiliations: none

Principal faculty: Ronald Bostick (ballet), Dafna Erlich (ballet), Herb Giron (children's classes, basic ballet), Ralf Harmer (jazz), Ed Kresley (ballet, jazz), Florence Lessing (ballet), Felicia Velasco (pre-ballet)

Summary statement: "We offer dedicated teaching no matter what the level. Beginner classes are never sloughed off. We stress individual corrections. The aims of the school are: to engender in the individual student a sense of poise and self-assurance; to develop muscular structure and coordination; and to lead the student to a deeper understanding and appreciation of the dance as an art form. Florence Lessing, the school's director, has performed in concert with José Limón and Charles Weidman. She was also the partner of the late Jack Cole in Broadway musicals, and afterward, a featured dancer in Paramount and R.K.O. films."

NEW YORK CONSERVATORY OF DANCE

226 West 56th Street
New York, New York 10019
(212-581-1908)

Techniques offered: BALLET

Established: 1977

Director: Vladimir Dokoudovsky

Facilities: 4 studios; dressing rooms; bathrooms; showers; lounges; sauna

Student enrollment: total: 600; average class: 15-20
Age: most 18-25; next 25-33; next 10-17 and 33-over in equal proportions
Level: most int and adv, in equal proportions; next beg and adv beg, in equal proportions

Entrance requirements: minimum age is 7

Classes: BALLET: adult beg, adv beg, int, adv int, open adv, pro, adv pro; toe; pas de deux
Adult beg: see adult beg ballet class above
Children (ages 7 and up): beg ballet class (Saturdays only)

Accompaniment: piano

Holidays: major national holidays; Sundays

Fees: $4/class, $30/10 classes

Scholarships: fluctuate, depending on needs of the school

Company affiliations: none

Principal faculty: William Badolato (int), Vladimir Dokoudovsky (children's beg, adv beg, int-adv, pro, toe, pas de deux), Patricia Heyes (adult beg, adv beg), Celene Keller (adv beg); Igor Schwezoff (pro), Nina Stroganova (int, variations), Rochelle Zide (int)

Summary statement: (from director Vladimir Dokoudovsky): "I have dedicated the opening of the New York Conservatory of Dance to Mme. Olga Preobrajenska, a truly great teacher to whom so many, myself included, are indebted; to Colonel W. de Basil, director of the Monte Carlo Ballet Russe (later known as the Original Ballet Russe), and finally to the second wave of dance pioneers, my colleagues of the thirties and forties. Few things are more rewarding for a teacher than to see a student improving, but to me the reward is even greater when the student understands the logic of the traditional academic training. During my twenty-eight years of teaching in New York City, I have seen various styles of ballet come and go; many were based on exaggeration, which is often mistaken for beauty. It is my view, however, that simplicity is purity, purity is beauty, and beauty may one day save the world. I would like to help conserve that pure, unadorned academism which in the past has fostered so many outstanding artists. My dream is to conserve the Maryinsky-Preobrajenska method. The Conservatory offers as many 'open' classes as possible because I do not believe that one can judge who will or will not be a dancer. The exercise of such judgments in the past would have deprived the world of some of its greatest dancers, teachers and choreographers. We have future plans to invite guest teachers from all over the world to conduct classes; and to hold an annual competition for students ages 14 to 16, with the winners (one boy and one girl) receiving a one-year scholarship to the school of their choice."

Authors' note: Although this is a relatively new school, its staff is comprised of some of the best known and most highly respected teachers in the city. Vladimir Dokoudovsky, for example, made his professional debut at the age of thirteen as a soloist with Colonel de Basil's Original Ballet Russe. He performed with the Polish Ballet under the direction of Bronislava Nijinska, the Ballet Russe de Monte Carlo, the Mordkin Ballet, and American Ballet Theatre. His wife, Nina Stroganova, was also trained in Europe and performed with the Ballet Russe de Monte Carlo, the Original Ballet Russe, American Ballet Theatre, and the Royal Danish Ballet. Igor Schwezoff was trained at the Kirov school in Leningrad. He was a soloist with the Ballet Russe de Monte Carlo and the Original Ballet Russe, directed his own company and school in Manhattan, and for many years taught at the American Ballet Theatre School.

NEW YORK SCHOOL OF BALLET

2291 Broadway (81st Street)
New York, New York 10024
(212-799-5445/5446)

Techniques offered: BALLET

Established: 1964

Directors: Richard Thomas and Barbara Fallis

Facilities: 3 studios; dressing rooms; bathrooms; showers

Student enrollment: total: 400-500; average class: 30
Age: most 10-25, in equal proportions; next 25-33; next 33-over
Level: most int and adv; next adv beg; next beg

Entrance requirements: miminum age is 8

Classes: BALLET: adult beg, adv beg, int, adv int, adv-pro

Adult beg: see adult beg ballet class above

Children (ages 6 and up): pre-ballet (for ages 6 and 7), and four levels of graded children's ballet classes from beg to int

Special courses/instruction: Master classes (taught by guest teachers); Coaching (for advanced and professional dancers only)

Accompaniment: piano

Holidays: most national holidays; Sundays

Fees: \$3.50/class, \$25/10 classes; special semester rates (September to May) for children; pro rates for union members

Scholarships: Full scholarships are available to boys 8-14 years old; and full and work scholarships are available to students performing in the company, U.S. Terpsichore.

Company affiliations: U.S. Terpsichore

Principal faculty: Dick Andros, Barbara Fallis, Richard Thomas

Summary statement: "We teach a combination of Italian and Russian training. Besides the study of technique in class, an emphasis is placed on intellectual development and on understanding the various balletic styles, ballet history, and tradition."

Authors' note: Richard Thomas and Barbara Fallis, who are husband and wife, have danced with Alicia Alonso's Ballet de Cuba, the American Ballet Theatre, and the New York City Ballet, and have served as ballet master and mistress to Eliot Feld's American Ballet Company. They have a loyal and affectionate following among New York's professional and amateur dancers alike. Perhaps one reason is the gift they share for creating beautiful and challenging movement for classes. The Thomases' studio is comfortably worn and has a homey atmosphere, complete with occasional dogs (which they breed as a hobby) and babies roaming around the front desk area. (Twyla Tharp's young son and the children of Anne Byrne and Dustin Hoffman—she's a fine dancer and longtime pupil of the Thomases—practically grew up there.) Among their other current and former students are choreographer Eliot Feld, the New York City Ballet's Sean Lavery, Daniel Levans (the former American Ballet soloist who played the part of the brash young choreographer in ***The Turning Point***), and ballerinas Christine Sarry and Cynthia Gregory. The Thomases are the parents of ballet dancer Bronwyn Thomas and actor Richard Thomas, Jr.

MAY O'DONNELL MODERN DANCE CENTER

439 Lafayette Street (between Astor Place
and East 8th Street)
3rd Floor
New York, New York 10003
(212-777-0744)

Techniques offered: MODERN

Established: 1945

Director: May O'Donnell

Facilities: 1 studio; dressing rooms; bathrooms; showers

Student enrollment: total: 100; average class: 15-20
Age: most 18-25; next 25-33; next 33-over
Level: most adv; next int; next beg

Entrance requirements: no children

Classes: MODERN: beg, adv beg, int, adv int, adv
Adult beg: 1-hour adult beg class, given evenings

Special courses/instruction: Winter and summer workshops are given during school vacations so that out-of-town students can attend; they include technique, repertory, composition, and study of percussion accompaniment.

Accompaniment: voice, drum

Holidays: national holidays; Sundays

Fees: $4/class; $36/10 classes (with time limit); other discounts available depending on the number of classes taken per week

Scholarships: work scholarships; for potential company members

Company affiliations: The May O'Donnell Concert Dance Company

Principal faculty: Sheila Zadra Goldstein, May O'Donnell, Sophia Paluszek, and members of the O'Donnell company

Summary statement:* On its small and personal scale, the May O'Donnell Modern Dance Center, formerly located on West 19th Street, is among the oldest and most highly respected modern dance studios in New York. Until recently it was known as the O'Donnell-Shurr Studio (three years ago O'Donnell's partner, Gertrude Shurr, retired from teaching). O'Donnell says that the training is primarily aimed at developing professional dancers; but in addition, the school offers beginning classes for adults, which stress the same high standards and sense of personal achievement as the professional training. Although O'Donnell's technique is based on the contraction-release principles of Martha Graham in whose company she was a soloist for many years, her classes further emphasize "a free, open, and energetic use of the body." She says she tries "to give students basic skills and training for the body without personal mannerisms, so they will have a broad technical range that will enable them to work with a variety of choreographers." "Graduates" of the O'Donnell company and school include Dudley Williams, Robert Joffrey, Gerald Arpino, Norman Walker, Cora Cahan, Mabel Robinson, Ramon Seguerra, and actor Ben Vareen.

Authors' note: May O'Donnell is originally from California and, although she is close to seventy, still looks as though she could cross the Rockies in a covered wagon. Some people say that O'Donnell's studio is one of the best places to study Graham technique because she produces dancers who are both strong and natural looking.

*This was obtained from May O'Donnell by interview.

PUERTO RICAN DANCE THEATRE

215 West 76th Street
New York, New York, 10024
(212-724-1195)

Techniques offered: BALLET, JAZZ, MODERN, ETHNIC (AFRO-CUBAN), FLAMENCO

Established: 1970

School administrator: Sandy Levitt

Artistic director: Julio Torres

Facilities: 1 studio; dressing rooms; bathrooms

Student enrollment: total: 300-400; average class: 15
Age: most 10-17; next 18-33; next 33-over
Level: most beg and adv beg; next int; next adv

Entrance requirements: none

Classes: BALLET: adult basics, beg, int, adv, pro; JAZZ: adult basics, beg, int, adv, pro; MODERN: beg, int, adv, pro; FLAMENCO (given occasionally): beg

Adult beg: see adult basics and beg classes in ballet, jazz, modern dance, and flamenco above

Children: BALLET: pre-ballet (ages 4-7), children's ballet I (ages 7-10), children's ballet II (ages 10-14); JAZZ: beg jazz for children of combined ages (given on Saturdays); MODERN: beg modern for children of combined ages; ETHNIC (Afro-Cuban combined with modern dance): beg class for children of combined ages

Special courses/instruction: Private classes; Coaching

Accompaniment: piano, drum

Holidays: national holidays; Sundays; weekends in summer

Fees: $5/annual registration fee; $3.75/class; $30/10 classes; pro rate: $3/class, $25/10 classes

Scholarships: Full and part are available to students with dance aptitude and financial need.

Company affiliations: The Puerto Rican Dance Theatre; Puerto Rican Dance Theatre Workshop (a student apprentice group that performs in conjunction with the Puerto Rican Dance Theatre); Children's Performing Group (appears at public school assembly programs and the annual student recital)

Principal faculty: Teresa Cassese (ballet), Sandy Levitt (ballet), Polly Rogers (jazz, ethnic), Tee Ross (modern, ballet)

Summary statement: "The Puerto Rican Dance Theatre was founded in 1970 by Mr. Torres to expand the cultural base of the Hispanic population in the New York metropolitan area. The school offers bilingual classes in all forms of dance and maintains an extensive scholarship program. The company also gives some free performances in an effort to reach out to the community, and lecture/demonstrations to encourage the study of dance among Hispanics. The primary goal of the Puerto Rican Dance Theatre School is to train young students for careers as professional dancers. In addition, we try to maintain a varied curriculum to expose students to several different styles of dance such as ballet, modern, primitive, jazz, and flamenco. It is our belief that students should have a wide range of knowledge in their chosen craft. The faculty has been carefully selected to bring to the students the best teachers for each technique taught in our school."

Authors' note: The school's founder and artistic director, Julio Torres, performed with the José Greco Spanish Dance Company and the George Chaffee Ballet Company. Sandy Levitt was the lead dancer in the Broadway show ***Gypsy*** and former soloist with the Garden State Ballet. Tee Ross dances with the Pepsi Bethel Authentic Jazz Dance Theatre.

LARRY RICHARDSON'S DANCE GALLERY

242 East 14th Street
New York, New York 10003
(212-685-5972)

Techniques offered: MODERN, BALLET

Established: 1967

Administrator: J. Antony Siciliano

Artistic director: Larry Richardson

Facilities: 1 studio; dressing rooms; bathrooms; showers

Student enrollment: total: 40-50
Age: most 18-32
Level: most beg; next int

Entrance requirements: none

Classes: MODERN: elem, int, adv; BALLET: beg

Special courses/instruction: Private classes; Coaching

Accompaniment: tape, drums, piano

Holidays: national holidays; July and August; weekends

Fees: $5/class; $30/10 classes

Scholarships: none

Company affiliations: Larry Richardson and Dance Company; Viola Farber Dance Company

Principal faculty: Viola Farber (int-adv Cunningham technique), Shelagh Gonzalez (ballet), Larry Richardson (modern), Wendy Stein (modern)

Summary statement: "We are primarily interested in teaching professionally minded and serious dance students. We emphasize technique. There is no improvisation as such. We are not an avant-garde school. The modern dance classes of Larry Richardson and Wendy Stein are Limón and Graham-oriented."

Authors' note: Viola Farber, who is new on the teaching staff, was a leading dancer with Merce Cunningham for twelve years. She has had her own company since 1968. Farber is known for a rhythmically complex and quirky but virtuoso movement style, and until recently she taught at her own school.

ROD RODGERS DANCE STUDIO
8 East 12th Street
New York, New York 10003
(212-924-7560)

Techniques offered: MODERN, JAZZ, AFRO-HAITIAN

Established: 1972

Director: Rod Rodgers

Facilities: 1 studio; dressing rooms; bathrooms

Student enrollment: average class: 10
Age: most 16-25; next 25-33; next 33-over
Level: most beg; next adv beg; next int; next adv

Entrance requirements: minimum age, 16

Classes: MODERN: elementary-beg, int; ETHNIC (Dunham): beg-int; MODERN-JAZZ: beg-int; JAZZ: beg-int, adv; ETHNIC JAZZ: beg-int; AFRO-HAITIAN: int, int-adv
Adult beg: see elementary-beg modern class above

Special courses/instruction: Workshop in advanced technique and repertory (by invitation only).

Accompaniment: tapes, records, drum

Holidays: New Year's Day, Thanksgiving, Christmas; Sundays

Fees: $1.50/introductory class; $3/class; $25/10 classes

Scholarships: Work-study available for students with interest, professional dance potential, and financial need

Company affiliations: Rod Rodgers Dance Company

Principal faculty: Rhema Pinnock (Afro-Haitian), Sloan Robinson (jazz), Rod Rodgers (repertory workshop), Shirley Rushing (modern, jazz), Theresa Stephens (Dunham)

Summary statement: "The philosophy of the school echoes the philosophy of Rod Rodgers Dance Company, combining ethnic or traditional Afro-American styles with classical modern dance and jazz-blues idioms. The dance student's experience is enhanced by the studio's relaxed atmosphere and the individual attention given each participant."

Authors' note: Rodgers worked with Erick Hawkins before forming his own company, and his choreography combines the fluidity of Hawkins's style with African and jazz dance influences. Rhema Pinnock has performed with Jean-Leon Destiné's Afro-Haitian Dance Company. Shirley Rushing has danced in Rodgers's company, as well as with Walter Nicks and Eleo Pomare.

ZENA ROMMETT STUDIO

70 West 3rd Street
New York, New York 10012
(212-982-8033)

Techniques offered: BALLET

Established: 1971

Director: Zena Rommett

Facilities: 1 studio; dressing rooms; bathrooms

Student enrollment: average class: 25-35

Entrance requirements: no children

Classes: BALLET: basic placement and ballet class, level 1; basic placement and ballet class (for more experienced beginners); int placement and ballet class; adv placement and ballet class

Accompaniment: piano (for barre and center work)

Holidays: major national holidays; Sundays

Fees: $5/class; $4/registration fee for initial series card; $32/8 classes ($4 per class); $42/12 classes ($3.50 per class); all series cards expire 1 month from date of purchase

Scholarships: none

Company affiliations: none

Principal faculty: Ernest Pagnano, Zena Rommett

Summary statement: "Zena Rommett introduced into the field of dance education a system of exercises related to the physical dynamics of the body in motion. The intention of these logical and scientific floor exercises is to provide the dancers with a private and confident knowledge of the mechanics and capabilities of their bodies in relationship to alignment, energy, and movement. The terms used are familiar ballet vocabulary so that the dancers relate what they have learned to their standing position at the barre or at center. The isolated exercises permit the dancer to concentrate on specific or problem areas, developing an awareness of turnout, correct muscle usage and mobility. While the floor positions allow the dancers to build strength, their energy is being used efficiently without the added tension of retaining their standing balance. In this manner of training, the dancer's body is warmed up and develops control of an unmannered technique and a basic placement foundation suitable for a career in either modern or classical dance."

Authors' note: Classes at Zena Rommett's studio begin with a slow, careful warmup composed of a series of progressive exercises which are done lying down on the floor. The purpose of the hour-long floor workout is to establish good body placement and develop stretch and strength in key areas of the body such as the pelvic and stomach muscles, back, legs, and feet. This is followed by a standard ballet barre (performed standing up) and finally, center-floor exercises and combinations. A typical lesson lasts about two hours, but students sometimes leave after the floor warmup, or after taking the warmup and the barre. The Rommett method has proved to be wonderfully effective for beginners, since it gives them a sound foundation in technique, and helps sensitize them to the individual way in which their bodies work. Professional dancers often take Zena's classes to get "set up" for the day's rehearsals and performances, or to get back into shape after touring or injury. Zena is an ever-growing and devoted teacher who is genuinely interested in helping dancers. Ernie Pagnano, a new member of the teaching staff, has performed with the Alvin Ailey American Dance Theatre, the Harkness Ballet, the Netherlands Dance Theatre, Dennis Wayne's Dancers, the Lar Lubovitch Dance Company, and the Cliff Keuter Dance Company.

SCHOOL OF AMERICAN BALLET
The Juilliard School Building
3rd Floor
144 West 66th Street
New York, New York 10023
(212-877-0600)

Techniques offered: BALLET

Established: 1934

Directors: Natalie Molostwoff and Nathalie Gleboff

Chairman of Faculty: George Balanchine

Facilities: 4 studios; dressing rooms; bathrooms; showers

Student enrollment: total: 325; average class: 25-30 (maximum)
Age: most 8-17; next 18-25
Level: equal proportions of all levels

Entrance requirements: age and audition, reevaluated annually. The minimum age for enrollment is 8, and there are age limits for each level of technique. In general, children with no previous ballet training are preferred. Auditions for beginners ages 10-14 and all students with previous ballet instruction are held the Tuesday after Labor Day; 8- and 9-year-old beginners are auditioned in mid-September. Auditions for new students are also held once a week throughout the school year; parents should call for an appointment.

Classes: BALLET: fourteen progressive divisions of academic ballet technique, from First Children's Division to Graduating Division; toe variations, supported adagio; MUSIC THEORY; ETHICS AND ESTHETICS

Children and teens: several graded levels of ballet classes for ages 8 and up

Men: men's ballet classes from the int level on

Special courses/instruction: Five-week summer intensive course (open to outside students by audition; teachers may observe classes)

Accompaniment: piano

Holidays: major national holidays, 5 weeks in summer, 2 weeks for Christmas; Sundays

Fees: yearly and monthly rates, depending on the division and number of classes taken per week; tuition for the First and Second Children's Division must be paid by the year; $35/10 classes, pro rate

Scholarships: 80 to 105 scholarships are available to students of exceptional talent and financial need; half of these pay for full tuition and half for tuition plus living expenses. Most scholarships are awarded to dancers between the ages of 13 and 16. Both summer and school-year scholarships are available.

Company affiliations: New York City Ballet; children are chosen from the school to perform in NYCB productions such as ***The Nutcracker, Coppelia,*** and ***A Midsummer Night's Dream***; older students apprentice with the company. There is also a Performance Workshop in which ballets from the NYCB's repertory are rehearsed during the school year and presented at a public performance each spring that is reviewed by the New York critics.

Principal faculty: Alexandra Danilova, Felia Doubrovska, Helene Dudin, Andrei Kramarevsky, Richard Rapp, Elise Reiman, Suki Schorer, Muriel Stuart, Antonina Tumkovsky, Stanley Williams, and guest teachers from the New York City Ballet.

Summary statement: "The principal aim of the School of American Ballet is to prepare students for performing careers in the New York City Ballet or any other professional ballet company. The school is therefore extremely selective in admitting new students and renewing their enrollment from year to year. It provides a program of progressive training which meets the ever-accelerating demands of accuracy, speed, and acrobacy of which George Balanchine's choreography is a contemporary criterion. Its fourteen separate divisions enable the school to place each student in the grade best suited to his age and proficiency. The school's distinguished faculty, some of whom Mr. Balanchine brought here from Russia, are world famous."

JUDITH SCOTT—CLASSES IN MODERN DANCE
Satoru Shimazaki Studio
43 East 19th Street
New York, New York 10003
(212-749-4714)

Techniques offered: MODERN, IMPROVISATION, BODY CONDITIONING

Established: 1976

Director: Judith Scott

Facilities: 1 studio; dressing rooms; bathrooms

Student enrollment: total: 35; average class: 8-9
Age: most 25-33; next 18-25; next 33-over; next 10-17
Level: most adv beg; next beg; next int; next adv

Entrance requirements: none

Classes: MODERN: adv beg, int; MOVEMENT IMPROVISATION (a 2-hour class given twice weekly as part of a 10-week workshop; "explores dance as a process integrating body, feelings, mind, and spirit through breath, sound, natural movement, games, ritual, and other structures leading to creation and performance"); ENDURADANCE ("for the dancer or nondancer who wishes to improve cardiovascular fitness through repetitious running without developing muscle bulk; consists of a 20-minute warmup, 20 minutes of movement combinations using running, jumping, sliding and other rigorous activities, and a 20-minute cool-down")

Children (ages 4-12): CREATIVE MOVEMENT: classes graded by age

Special courses/instruction: Private classes; Coaching

Accompaniment: percussion, records

Holidays: month of August; 2 weeks around Christmastime; Sundays

Fees: technique classes: $6/class, $32/8 classes; improvisation: $10/class, $48/8 classes, $90/16 classes; endurance: $35/10 classes; all series expire 1 month from date of purchase.

Scholarships: Two work scholarships are available; students are chosen by interview and according to financial need.

Company affiliations: Judith Scott Dance Company

Principal faculty: Judith Scott

Summary statement: "The dance technique I teach is based on relaxation and proper body alignment, progressing to movement patterns that evolve naturally from oneself. In our improvisation classes students work on techniques to release the natural voice, free the body, and provide structures for collaborative performance."

Authors' note: Judith Scott is a graduate of Northwestern University, with degrees in theatre, music, and dance education. She has studied with Martha Graham, Charles Weidman, Erick Hawkins, Murray Louis, Alwin Nikolais, Anna Halprin, Merce Cunningham, Zena Rommett, Raoul Gelabert, and Luigi, among others. While teaching at Northwestern University she formed the Judith Scott Dance Company, which performs multimedia, outdoor, and environmental works. Scott has also taught at Barnard College, Dance Theatre Workshop, the University of the West Indies in Kingston, Jamaica, and at the Paris-American Academy in France. She is presently an assistant professor in dance education at New York University. In addition to concert works, Scott has choreographed for musical theatre and in 1973 was one of six choreographers chosen to be recipients of National Endowment for the Arts fellowships at Connecticut College's Dance/TV Workshop. She is on the board of directors of Dance Theatre Workshop.

SOUNDS IN MOTION SCHOOL
290 Lenox Avenue (125th Street)
New York, New York 10027
(212-348-2460)

Techniques offered: MODERN, EXERCISE

Established: 1973

Director: Dianne R. McIntyre

Facilities: 1 studio; dressing rooms; bathrooms

Student enrollment: total: 300; average class: 15

Entrance requirements: none

Classes: MODERN: beg, int-adv; MODERN (Horton): beg-int; EXERCISE CLASS FOR ADULTS (45 minutes)

Adult beg: see beg and exercise classes above
Children (ages 3-11): MODERN: beg (Saturdays only)

Accompaniment: piano

Holidays: national holidays; Sundays; other breaks announced in advance

Fees: $3/class, adults; $2.50/class, children; $20/10 classes, adults; $15/12 classes, children

Scholarships: A limited number of work scholarships are available for regular students who express interest and need.

Company affiliations: Sounds in Motion Dance Company

Principal faculty: Mickey Davidson, Bernadine Jennings, Dianne McIntyre

Summary statement: "We are a school that primarily serves the black community, offering instruction in modern dance to expand the concept of dance in the community we serve. To that end we give evening beginning classes for working men and women, and a Saturday children's class. We hope, in the future, to add more daytime classes."

STUDIO OF CREATIVE MOVEMENT
60 West 25th Street
New York, New York 10010
(212-CH3-7758)

Techniques offered: MODERN

Established: 1963

Director: Merle Lister

Facilities: 1 studio; dressing rooms; bathrooms

Student enrollment: average class: 10
Age: most 18-33; next 33-over
Level: equal proportions of all levels

Entrance requirements: An interview is required for students who wish to take intensive study (several classes per week); the modern dance technique class is the prerequisite for the Unity of Arts Workshop.

Classes: MODERN DANCE TECHNIQUE: beg, int, adv; UNITY OF ARTS WORKSHOP (combines dance with other creative arts such as playwriting and poetry)

Special courses/instruction: Private classes for students who want more individual work, who have specific creative or physical (handicap) problems, or who need help in areas where movement is vital to their work.

Accompaniment: tapes and records, piano, vocal sounds

Holidays: most national holidays; weekends

Fees: $6/class, $25/5 classes; $40/10 classes; reduced rates for students taking more than 2 classes per week; $15/1½-hour private class

Scholarships: Two partial scholarships are available; students assist with office and studio chores and help set up performing programs.

Company affiliations: The Lister Complex Theatre; students also participate in workshop performances during the year.

Principal faculty: Secorra Jones, Merle Lister

Summary statement: "Along with the study of the individual skills of dance movement and other arts and creative forms, the studio teaches an inner process that ties the dance and these forms together. Students have an opportunity to experience this process in performance and also can create their own work. Because of the ongoing poets' and writers' program, written material of different structures, such as plays, dialogues, and poetry, are also fed into the studio work for workshops and performances. The courses at the studio are adaptable for laymen and children who want to extend their range of movement and creativity and to gain a general sense of well-being about themselves; and also for professionals (i.e., educators, recreational personnel, therapists, other performers, and anyone who can incorporate the studio work into their own work). High school and college students who have special programs at their schools can get credit toward their curriculum study."

Authors' note: Merle Lister performed with the late James Waring and is herself a choreographer.

STUDIO REVENE
55 West 16th Street
New York, New York 10011
(212-242-5878)

Techniques offered: BALLET, MODERN, T'AI CHI CH'UAN

Established: 1976

Director: Nadine Revene

Facilities: 1 studio; dressing rooms; bathrooms; showers

Student enrollment: total: 300; average class: 30
Age: most 18-25
Level: most int

Entrance requirements: none

Classes: The following classes are taught by Nadine Revene: BALLET: beg, adv-int, adv-pro; pointe: beg, adv. The studio is also rented out to other teachers who offer their own classes. Currently they are: BALLET: basics (taught by choreographer and former Cunningham dancer Peter Saul); MODERN DANCE TECHNIQUE AND BODY AWARENESS; beg (taught by Paula Mason, chairman of the dance department at Bryn Mawr College); T'AI CHI CHU'AN: beg (taught by New York University faculty member Joshua Whiting).

Adult beg: see ballet basics, beg modern dance, and T'ai Chi classes above

Special courses/instruction: Private classes; Coaching

Accompaniment: piano

Holidays: major holiday weekends; Sundays

Fees: $4/class, $3/class, barre only; $35/10 classes: $12.50/half-hour, private class; classes taught by outside teachers are separately priced

Scholarships: Two work scholarships are available to conscientious students who are "willing to do cleaning and other chores despite a talent for ballet!"

Company affiliations: none

Principal faculty: Nadine Revene (ballet)

Summary statement: "Studio Revene wishes to inspire dancers to lift and stretch their bodies out into space; to place dancers where they can expand themselves completely; to enjoy the feeling of freedom within the boundaries of two great arts—music and dance—boundaries which have within them unlimited expression. We make a special effort to get good pianists for classes. Other than Nadine Revene, there is no permanent faculty per se; we offer space to teachers who wish to do serious concentrated work. Trained by Helene Platova, Vincenzo Celli, Mia Slavenska, and Igor Schwezoff, Ms. Revene has performed as a soloist with American Ballet Theatre, the First Chamber Dance Quartet, and the New York City Opera; and as a principal dancer with the Pennsylvania Ballet and the Bremen Opera in Germany. She has also appeared with the New York City Ballet and danced in several Broadway musicals. Before opening her own studio, she taught at Lehman College, the Finis Jhung studio, and the Morelli Ballet in New York, and was ballet mistress and coach for the Pennsylvania Ballet."

Authors' note: Nadine Revene's classes move beautifully and are very musical. Revene is a dancer's dancer, articulate and expressive, from whose example one can learn a great deal. She seems to be particularly interested in the refinements of dancing and has a gift for drawing out of each student his or her own special movement qualities.

Nadine Revene corrects a student in her advanced intermediate class. ***courtesy of Studio Revene***

Jerry Ames, front and center, leads an adult beginner tap class at the Theatre Teachers Alliance. ***courtesy of Theatre Teachers Alliance***

THEATRE TEACHERS ALLIANCE
Act 48th Studios
209 West 48th Street
New York, New York 10036
(212-541-9518)

Techniques offered:	TAP, BALLET, JAZZ
Established:	1973
Executive director:	Judd Mathison
Artistic director:	Jerry Ames
Facilities:	6 studios; dressing rooms; bathrooms
Student enrollment:	total: 200; average class: 15 Age: most 18-25 and 25-33; next 10-17; next 33-over Level: most beg to int; next adv
Entrance requirements:	none
Classes:	TAP: new beg, beg, adv beg, int-adv; BALLET: beg-int, int; JAZZ: new beg *Adult beg*: see new beg tap and jazz classes above *Children*: (ages 7-14, Saturdays only): TAP: beg, beg-int
Special courses/instruction:	Private classes; Coaching
Accompaniment:	records
Holidays:	national holidays; Sundays
Fees:	$5/class; $4.50/class for pros who are union members; $40/10 classes, 1 per week; $35/10 classes, 2 per week; $30/10 classes, 3 per week; $20/hour, private class or coaching; $25/hour, special material
Scholarships:	none
Company affiliations:	The Jerry Ames Tap Dance Company
Principal faculty:	Jerry Ames (tap), Amelia Gilmore (ballet), Lilian Scroppo (jazz)
Summary statement:	"Theatre Teachers Alliance is a professional training center. Our faculty consists of established performers with extensive credits in their respective fields. Our goal is to provide the best possible training in a clean, pleasant atmosphere. Known for his dancing, teaching, and choreography, Artistic Director Jerry Ames is considered to be one of America's foremost exponents of the art of tap dancing. He is coauthor of ***The Book of Tap.*** Amelia Gilmore has performed with the Metropolitan Opera and in theatre and nightclubs in the U.S., Canada, Europe, and South America. She has also choreographed for clubs and television. Lilian Scroppo was a featured dancer with both Martha Graham and Pearl Lang, and has appeared on Broadway and television."

TOKUNAGA DANCE KO. STUDIO

874 Broadway (17/18th Street)
3rd Floor
New York, New York 10003
(212-929-8937/255-4641)

Techniques offered: BALLET, MODERN

Established: 1975

Directors: Emiko and Yasuko Tokunaga

Facilities: 1 studio; dressing rooms; bathrooms

Student enrollment: total: 185; average class: 15
Age: most 18-25; next 25-33; next over 33
Level: most adv; next int; next adv beg

Entrance requirements: students must be at least at the advanced beginner level and able to keep up with the class

Classes: BALLET: int beg, adv-pro, pointe; MODERN: int beg, adv-pro

Special courses/instruction: Summer workshop (ballet, modern, and repertory classes at the advanced intermediate level, ending with student performances); Private classes; Coaching (upon request)

Accompaniment: tapes

Holidays: national holidays; weekends

Fees: $4/class; $3.50/class, pro rate; $37.50/10 classes (with 2-month time limit); $30/10 classes, pro rate; other rates for other series; $400/8-week summer workshop; $25/hour, private class

Scholarships: Work-study scholarships are available according to students' needs, abilities, and references

Company affiliations: Tokunaga Dance Ko.

Principal faculty: All classes are taught by Emiko and Yasuko Tokunaga.

Summary statement: "The Tokunaga sisters' classes are unique in that they are team taught and combine ballet with modern dance. One teacher at the front of the class and one in the back enable students to get twice the amount of correction and attention. The Tokunagas begin with a strength-building hour-and-a-half ballet class in which they establish certain basic lines of action. This is followed by a modern dance class in which the same final movement combinations already established in the ballet class are taught, but from a modern dance point of view: quality differences are emphasized, such as level changes, body falls, etc. They teach two modern dance techniques: the fall/rebound/suspension/style inspired by Doris Humphrey, Charles Weidman, and José Limón; and the contraction/release system inspired by Martha Graham. The Tokunagas devised this concept of coordinated ballet and modern classes because they felt that dancers needed to understand the similarities as well as the differences in movement. Students are always challenged to their fullest capacity and each exercise is meaningfully related to the final big movement combination given at the end of class. There is careful work on body placement, and dancers are helped to move with a musical and muscular efficiency. Emiko and Yasuko Tokunaga both have backgrounds in ballet, modern, and classical Japanese dance. They have taught extensively at American universities and are experienced performers; they also direct their own company of dancers and musicians. Emiko has a B.F.A. degree from the University of Utah and trained with Martha Graham, Mary Hinkson, Takako Asakawa, and Alfredo Corvino. Yasuko studied with William Christensen, Alfredo Corvino, and Mary Hinkson, as well as with José Limón and Anna Sokolow at the Juilliard School."

Authors' note: Although the way to get the most out of the Tokunagas' teaching approach is to take both the ballet and modern dance classes, this is not required by the school.

Eleo Pomare's advanced repertory class at the Vital Arts Center. *Frank Gimpaya*

VITAL ARTS CENTER

325 West 16th Street
New York, New York 10011
(212-675-1136)

Techniques offered: MODERN, JAZZ, MIME

Established: 1971

School administrator: Virgil Akins

Artistic director: Eleo Pomare

Facilities: 1 studio; dressing rooms; bathrooms

Student enrollment: total: 325; average class: 18-23
Age: most 18-25; next 10-17; next 25-33; next 33-over
Level: most beg; next adv beg; next int and adv in equal proportions

Entrance requirements: none

Classes: (offered September-June): MODERN: beg, int, adv repertory/choreographer's workshop (the first part of the class combines advanced technique with the study of repertory, after which students work on their own choreography); JAZZ: beg, int; MIME: combined levels

Adult beg: see beg modern dance and jazz classes above
Children: CREATIVE MOVEMENT FOR CHILDREN (ages 3-5)

Special courses/instruction: Weekend interaction series, a new choreographer's showcase which takes place almost every weekend and usually features the work of students from the advanced repertory/choreographer's workshop; Summer course offered according to student demand

Accompaniment: drums

Holidays: national holidays; summer (July and August); weekends

Fees: $3.50/class; $30/10 classes (5-week time limit)

Scholarships: Work scholarships are available to students with merit and financial need.

Company affiliations: Eleo Pomare Dance Company

Principal faculty: Loris Beckles (modern), Lonetta Gaines (children's creative movement), Charles Grant (modern), Patricia Jones (modern), John Juhl (modern), Strody Meekins (modern), Eleo Pomare (modern, advanced repertory/choreographer's workshop), June Segal (jazz), Gil Torres (mime)

Summary statement: "The Vital Arts Center was founded in 1971, with the assistance and financial support of the New York State Council on the Arts, in order to offer basic to advanced dance training to capable but needy aspiring dancers. The school at this point has expanded its scope to become a hub of training activities directed toward the making of a complete professional dancer with knowledge of the history, the technique, and performing capability of the dance. Eleo Pomare, director of the school, was born in Cartagena, Colombia, South America, and lived in Panama before coming to New York at the age of ten. After attending the High School of Performing Arts, he continued to study dance with Louis Horst, Curtis James, José Limón, and Kurt Jooss (in Germany). In 1962 he went to Europe on a John Hay Whitney Foundation Fellowship. Since returning to this country in 1964 he has choreographed for his own company, theatre, and television in both the United States and Europe. Pomare's work has continued to be supported by a Guggenheim Fellowship and grants from the National Endowment for the Arts."

LEE WELLES MADISON BALLET SCHOOL
1236 Madison Avenue (97/98th Street)
New York, New York 10028
(212-534-4612)

Techniques offered: BALLET, BALLET EXERCISE

Established: 1976

Director: Lee Welles

Facilities: 1 studio; dressing rooms; bathrooms; showers

Student enrollment: total: 300; classes limited to 20 students
Age: most 10-17; next 18-33; next 33-over
Level: most beg; next adv beg; next int; next adv

Entrance requirements: All adult beginners must take the ballet exercise class twice a week; since enrollment is limited, it is recommended that students sign up in advance.

Classes: BALLET: beg, int; BALLET EXERCISE (a body conditioning class which utilizes basic ballet barre and floor exercises)

Adult beg: see ballet exercise class above

Children and teens: CREATIVE MOVEMENT FOR CHILDREN (ages 3½-5); BALLET: beg and int classes for children in first grade through high school, graded according to age and ability

Special courses/instruction: Private classes

Accompaniment: piano

Holidays: private school holidays; month of August; Sundays (from September to May); weekends in June and July

Fees: $7/trial class (this is deductible from the term fee, should you decide to take more classes); all other tuition is paid by the term and set on a sliding scale according to the number of lessons taken per week. Adults, for example, pay $145/12-week term, 2 classes per week; and children's classes cost $112/16-week term (September to June), 1 class per week —$195/16-week term, 2 classes per week

Scholarships: Scholarships are available to students with ability.

Company affiliations: none

Principal faculty: Lee Welles, and guest faculty

Summary statement: "Lee Welles performed with Colonel de Basil's Original Ballet Russe, and her teaching is entirely based on Russian classical technique, with emphasis on individual attention and guidance."

NED WILLIAMS SCHOOL OF DANCE
525 Avenue of the Americas (14th Street)
New York, New York 10011
(212-CH3-3688)

Techniques offered: PRIMITIVE (AFRICAN), JAZZ, TAP, BALLET

Established: 1970

Director: Ned Williams, Jr.

Facilities: 2 studios; dressing rooms; bathrooms

Student enrollment: total: 200; average class: 14
Age: most 18-25; next 25-33; next 33-over; next 10-17
Level: most beg; next int; next adv

Entrance requirements: none

Classes: PRIMITIVE (AFRICAN DANCE): beg, int, adv; JAZZ: beg, int; TAP: beg, adv beg, int; BALLET: beg, int

Special courses/instruction: Theatre workshop for dancers, for students who have been in school at least six months

Accompaniment: records, drum

Holidays: Easter, Memorial Day weekend, July 4, Thanksgiving Day, Christmas, New Year's; Sundays

Fees: $4/class; $33/10 classes; $60/20 classes

Scholarships: Work scholarships are awarded according to ambition, talent, and the studio's needs.

Company affiliations: none, but there is an annual school concert in which all students willing to attend rehearsals may participate

Principal faculty: Betty Johnson (ballet), José (primitive), Ethel Newbold (tap), Cynthia Rogers (primitive), Ned Williams, Jr. (primitive, jazz, ballet), Eddie Wright (tap, jazz)

Summary statement: "We have good teachers who care about the students. We have only fourteen students to a class, so everyone can get special attention. Mr. Williams trained with Katherine Dunham and was her teaching assistant for a number of years. He also taught at the school of the late Syvilla Forte."

IGOR YOUSKEVITCH SCHOOL OF BALLET

846 Seventh Avenue (54th Street)
New York, New York 10019
(212-245-9684)

Techniques offered: BALLET, JAZZ, SPANISH DANCE

Established: 1962

Directors: Igor Youskevitch and Anna Youskevitch

Facilities: 2 studios; dressing rooms; bathrooms

Student enrollment: total: 300; average class: 15
Age: most 18-25; next 25-33; next 33-over; next 10-17
Level: most int; next adv beg; next adv; next beg

Entrance requirements: none

Classes: BALLET: beg, int, int-adv, adv-pro, pointe, character; JAZZ: beg, int, adv-pro; SPANISH: adv int

Adult beg: BALLET: adult beginner class (evenings)
Children: BALLET: beg and int

Special courses/instruction: Private classes, Coaching

Accompaniment: piano

Holidays: national holidays; summer break; Sundays

Fees: $4/class; $3.50/class, pro rate; $35/10 classes (must be taken within 3 months); $30/10 classes, pro rate; $25/hour, private classes or coaching

Scholarships: Partial and work scholarship are occasionally available to regular students with talent and financial need.

Company affiliations: none

Principal faculty: Myron Curtis (ballet), Ronnie DeMarco (jazz), Rosario Galan (Spanish), Katia Geleznova (ballet), Mary Jane Houdino (jazz), Nicolas Orloff (character, ballet), Cleo Quitman (jazz), Larry Stevens (ballet), Anna Youskevitch (ballet), Igor Youskevitch (ballet), Maria Youskevitch (ballet)

Summary statement: "The school employs exclusively professional faculty. Although we are primarily a classical ballet school, we offer classes in jazz and Spanish dance. All students are trained for professional careers regardless of their individual personal reasons for studying dance. Students receive individual attention due to the manageable size of the classes. We believe that dance technique is based on scientific laws and the approach to its study should be rational and physical. We also believe that dance is a part of the theatre, and the importance of the expression of emotions or ideas in performance is stressed."

Authors' note: To the Youskevitches ballet is a family business. Igor and his wife Anna are Russian-trained and both appeared with the Ballet Russe de Monte Carlo. Youskevitch went on to perform with American Ballet Theatre, and partnered the legendary Cuban ballerina Alicia Alonso. In his prime he was considered to be one of the great male classical dancers of the twentieth century. After retiring from the stage, Madame Youskevitch taught at the American Ballet Theatre School for many years. The Youskevitches' daughter, Maria, also teaches at their school. Katia Geleznova and Nicolas Orloff are products of Russian training too, and performed with the Ballet Russe de Monte Carlo. Jazz teacher Mary Jane Houdino has assisted choreographer Peter Gennaro in a number of Broadway and television productions; and Ronnie DeMarco was a former instructor at Luigi's Jazz Center.

Quick-reference indices

Adult-beginner classes:

ALVIN AILEY AMERICAN DANCE CENTER
AMERICAN BALLET CENTER
AMERICAN BALLET THEATRE SCHOOL
AMERICAN DANCE MACHINE TRAINING FACILITY
MARY ANTHONY DANCE STUDIO
BALLET CLASSIQUE
BALLET SCHOOL OF LINCOLN SQUARE
COLLETTE BARRY AND SUSAN KLEIN SCHOOL OF DANCE
VALERIE BETTIS DANCE STUDIO
LA ROCQUE BEY SCHOOL OF DANCE THEATRE
ALONSO CASTRO DANCE THEATRE
CHAMBER DANCE GROUP
CHILDREN'S DANCE THEATRE, see Gloria Kosowski Children's Dance Theatre
CLARK CENTER FOR THE PERFORMING ARTS
CAROL CONWAY SCHOOL OF DANCE
MERCE CUNNINGHAM DANCE STUDIO
DANCE CENTER-92ND STREET YM-YWHA
DANCE CIRCLE
THE DANCE CONNECTION
DANCE MEWS
THE DANCE MOVEMENT
DANCERSCHOOL
DANCE THEATRE OF HARLEM
MADAME DARVASH BALLET STUDIO
DAVIS DANCE CENTER
DOWNTOWN DANCE STUDIOS and DOWNTOWN COMMUNITY DANCE WORKSHOP
FARNWORTH AND HAUER SCHOOL OF DANCE
FOKINE BALLET SCHOOL
FORELLA STUDIO
GELABERT STUDIOS
THE MARTHA GRAHAM SCHOOL
HARKNESS BALLET SCHOOL
HARLEM DANCE STUDIO
ERICK HAWKINS SCHOOL OF DANCE
MELISSA HAYDEN STUDIO
HENRY STREET SETTLEMENT DANCE SCHOOL
NAT HORNE MUSICAL THEATRE SCHOOL
DAVID HOWARD SCHOOL OF BALLET
INTERNATIONAL DANCE SCHOOL

FINIS JHUNG BALLET
JOFFREY SCHOOL, see American Ballet Center
JO JO'S DANCE FACTORY
SALVADOR JUAREZ SCHOOL OF BALLET
HAVA KOHAV THEATRE/DANCE FOUNDATION
THE GLORIA KOSOWSKI CHILDREN'S DANCE THEATRE
HENRY LE TANG PROFESSIONAL SCHOOL OF DANCE
VALENTINA LITVINOFF STUDIO OF DANCE
LOUIS-NIKOLAIS DANCE THEATRE LAB
LUIGI'S JAZZ CENTRE
MANHATTAN SCHOOL OF DANCE
MONSALVE DANCE STUDIO
MORELLI BALLET, INC.
VERA NEMTCHINOVA SCHOOL OF CLASSICAL BALLET
NEUBERT BALLET INSTITUTE
THE NEW BALLET SCHOOL
NEW DANCE GROUP STUDIO
NEW YORK ACADEMY OF BALLET
NEW YORK CONSERVATORY OF DANCE
NEW YORK SCHOOL OF BALLET
MAY O'DONNELL MODERN DANCE CENTER
PUERTO RICAN DANCE THEATRE
ROD RODGERS DANCE STUDIO
SOUNDS IN MOTION SCHOOL
STUDIO REVENE
THEATRE TEACHERS ALLIANCE
VITAL ARTS CENTER
LEE WELLES MADISON BALLET SCHOOL
IGOR YOUSKEVITCH SCHOOL OF BALLET

Children's classes:

ALVIN AILEY AMERICAN DANCE CENTER
AMERICAN BALLET CENTER
AMERICAN BALLET THEATRE SCHOOL
AMERICAN DANCE MACHINE TRAINING FACILITY
BALLET CLASSIQUE
BALLET SCHOOL OF LINCOLN SQUARE
VALERIE BETTIS DANCE STUDIO
LA ROCQUE BEY SCHOOL OF DANCE THEATRE
PHIL BLACK DANCE STUDIO
CHAMBER DANCE GROUP
CHILDREN'S DANCE THEATRE, see Gloria Kosowski Children's Dance Theatre
CLARK CENTER FOR THE PERFORMING ARTS
CAROL CONWAY SCHOOL OF DANCE
DANCE CENTER-92ND STREET YM-YWHA
THE DANCE CONNECTION
DANCE MEWS
THE DANCE MOVEMENT
DANCERSCHOOL
DANCE THEATRE OF HARLEM
DOWNTOWN DANCE STUDIOS and DOWNTOWN COMMUNITY DANCE WORKSHOP
FOKINE BALLET SCHOOL
GELABERT STUDIOS
THE MARTHA GRAHAM SCHOOL
HARKNESS BALLET SCHOOL
HARLEM DANCE STUDIO

HENRY STREET SETTLEMENT DANCE SCHOOL
NAT HORNE MUSICAL THEATRE SCHOOL
JOFFREY SCHOOL, see American Ballet Center
JO JO'S DANCE FACTORY
HAVA KOHAV THEATRE/DANCE FOUNDATION
THE GLORIA KOSOWSKI CHILDREN'S DANCE THEATRE
HENRY LE TANG PROFESSIONAL SCHOOL OF DANCE
MANHATTAN SCHOOL OF DANCE
MONSALVE DANCE STUDIO
VERA NEMTCHINOVA SCHOOL OF CLASSICAL BALLET
NEUBERT BALLET INSTITUTE
THE NEW BALLET SCHOOL
NEW DANCE GROUP STUDIO
NEW YORK ACADEMY OF BALLET
NEW YORK CONSERVATORY OF DANCE
NEW YORK SCHOOL OF BALLET
PUERTO RICAN DANCE THEATRE
SCHOOL OF AMERICAN BALLET
JUDITH SCOTT—CLASSES IN MODERN DANCE
SOUNDS IN MOTION SCHOOL
THEATRE TEACHERS ALLIANCE
VITAL ARTS CENTER
LEE WELLES MADISON BALLET SCHOOL
IGOR YOUSKEVITCH SCHOOL OF BALLET

Men's classes:

ALVIN AILEY AMERICAN DANCE CENTER
AMERICAN BALLET CENTER
DANCE CIRCLE
DANCERSCHOOL
DANCE THEATRE OF HARLEM
HARKNESS BALLET SCHOOL
MELISSA HAYDEN STUDIO
MANHATTAN SCHOOL OF DANCE
NEUBERT BALLET INSTITUTE
SCHOOL OF AMERICAN BALLET

Intensive or short-term courses:

AMERICAN BALLET CENTER
AMERICAN BALLET THEATRE SCHOOL
LA ROCQUE BEY SCHOOL OF DANCE THEATRE
ALONSO CASTRO DANCE THEATRE
CHAMBER DANCE GROUP
CLARK CENTER FOR THE PERFORMING ARTS
CAROL CONWAY SCHOOL OF DANCE
MERCE CUNNINGHAM DANCE STUDIO
DANCERSCHOOL
MADAME DARVASH BALLET STUDIO
DOWNTOWN DANCE STUDIOS and DOWNTOWN COMMUNITY DANCE WORKSHOP
FARNWORTH AND HAUER SCHOOL OF DANCE
GELABERT STUDIOS
THE MARTHA GRAHAM SCHOOL
HARKNESS BALLET SCHOOL
HARLEM DANCE STUDIO
ERICK HAWKINS SCHOOL OF DANCE
VALENTINA LITVINOFF STUDIO OF DANCE
LOUIS-NIKOLAIS DANCE THEATRE LAB

NEUBERT BALLET INSTITUTE
THE NEW BALLET SCHOOL
MAY O'DONNELL MODERN DANCE CENTER
SCHOOL OF AMERICAN BALLET
TOKUNAGA DANCE KO. STUDIO

Teachers:

ADAMS, CAROLYN, Harlem Dance Studio
ADCOCK, STEVEN, Finis Jhung Ballet
AGUIRRE, GENE, International Dance School
ALBERT, JILL, Clark Center for the Performing Arts
ALTMAN, ROBERTA, The Dance Movement
AMES, JERRY, Theatre Teachers Alliance
ANDROS, DICK, New York School of Ballet
ANSORGE, WILL, Carol Conway School of Dance
ANTHONY, MARY, Mary Anthony Dance Studio
ANTONIO, JUAN, Louis Falco Studio
ARPINO, GERALD, American Ballet Center
ASAKAWA, TAKAKO, Asakawalker Dance Studio
ASHLEY, FRANK, Henry Street Settlement Dance School
ATWOOD, ROBERT, Farnworth and Hauer School of Dance
BADOLATO, WILLIAM, New York Conservatory of Dance
BALESTRACCI, SANDRA, Neubert Ballet Institute
BALLARD, MICHAEL, Louis-Nikolais Dance Theatre Lab
BARBOUR, MARY, Dance Theatre of Harlem
BARKER, WENDY, Mary Anthony Dance Studio
BARNES, RUTH, Merce Cunningham Dance Studio
BARRY, COLLETTE, Collette Barry and Susan Klein School of Dance
BAYLIS, MEREDITH, American Ballet Center
BECKLES, LORIS, Vital Arts Center
BELL, CHERYL, New Dance Group Studio
BENJAMIN, FRED, Clark Center for the Performing Arts
BERGMAN, JOEL, Jo Jo's Dance Factory
BERKE, STANLEY, New Dance Group Studio
BETHEL, PEPSI, Alvin Ailey American Dance Center; Clark Center for the Performing Arts
BETTIS, VALERIE, Valerie Bettis Dance Studio
BEY, LA ROCQUE, La Rocque Bey School of Dance Theatre
BIELSKI, NANCY, Dance Center-92nd Street YM-YWHA; Harkness Ballet School
BLACK, PHIL, Phil Black Dance Studio
BLACK, ROBIN, Phil Black Dance Studio
BLISS, SALLY, American Ballet Center
BLOCK, BRUCE, Dance Center-92nd Street YM-YWHA
BLOSSOM, BEVERLY, Louis-Nikolais Dance Theatre Lab
BONELLE, DICK, DancerSchool
BOSTICK, RONALD, New York Academy of Ballet
BRAGG, OCEOLA, International Dance School
BROWN, ANDREA, Morelli Ballet Inc.
BROWN, DALE, The Dance Movement
BROWN, DELORES, Alvin Ailey American Dance Center
BROWN, MARY JANE, International Dance School
BURMANN, WILHELM, Melissa Hayden Studio
BYE, GWENDOLYN, Mary Anthony Dance Studio
CAHILL, KIM, Dance Center-92nd Street YM-YWHA
CARROLL, KELLY, Jo Jo's Dance Factory
CASEY, DIANE, Harlem Dance Studio
CASSESE, TERESA, Puerto Rican Dance Theatre

CASTRO, ALONSO, Alonso Castro Dance Theatre
CATÁ, ALFONSO, Melissa Hayden Studio
CHARISSE, NENETTE, American Dance Machine; Harkness Ballet School
CHIARELLO, LOIS, Gelabert Studio
CHISMAR, NANCY, American Dance Machine
CHO, MACHIKO, Downtown Dance Studios
CHORNEY, SHERRY, Henry Street Settlement Dance School
CHRISTEL, DAVID, High School of Performing Arts
CHRISTOPHER, ROBERT, Alvin Ailey American Dance Center
CLARK, ANN. Gelabert Studios
CLEMENT, NANSI, American Ballet Theatre School
COLBERT, MARGOT, New Dance Group Studio
COLE, BARBARA, Alvin Ailey American Dance Center
CONWAY, CAROL, Carol Conway School of Dance
COOK, PHILLIP, Farnworth and Hauer School of Dance
COOPERMAN, TOM, DancerSchool
CORVINO, ALFREDO, Dance Circle
CORVINO, ANDRA, Dance Circle
CORVINO, ERNESTA, Dance Circle
CRASKE, MARGARET, Manhattan School of Dance
CUNNINGHAM, MERCE, Merce Cunningham Dance Studio
CURTIS, MYRON, Igor Youskevitch School of Ballet
CUTLER, ROBYN, Dance Center-92nd Street YM-YWHA
DAKIN, CHRIS, The Martha Graham School
DALEL, International Dance School
DAMESTOY, SIMA, Downtown Dance Studios
DANIELIAN, LEON, American Ballet Theatre School
DANILOVA, ALEXANDRA, School of American Ballet
DARLING, JAMES, Nat Horne Musical Theatre School
DARVASH, GABRIELLA, Madame Darvash Ballet Studio
DAVIDSON, MICKEY, Sounds in Motion School
DAVIS, JOE, Davis Dance Center
DE MARCO, RONNIE, Igor Youskevitch School of Ballet
DENNEHEY, DENNIS, Phil Black Dance Studio
DESTINÉ, JEAN-LEON, New Dance Group Studio
DIAZ, MONICA, Chamber Dance Group
DLUGOSZEWSKI. LUCIA, Erick Hawkins School of Dance
DOBROVINSKA, SONYA, Chamber Dance Group
DOKOUDOVSKY, VLADIMIR, New York Conservatory of Dance
DOUBROVSKA, FELIA, School of American Ballet
DUDIN, HELENE, School of American Ballet
DUDLEY, JANE, The Martha Graham School
DUSING, DAVID, Nat Horne Musical Theatre School
DYNOWSKA, OLDYNA, Davis Dance Center
EDDINGTON. LAWRENCE, High School of Performing Arts
EDELSTEIN, AMY, Asakawalker Dance Studio
ENSLEY, BARBARA, Merce Cunningham Dance Studio
ERLICH, DAFNA, New York Academy of Ballet
ESTES, BONNIE, Valerie Bettis Dance Studio
EXTER, RENITA, Harkness Ballet School
FALLIS, BARBARA, New York School of Ballet
FANIZZI, ANNA MARIA, Forella Studio
FARBER, VIOLA, Larry Richardson's Dance Gallery
FARNWORTH, DON, Farnworth and Hauer School of Dance
FEDINE, VICKI, Dance Theatre of Harlem

FELSHER, BLANCHE, International Dance School
FERNANDEZ, CARLOS, International Dance School
FIGUEROA, WILLIAM, Alvin Ailey American Dance Center
FOKINE, CHRISTINE, Fokine Ballet School
FORELLA, RONN, Forella Studio
FORSYTHE, ANA MARIE, New Dance Group Studio
FRANK, PENNY, New Dance Group Studio; High School of Performing Arts
FRANKEL, SHELLEY, Clark Center for the Performing Arts
FREEMEN, GALE, Hava Kohav Theatre/Dance Foundation
FRIEDMAN, RISA, Nancy Meehan Dance School
FUGATE, JODY, Madame Darvash Ballet School
GAINES, LONETTA, Vital Arts Center
GAL, HILLARY, Dance Center-92nd Street YM-YWHA
GALAN, ROSARIO, Igor Youskevitch School of Ballet
GALLERON, PAULA, Dance Studio
GASPARINETTI, TRUTTI, American Chamber Ballet Center
GELABERT, RAOUL, Gelabert Studios
GELEZNOVA, KATIA, Igor Youskevitch School of Ballet
GILMORE, AMELIA, Theatre Teachers Alliance
GIORDANO, JEAN, Phil Black Dance Studio
GIRON, HERB, New York Academy of Ballet
GITELMAN, CLAUDIA, Louis-Nikolais Dance Theatre Lab
GOLDENSHTEIN, ESFIR, DancerSchool
GOLDMAN, PHYLLIS, American Dance Machine
GOLDSTEIN, SHELIA ZADRA, May O'Donnell Modern Dance Center
GONZALEZ, SHELAGH, Larry Richardson's Dance Gallery
GOODMAN, ERICA, Neubert Ballet Institute
GORDON, MARVIN, International Dance School; Chamber Dance Group
GRANT, CHARLES, Vital Arts Center
GRATZ, ZAHAVA, Ballet School of Lincoln Square
GREEN, ALICE TEMPKIN, Manhattan School of Dance
GREY, DIANE, The Martha Graham School
GUZIKOVA, K., Madame Darvash Ballet School
GUZMAN, PASCHAL, Downtown Dance Studios
HAACK, CHARLES, Downtown Dance Studios
HAKEK, DIANNE, International Dance School
HARMER, RALF, New York Academy of Ballet
HARPER, MEG, Merce Cunningham Dance Studio
HARRIS, ELEANOR, Clark Center for the Performing Arts
HARRIS, PAUL, La Tocque Bey School of Dance Theatre
HASLAM, HENLEY, The New Ballet School
HATCHETT, FRANK, Henry Le Tang Professional School of Dance
HAUG, BETSY, American Chamber Ballet Center
HAWKINS, ERICK, Erick Hawkins School of Ballet
HAYDEN, MELISSA, Melissa Hayden Studio
HEBARD, ANNE, Harkness Ballet School
HEITZMAN, LILLIAN, International Dance School
HERRING, JOYCE, Fokine Ballet School
HERTER, BILL, International Dance School
HERTZOG, JACK, The Dance Movement
HESS, CAROL, International Dance School
HEYES, PATRICIA, New York Conservatory of Dance
HIGHTOWER, LOREN, Manhattan School of Dance

HILL, DOROTHY, Manhattan School of Dance
HILZINGER, JEAN, Davis Dance Center
HIMELSTEIN, ELIZABETH, The Gloria Kosowski Children's Dance Theatre
HINKSON, MARY, Dance Theatre of Harlem; Marjorie Mussman Studio
HODES, LINDA, The Martha Graham School
HOFF, STEFAN, Neubert Ballet Institute
HOGAN, JUDY, The Martha Graham School
HOLM, HANYA, Louis-Nikolais Dance Theatre Lab
HORNE, NAT, Alvin Ailey American Dance Center; Nat Horne Musical Theatre School
HOROSKO, MARIAN, Chamber Dance Group
HORVATH, JULLIU, Neubert Ballet Institute
HOUDINO, MARY JANE, Igor Youskevitch School of Ballet
HOWARD, DAVID, David Howard School of Ballet
HOWARD, RAND, Erick Hawkins School of Dance
ICHINOHE, SAEKO, Davis Dance Center
JAMES, JEFFREY, Chamber Dance Group
JEFFERSON, DENISE, Ailvin Ailey American Dance Center
JENNINGS, BERNADINE, Sounds in Motion School
JHUNG, FINIS, Finis Jhung Ballet
JOEL, LYDIA, High School of Performing Arts
JOFFREY, ROBERT, American Ballet Center
JOHNSON, AGNES, Nat Horne Musical Theatre School
JOHNSON, BETTY, Ned Williams School of Dance
JONES, PATRICIA, Vital Arts Center
JONES, SECORRA, Studio of Creative Movement; Downtown Dance Studios
JOSÉ, Ned Williams School of Dance
JOYCE, DEBBIE, Jo Jo's Dance Factory
JUAREZ, SALVADOR, Salvador Juarez School of Ballet
JUHL, JOHN, Vital Arts Center
KACHADURIAN, GAIL, The Dance Movement
KAHLIL, AISHA, Henry Street Settlement Dance School
KAPLAN, ROBBIE, The Dance Movement
KASNI, JANIS, International Dance School
KELLER, CELENE, New Dance Group Studio; New York Conservatory of Dance
KELLEY, CHARLES, Farnworth and Hauer School of Dance
KEOUGH, MARY, DancerSchool
KINGERY, LARRY, Harkness Ballet School
KIRIK, International Dance School
KLEIN, SUSAN, Collette Barry and Susan Klein School of Dance
KOGAN, ELLEN, Dance Center-92nd Street YM-YWHA
KOHAV, HAVA, Hava Kohav Theatre/Dance Foundation
KOROGODSKI, MIKHAIL, Neubert Ballet Institute
KOVACH, NORA, Madame Darvash Ballet Studio
KRAMAREVSKY, ANDREI, School of American Ballet
KRESLEY, ED, New York Academy of Ballet
KRUGER, SHELAGH, Downtown Dance Studios
KRYSANOWSKA, ROMANA, Clark Center for the Performing Arts
KUBALA, MICHAEL, Forella Studio
LANE, ROBERT, Davis Dance Center

LANG, PEARL, Alvin Ailey American Dance Center; The Martha Graham School
LASKO, JUDY, Clark Center for the Performing Arts
LATIMER, LENORE, Clark Center for the Performing Arts
LAUB, ARLENE, Louis-Nikilais Dance Theatre Lab
LE CLERCQ, TANAQUIL, Dance Theatre of Harlem
LEE, KEITH, Chamber Dance Group
LENGYEL, ANDRE, Asakawalker Dance Studio
LENSKY, FEDOR, International Dance School
LESSING, FLORENCE, New York Academy of Ballet
LE TANG, ELLIE, Henry Le Tang Professional School of Dance
LE TANG, HENRY, Henry Le Tang Professional School of Dance
LEVI, RICHARD, Clark Center for the Performing Arts
LEVIEN, JULIA, New Dance Group Studio
LEVINE, LYNN, Louis-Nikolais Dance Theatre Lab
LEVITT, SANDY, Puerto Rican Dance Theatre
LEWIS, CAROL ANN, Valerie Bettis Dance Studio
LILE, RICHARD, Dance Circle
LISTER, DOROTHY, American Ballet Center
LISTER, MERLE, Studio of Creative Movement
LITVINOFF, VALENTINA, Valentina Litvinoff Studio of Dance
LOREMIL, Clark Center for the Performing Arts
LORENZ, JOCELYN, Morelli Ballet Inc.
LOUIS, MURRAY, Louis-Nikolais Dance Theatre Lab
LOVELY, ALICIA, American Chamber Ballet Center
LOWENTHAL, SIDNEY, American Ballet Center
LUCKMAN, SHARON, Dancer Center-92nd Street, YM-YWHA
LUIGI, Luigi's Jazz Center
LYALL, CHRISTOPHER, Manhattan School of Dance
MACKAY, GARY, Henry Street Settlement Dance School
MADDOX, ARTHUR, La Rocque Bey School of Dance Theatre
MAGEE, JUDY, American Dance Machine
MAHLER, DONALD, Madame Darvash Ballet Studio
MAIORANO, ROBERT, Ballet School of Lincoln Square
MALAMENT, SARAH, High School of Performing Arts
MALINKA, BELLA, High School of Performing Arts
MALONEY, DANIEL, Mary Anthony Dance Studio
MAPP, KATHERINE, Nancy Meehan Dance Company and School
MARCEAU, MICHELLE, DancerSchool
MARTINET, FRANÇOISE, American Ballet Center
MASLOW, SOPHIE, New Dance Group Studio
MASON, PAULA, The Gloria Kosowski Children's Dance Theatre; Studio Revene
MATTEO, High School of Performing Arts
MAULE, MICHAEL, American Ballet Theatre School
MAXIMILIAN, OTTO, Nat Horne Musical Theatre School
McENTEE, DONNA, Ballet School of Lincoln Square
McINTYRE, DIANNE, Sounds in Motion School
McLAIN, SUSAN, The Martha Graham School
McPHERSON, WILLIAM, La Rocque Bey School of Dance Theatre
MEDERIOS, JOHN, Forella Studio; International Dance School

MEEHAN, NANCY, Nancy Meehan Dance Company and School
MEEKINS, STRODY, Vital Arts Center
MELIKOVA, GENIA, Alvin Ailey American Dance Center
MERCEDES, LOIS, Downtown Dance Studios
MERINOWA, OLGA, American Ballet Theatre School
MIKOTA, NANCY, Morelli Ballet Inc.
MILLER, BUZZ, American Dance Machine
MITCHELL, ARTHUR, Dance Theatre of Harlem
MONSALVE, JORGE, Monsalve Dance Studio
MOORE, CHARLES, Clark Center for the Performing Arts
MORARU-WECHSLER, DOYNA, Neubert Ballet Institute
MORELLI, WILSON, Morelli Ballet Inc.
MUNDY, PAM, The Dance Movement
MUSSMAN, MARJORIE, Marjorie Mussman Studio
MYERS, MILTON, Alvin Ailey American Dance Center
NEMTCHINOVA, VERA, Vera Nemtchinova School of Classical Ballet
NEUBERT, CHRISTINE, Neubert Ballet Institute
NEWBOLD, ETHEL, Ned Williams School of Dance
NIKOLAIS, ALWIN, Louis-Nikolais Dance Theatre Lab
NORA, MARIA, Alonso Castro Dance Theatre
O'DONNELL, MAY, May O'Donnell Modern Dance Center
ORLOFF, NICOLAS, Igor Youskevitch School of Ballet
OSSORIO, ROBERT, Manhattan School of Dance
OTTE, GERALD, Louis-Nikolais Dance Theatre Lab
OWENS, HAYNES, DancerSchool
PACKER, IDELLE, Dance Center-92nd Street YM-YWHA
PAGNANO, ERNEST, Zena Rommett Studio
PALUSZEK, SOPHIA, May O'Donnell Modern Dance Center
PARADISE, DON, Jo Jo's Dance Factory
PARKER, FRAN, Dancer Center-92nd Street YM-YWHA
PARKES, ROSS, Mary Anthony Dance Studio
PATRELLE, FRANCIS, Fokine Ballet School
PEARL, KENNY, The Martha Graham School
PEARSON, GAIL, Davis Dance Center
PEARSON, GERALD, Louis-Nikolais Dance Theatre Lab
PEARSON, SARA, Louis-Nikolais Dance Theatre Lab
PERCES, MARJORIE, Alvin Ailey American Dance Center; Clark Center for the Performing Arts
PEREYASLAVEC, VALENTINA, American Ballet Theatre School
PETERS, JOAN, Alvin Ailey American Dance Center
PHAEDRA, International Dance School
PIETRI, FRANK, Davis Dance Center
PINES, TERRY, Manhattan School of Dance
PINNOCK, RHEMA, Rod Rodgers Dance Studio
PLANE, LIANE, Finis Jhung Ballet
PLOCH, RICHARD, DancerSchool
POMARE, ELEO, Vital Arts Center
POPOVA, NINA, Neubert Ballet Institute
PRINZ, JOHN, Harkness Ballet School
PURNELL, MELVIN, Dance Theatre of Harlem
QUITMAN, CLEO, Igor Youskevitch School of Ballet
RAITT, JIM, American Dance Machine
RANSOM, LUCINDA, Alvin Ailey American Dance Center; Clark Center for the Performing Arts
RAPP, RICHARD, School of American Ballet

REDLICH, DON, Dance Center-92nd Street YM-YWHA
REID, ALBERT, Merce Cunningham Dance Studio
REIMAN, ELISE, School of American Ballet
REVENE, NADINE, Studio Revene
REYNOLDS, CYNTHIA, Erick Hawkins School of Dance
RHODES, LAWRENCE, DancerSchool
RICHARDSON, DORENE, New Dance Group Studio
RICHARDSON, LARRY, Larry Richardson's Dance Gallery
RIDDICK, BERNARD, Henry Street Settlement Dance School
RINCON, SYLVIA, Henry Street Settlement Dance School
ROBENS, KATHY, Dancer Center-92nd Street YM-YWHA
ROBINSON, SLOAN, Rod Rodgers Dance Studio
RODGERS, ROD, Rod Rodgers Dance Studio
ROGERS, CYNTHIA, Ned Williams School of Dance
ROGERS, POLI, New Dance Group Studio
ROGERS, POLLY, Puerto Rican Dance Theatre
ROMMETT, ZENA, Zena Rommett Studio
ROSENBLUTH, BETH, Downtown Dance Studios
ROSS, BERTRAM, Alvin Ailey American Dance Center
ROSS, JOANNA, Neubert Ballet Institute
ROSS, TEE, Puerto Rican Dance Theatre
RUIZ, BRUNILDA, The New Ballet School
RUSHING, SHIRLEY, Rod Rodgers Dance Studio
RYBURN, CAROLINE, Valerie Bettis Dance Studio
SALINAS, RIC, Luigi's Jazz Center
SAMBOGNA, AL, International Dance School
SAMUELS, KEN, Jo Jo's Dance Factory
SANFILIPPO, PHYLLIS, The Gloria Kosowski Children's Dance Theatre
SASAKI, YAEKO, Nat Horne Musical Theatre School
SAUL, PETER, Studio Revene
SCHORER, SUKI, School of American Ballet
SCHWEZOFF, IGOR, New York Conservatory of Dance
SCOTT, JUDITH, Judith Scott-Classes in Modern Dance
SCROPPO, LILIAN, Theatre Teachers Alliance
SEETOO, DENNIS, Neubert Ballet Institute
SEGAL, JUNE, Vital Arts center
SERAVALLI, ROSANNA, Madame Darvash Ballet Studio
SETTERFIELD, VALDA, Merce Cunningham Dance Studio
SHIFRIN, WENDY, Nancy Meehan Dance Company and School
SHIMAZAKI, SATORU, Dance Mews
SHOOK, KAREL, Dance Theatre of Harlem
SHULTERBRANDT, MICHELE, Harlem Dance Studio
SIMON, VICTORIA, Dance Theatre of Harlem
SIMONSON, LYNN, Morelli Ballet Inc
SIMPSON, CAROL, Henry Street Settlement Dance School
SMALL, ROBERT, Louis-Nikolais Dance Theatre Lab
SMITH, JO JO, Jo Jo's Dance Factory
SORINE, STEPHANIE, The Dance Movement
STEIN, RANDY, The Gloria Kosowski Children's Dance Theatre
STEIN, WENDY, Larry Richardson's Dance Gallery
STEINWAY, TINA, Clark Center for the Performing Arts
STEPHENS, THERESA, Rod Rodgers Dance Studio
STEVENS, LARRY, Igor Youskevitch School of Ballet
STEVENS, TOM, Alvin Ailey American Dance Center

STRANDBERG, JULIE ADAMS, Harlem Dance Studio
STROGANOVA, NINA, New York Conservatory of Dance
STUART, MURIEL, School of American Ballet
SUMNER, CAROL, Dance Theatre of Harlem
TCHERNISHOVA, ELENA, Harkness Ballet School
TERRY, CORI, Erick Hawkins School of Dance
THEODORE, LEE, American Dance Machine
THOMAS, BETTY, Phil Black Dance Studio
THOMAS, PATRICIA, Alvin Ailey American Dance Center
THOMAS, RICHARD, New York School of Ballet
THOMPSON, BASIL, American Ballet Center
TOKUNAGA, EMIKO, Tokunaga Dance Ko. Studio
TOKUNAGA, YASUKO, Tokunaga Dance Ko. Studio
TOMAL, GEORGE, International Dance School
TOMC, P.J., Farnworth and Hauer School of Dance
TORRES, GIL, Vital Arts Center
TUMKOVSKY, ANTONINA, School of American Ballet
TURNBAUGH, DOUGLAS, Alonso Castro Dance Theatre
TYUS, ANN, Dance Theatre of Harlem
URSIN, MARYA, Merce Cunningham Dance Studio
VANN, JANE, Ballet Classique
VELASCO, FELICIA, New York Academy of Ballet
VON BARDELEBED, ARMGARD, The Martha Graham School
WAGNER, FRANK, International Dance School
WALCZAK, BARBARA, Ballet School of Lincoln Square
WALKER, DAVID HATCH, Asakawalker Dance Studio
WALKER, SUZANNE, High School of Performing Arts
WARD, CATHY, Erick Hawkins School of Dance
WASHINGTON, DON,JR., Dance Center-92nd Street, YM-YWHA
WASSELL, DOUGLAS, David Howard School of Ballet
WATERMAN, GAIL, Downtown Dance Studios
WATTLEY, PATRICIA M., Ballet Classique
WELLES, LEE, Lee Welles Madison Ballet School
WELLS, BRUCE, The Dance Movement
WENGARD, TIM, The Martha Graham School
WILDE, PATRICIA, American Ballet Theatre School
WILLIAMS, NED, JR., Ned Williams School of Dance
WILLIAMS, STANLEY, School of American Ballet
WILSON, DEBBIE, La Rocque Bey School of Dance Theatre
WILSON, HERB, Phil Black Dance Studio
WILSON, SALLY, Manhattan School of Dance
WOODBURY, JOAN, Louis-Nikolais Dance Theatre Lab
WOODEN, ANTHONY, La Rocque Bey School of Dance Theatre
WOOLEVER, HARRY, International Dance School
WRAY, SUSANNE, Monsalve Dance Studio
WRIGHT, EDDIE, Ned Williams School of Dance
WYNN, ZELDA, Dance Theatre of Harlem
YOUSKEVITCH, ANNA, Igor Youskevitch School of Ballet
YOUSKEVITCH, IGOR, Igor Youskevitch School of Ballet
YOUSKEVITCH, MARIA, Igor Youskevitch School of Ballet
ZIDE, ROCHELLE, New York Conservatory of Dance
ZIMMERMAN, STEFANIE, High School of Performing Arts

Independent teachers

Some of New York's finest dance instructors are not permanently affiliated with a school but instead choose to operate independently by renting studio space or teaching in their own lofts. Several teachers in this category are active performers and/or choreographers who tour frequently and therefore cannot maintain a full-time school, so they offer classes periodically, a few weeks or months at a time. By and large, their fees are comparable to those charged at dance schools (that is, in the $3.50 to $4.50 price range), and sometimes slightly lower. In the listings that follow we have given the addresses and phone numbers either of the teachers' permanent residences or of the rented studios where they are currently holding classes;* in some instances only phone numbers were supplied.

Bob Audy explaining a fine point to his advanced students.
Frank Gimpaya

ROBERT AUDY
c/o The Studio
152 West 56th Street
New York, New York 10019
(212-757-1941)

Classes: TAP: basic beg through pro; JAZZ: basic beg through pro; COACHING

Known in New York as the man who can teach anyone to tap dance, Bob Audy loves his work, and his enthusiasm for tap and jazz dancing is contagious. He is a clear teacher who makes sure students understand the basics before going on to learn complicated routines. "I break down the movement to an appropriate level for the class being taught," says Audy. "The basic beginner classes really start from the beginning and don't assume any prior knowledge of technique." But even in the most elementary classes Audy's students—who include secretaries and businessmen as well

*If you call a studio and find that the teacher you're interested in is no longer there, ask for a forwarding phone number or address.

as show biz types—learn an elegant carriage of the upper body, and he sees to it that all have a good time. Audy, who has worked with Shirley MacLaine, Joel Grey, and Ben Vereen among other celebrities, feels that one of his greatest strengths as a teacher lies in coaching. He has written two books: ***Teach Yourself How to Tap Dance: Bob Audy Method*** and ***Jazz Dancing: The Robert Audy Method***, both published by Vintage Books.

MARGARET BEALS
228 West Broadway
New York, New York 10013
(212-431-3869)

Classes: MODERN MOVEMENT AND IMPROVISATION; YOGA

In the twenty years that Maggie Beals has been working in New York, she has performed with the companies of José Limón, Valerie Bettis, Jean Erdman, Paul Sanasardo, and Lucas Hoving; in recent years she has been performing in solo concerts which combine poetry and live music with improvised and choreographed movement. Beals is a student of yoga and Eastern religion, and their influence can also be seen in her work. She sees dance "as an expression of our human time here" and believes that "everyone can dance regardless of technique." Beals further believes that students should learn to dance "from the 'inside being' first, and then develop those specific skills they feel they are in need of." She says "dance is not steps," and tries to build the kind of class atmosphere and confidence in her students that will allow them to "experience their own dance."

BEVERLY BROWN
c/o The Dancenter
388 Broadway
New York, New York 10013
(212-966-0709)

Classes: MODERN DANCE: elementary, int, adv

Beverly Brown was a principal dancer with the Erick Hawkins Dance Company for six years. She now directs her own company and has been choreographing since 1970. Brown is also a fine teacher who has been on the faculty of the Erick Hawkins Studio, the New York University School of the Arts, the American Dance Festival, and the University of Colorado. "I try to guide students toward achieving anatomically correct alignment and fulfilling their potential for vigor and tenderness," she says. "I teach a rhythmic, free-flowing technique—Hawkins-derived—using breath and voice as a means of centering and energizing the body during warmup, as well as to increase the dancer's awareness of and ability to express rhythm."

PAT CATTERSON
(212-695-3277)

Classes: TAP: basic, beg, int, adv; adults only

Modern dancer and choreographer Pat Catterson started her training as a child with acrobatics and tap dance lessons and later studied with virtuoso hoofers Charles Cook and Honi Coles. She also trained with Gus Giordano in Chicago, attended Connecticut College Summer School on scholarship, and studied dance composition with Bessie Schonberg. Catterson presented the first full evening concert of her own works at the Judson Church in 1970. Besides performing her own choreography, she has appeared with the companies of James Cunningham and Yvonne Rainer. As a teacher Catterson emphasizes "the clarity of tap sounds, musicality, and an understanding of weight shifts. This is not a jazz class," she reminds prospective students, "and is open to nondancers."

JANE GOLDBERG
65 East 4th Street # 15
New York, New York 10003
(212-533-4356)

Classes: JAZZ TAP: all levels

Jane Goldberg has been researching, studying, performing, teaching, and writing about tap dancing for the past six years. Her specialty is jazz tap, an improvisational form of tap dancing done to jazz music which was perfected during the twenties, thirties, and forties by virtuoso black hoofers such as Bill "Bojangles" Robinson, John Bubbles, Baby Lawrence, Charles Cook, and Honi Coles. Goldberg's mentors include Charles Cook (of the Cook and Brown team), with whom she performs and who guest teaches some of her classes; Chuck Green (of Chuck and Chuckles); Leslie "Bubba" Gaines (of The Three Dukes), who has also performed with Goldberg; Bert Gibson (of The Three Chocolateers); Sandman Sims; Paul Draper, and the late Stanley Brown (of The Brazilian Nuts). In recent years Goldberg has brought tap revues to the Village Vanguard and Dance Theatre Workshop in New York, as well as to the American Dance Festival and the Jacob's Pillow Dance Festival. She is something of a proselytizer for this historic art form, and her articles on the subject have been published in the ***Village Voice,*** the ***Soho Weekly News, Jazz Magazine,*** and ***Ballet Review.*** She is currently organizing the Changing Times Tap Dancing Company, which is dedicated to keeping the art of jazz tap alive by reviving old-time hoofing styles and creating new works in the same idiom. Goldberg, who has taught in New York for six years, says that in her classes she tries to provide an introduction to tap in which the primary emphasis is on the jazz music, with the dancer "treating the body as a musical instrument."

KATHY HARRIS
c/o the Whitby Hotel
325 West 45th Street
New York, New York 10036
(212-246-0430, ext. 509)

Classes: TAP: all levels and pro; adults' and childrens' classes; PRIVATE COACHING

Kathy Harris, who started performing in vaudeville, has been in show business all her life. She teaches what she calls "old-school tap, Bill Robinson-style" and guarantees that in less than a month students will be able to do shuffles, time steps, and the like for auditions. In her classes the emphasis in on learning tap routines.

JOAN LOMBARDI
55 West 16th Street
9th Floor
New York, New York 10011
(212-989-4513)

Classes: MODERN DANCE: int, adv; ages 14 and up

Joan Lombardi has performed with Paul Sanasardo, Manuel Alum, and the New York City Opera Ballet, and is currently the artistic director and choreographer of her own company. She has taught at Lehman College, Skidmore College, the Saratoga Performing Arts Center, and the Paul Sanasardo Studio. "My greatest strength as a teacher is that I look for individual qualities in each of my students," says Lombardi. "My approach to technique is to build a strong classical center and line—a solid base from which to grow."

ANNA MIRONNEAU
400 West 43rd Street #42A
New York, New York 10036
(212-594-6357)

Classes: BALLET FOR ADULTS: basic beg, int; ADULTS' EXERCISE

Trained at the French Conservatory at Versailles, Anna Mironneau also studied kinesiology in France for two years. She took further training in ballet with Zena Rommett and Maria Swoboda in New York and has been teaching her own classes for four years. "I try to keep my ballet classes small and also to work slowly and appropriately for the adult body," says Mironneau. "The exercise class concentrates on stretching and strengthening exercises on the floor and incorporates some yoga techniques."

HAYNES OWENS
(212-260-8367) at Dancerschool
(212-237-9332)

Classes: BALLET: int, adv, pointe

Haynes Owens, a seven-year member of the Joffrey Ballet, has taught at the New Jersey Ballet School and the New York University School of Education. He is currently on the faculty of Dancerschool (see the school listings earlier in this chapter). Owens says he primarily teaches "placement in movement. I try to show each student how to stand on his or her legs so that a minimum of tension is required to execute any given movement. I also break down each working part of the body in a conscious manner to show how optimal freedom comes from correct articulation." He adds that he offers "a quirky sense of humor as part of the working environment."

MYRNA PACKER
97 Crosby Street
New York, New York 10012
(212-966-3028)

Classes: MODERN DANCE: adult elementary

Myrna Packer has performed with Francis Alenikoff, Art Bauman, Ze'Eva Cohen, the Nimbus Dance Company, Doris Ginsberg, and in Two's a Company. She also teaches at the Dominican Academy High School. Her two-hour elementary modern dance class includes work on technique and relaxation and breathing exercises, as well as improvisation. "My class is easygoing and relaxed—different from studying at a formal dance school, which may intimidate students," she says.

MARLEEN PENNISON
117 Hudson Street
3rd Floor
New York, New York 10013
(212-966-0978)

Classes: MODERN DANCE: beg, int; TAP: beg, int; JAZZ: beg, int; PRIVATE CLASSES

Marleen Pennison has performed with the companies of Phoebe Neville, Rudy Perez, and Barbara Roan, and currently directs and choreographs for her own group. She has taught at the Stella Adler Studio, the National Shakespeare Company Conservatory, and the Erick Hawkins Dance Studio. Pennison says her classes "range from working on standard movement vocabulary to experimenting with the vocabulary." She believes in a "slow and thorough warmup."

CLEO QUITMAN
(212-767-3473)
(212-JU2-4240) answering service

Classes: BALLET: beg, int

Cleo Quitman has taught ballet and jazz at the June Taylor School, the Harkness Ballet School, and the Farnworth and Hauer School of Dance, as well as at dance conventions and universities. She has performed in musical theatre and on television, and choreographs for her own company, the Cleo Quitman Dance Experience. Quitman says her ballet classes "focus on individual body correction and placement." She feels that her method of teaching works well not only for classical technique but for any form of dance, and is especially good for dancers who start training late. "My beginners show improvement quickly," she says.

JUNE REED
c/o Showcase Studios
950 Eighth Avenue (56th Street)
New York, New York 10019
(212-586-7947)
(212-753-7213) home phone

Classes: BALLET: adult beg, int, adv; children's ballet classes

June Reed has taught in New York for seventeen years and has performed on Broadway and in concert. Her adult beginner ballet class is "specially designed to avoid the humiliation of being placed in either a children's beginner class or one that is too advanced."

ELLEN ROBBINS
173 Sullivan Street
New York, New York 10012
(212-254-0286)

Classes: MODERN DANCE: adults' int-adv; children's beg class (for ages 4 and up)

Ellen Robbins has performed with the companies of Don Redlich, Rod Rodgers, Rudy Perez, Barbara Roan, and Mary Anthony. She has taught dance at Sarah Lawrence College, the 92nd Street YM-YWHA, Dance Theatre Workshop, the Mary Anthony Studio, and has had her own classes since 1968. Robbins's great love is teaching children. In her classes youngsters learn technique, rhythm, improvisation, and dance appreciation at their own level, and they sometimes participate in informal performances. Since she believes that many intermediate and advanced dancers "have forgotten about the pleasures of dancing," Robbins tries to get her adult students to "enjoy and discover a variety of aesthetic possibilities while developing precise movement skills."

PETER SAUL
c/o Studio Revene
55 West 16th Street
New York, New York 10011
(212-242-5878)
(212-924-9054) home phone

Classes: BALLET: basic, int

Peter Saul has performed with the Merce Cunningham Company, American Ballet Theatre and in his own concert works, as well as on Broadway and television. He is an experienced teacher who has been on the faculty of the Merce Cunningham Studio, and the New Dance Group Studio and has taught at several American colleges and universities. He has had his own ballet classes since 1973 and is currently teaching an adults' basic beginner ballet class at Studio Revene (see the school listings earlier in this chapter).

Marcus Schulkind. ***courtesy of the Marcus Schulkind Dance Company***

MARCUS SCHULKIND
39 Great Jones Street
New York, New York 10012
(212-982-4264)
(212-427-6000 ext. 72) at the 92nd Street YM-YWHA

Classes: MODERN DANCE/BALLET: int, int-adv; PRIVATE COACHING

Marcus Schulkind has performed with Norman Walker, Pearl Lang, Martha Graham, the Bat Sheva Dance Company, Kathryn Posin, and Lar Lubovitch. He currently choreographs for his own company and also has a piece in the repertory of Dennis Wayne's Dancers. Schulkind has taught at the State University of New York at Purchase, Connecticut College, and the American Dance Festival. Next year he and his group are slated to replace the Don Redlich Dance Company as the company-in-residence* at the 92nd Street YM-YWHA (see the school listings earlier in this chapter). Schulkind's fast-paced classes begin with a strength-building ballet barre, followed by center work and across-the-floor phrases which combine balletic and modern dance movement (Limón- and Graham-influenced). He says the work is "based on centering, with an emphasis on using the body as a coordinated whole and moving through space with a sense of ease and form." Equally important, Schulkind gets students to move more fully, to enjoy the music, and to develop performing qualities. He also has a wonderful sense of humor about dancing.

*This means they will be teaching and performing there.

GUS SOLOMONS, JR
889 Broadway (18/19th Street)
New York, New York 10003
(212-242-5633)

Classes: MODERN DANCE: int-adv; INTENSIVE COURSES

Gus Solomons, Jr., performed with the companies of Martha Graham, Donald McKayle, Merce Cunningham, Joyce Trisler, and Pearl Lang before founding his own group (the Solomons Company/Dance) in the late 1960s. Solomons describes the technique he teaches as one "based on the principles of Merce Cunningham, though distilled through my own perceptions. It aims to develop the maximum range of possibilities of motion of each individual dancer and to make him adaptable, observant (capable of seeing and duplicating extended phrases), and intelligent. We also work on developing strength and flexibility with good placement and maximum efficiency of motion." Solomons and his company are in New York about half the year, so classes are offered intermittently.

WENDY SUMMIT
(212-228-0323)

Classes: MODERN DANCE: adult beg, int; children's classes; DANCE THERAPY

Wendy Summit holds a bachelor's degree in dance from Bennington College and a master's degree in dance therapy. She has performed with the Dance Theatre Workshop Company, and the Rudy Perez Dance Theatre and has taught in New York City for ten years. She also choreographs. Summit says that in her classes she emphasizes "creative as well as technical experience." She gives improvisation and composition exercises "to help students communicate through movement and work toward self-awareness," while the technique she teaches "focuses on alignment and strengthening exercises."

DAN WAGONER
20 East 17th Street
New York, New York 10003
(212-929-1018)

Classes: MODERN DANCE: int-adv

Dan Wagoner was a featured dancer with the companies of Paul Taylor and Martha Graham and is now director and choreographer of his own group, Dan Wagoner and Dancers. Classes are offered in between touring and performing engagements. Wagoner says his teaching approach "stresses movement, shape, energy, space, and phrasing."

CAROL WALTERS
(212-249-3553)

Classes: MODERN DANCE: beg through pro; JAZZ: beg through pro; teenagers' and adults' classes; ROUTINES AND PRIVATE COACHING

Carol Walters trained with Hanya Holm, Valerie Bettis, and José Limón. She has performed in concert and commercial work, and has choreographed. "I teach solid technique but also stress enjoyment of movement and free expression," she says.

BETTY WRAGGE
c/o Showcase Studios
950 Eighth Avenue (56th Street)
New York, New York 10019
(212-586-7947)
or at her home address:
Manhattan Plaza
400 West 43rd Street
New York, New York 10036
(212-564-5767)

Classes: TAP: beg, int, adv, routines; PRIVATE COACHING

Betty Wragge has performed in fifteen Broadway plays: she was Ruby's Keeler's understudy in ***No, No, Nannette*** and did Patsy Kelly's role in ***Ruby.*** An energetic instructor, she has taught everything from master classes at dance teachers' conventions to beginning tap and soft shoe classes for senior citizens. "I teach the basic fundamentals of tap technique in barre and center exercises, and concentrate on the things students have to know in order to pick up combinations from choreographers at auditions," Wragge says. She also works on routines and audition material. Wragge is currently teaching at Showcase Studios.

BATYA ZAMIR
137 West Broadway
New York, New York 10013
(212-267-8848)

Classes: MODERN DANCE: adult beg, int, adv; children's classes

Batya Zamir has directed her own company since 1969. A major influence on her work has been Alwin Nikolais, with whom she studied and performed. Zamir literally utilizes the entire space when she dances. She moves in the air and on the walls as well as the floor—with the help of sculptor Richard Van Buran's specially designed support systems of elastic ropes, swings, and pulleys—and she is primarily concerned with the elemental forces of gravity and air and their effect on movement. Her classes are an extension of her choreographic interests. And yes—students do get to work with the same aerial equipment she uses in performances. "I teach body alignment in relation to itself and to outside space," says Zamir. "The technique is aimed at achieving control, and exercises are given to help students work towards greater elasticity and flexibility. In the latter part of the class the emphasis is on improvisation, exploring the interaction of elements which initiate, direct, or change movement; and on extending the range of movement to incorporate dancing on the walls and in the air." Zamir teaches at two locations: children's classes are held at her loft on West Broadway, where there is a variety of equipment for "air dancing;" adult students are limited to the use of one aerial sculpture, which is rigged up at Studio 505 on Walker Street.

Aerial dancing on the "loop swing." ***courtesy of Batya Zamir***

KAROLY ZSEDENYI
315 West 86th Street
New York, New York 10025
(212-799-9440)

Classes: BALLET: adult beg, int, adv, pro; children's classes; COACHING

Karoly Zsedenyi, former premier danseur and director of ballet at the Royal Opera House of Budapest, has taught in New York for sixteen years. He has also taught and choreographed in Hungary, Brussels, and Chile. In order to provide enough individual attention, Zsedenyi's classes are limited to eight or ten students. He teaches "old-world academy-style Russian technique," which includes the study of music and ballet history. "No dilettantism," he says.

College dance: Full-time degree programs and continuing-education classes

Each year thousands of dancers come to study at the numerous metropolitan-area colleges and universities which grant a variety of degrees in dance. It's a way of having their cake and eating it too, since students attending New York colleges have all the advantages of a higher education as well as the wealth of outside dance classes, performances, resources, and professional opportunities that close proximity to the city offers. Recreational dancers can also take advantage of the continuing-education programs that several of these schools operate for nonmatriculating students.

ADELPHI UNIVERSITY

B.A. degree with performing arts majors in modern dance and ballet

for information, contact:
Norman Walker, Chairman of the Dance Department
Adelphi University
Garden City, New York 11530
(516-294-8700, ext. 7363)

faculty: Norman Walker, department head; full-time faculty: Harry Bernstein, Rochelle Zide Booth, Jo Ann Bruggeman, Samir Elias, Loren Hightower; also Robert Bowyer, Katia Geleznova, Sheila Zadra Goldstein, Celene Keller, Regina Larkin, Karen Levey, Nancy Lushington, Dana Manno, Evelyn Unger, Renée Wadleigh

BROOKLYN COLLEGE

B.A. and B.S. degrees, performing arts dance major

for information, contact:
Betsy M. Carden, Chairperson
Department of Dance
School of Performing Arts
Brooklyn College
Brooklyn, New York 11210
(212-780-5944/780-5485)

faculty: Betsy Martin Carden, chairperson; Karen Barracuda, Oldyna Dynowska, Sharon Filone, Howard Hormann, June Lewis, Paul Spong; also guest faculty and visiting artists

CITY COLLEGE OF NEW YORK, DAVIS CENTER FOR PERFORMING ARTS

B.F.A. degree, professional preparation program with majors in modern dance, ballet, and choreography

for information, contact:
Florence Waren, Chairperson of the Dance Program
Davis Center for the Performing Arts
City College of New York
Convent Avenue and 138th Street
New York, New York 10031
(212-690-6635/690-6666)

faculty: Florence Waren, chairperson; Jill Beck, Cheryl Bell, Marie Marchowsky, Walter Raines, Mariko Sanjo; and guest artists, Buzz Miller, Sahomi Tachibana, Norbert Vesak, Henry Yu

COLUMBIA UNIVERSITY, BARNARD COLLEGE

B.A. degree, dance concentration in program in the arts

for information, contact:
Jeanette Roosevelt, Program Coordinator
Barnard College, Columbia University
606 West 120th Street
New York, New York 10027
(212-280-2995)

faculty: Jeanette Roosevelt, Program Coordinator (presently on leave of absence); Sandra Genter, Janet Soares

COLUMBIA UNIVERSITY, TEACHERS COLLEGE

M.A. degree in dance education, program in department of physical education

for information, contact:
Office of Admissions
Teachers College, Columbia University
146 Horace Mann Hall
New York, New York 10027
(212-678-3710)

faculty: Thais Barry, director; Charles Dalbotten, Irene Dowd, Bob Dunn, Judith Willis Lesch, Linda Roberts

HUNTER COLLEGE

B.A. degree with dance education or performing arts major; M.S. degree in dance therapy; continuing education program

Undergraduate program
for information, contact:
Dorothy Vislocky, dance coordinator
Hunter College of the City University of New York
695 Park Avenue (69/70th Street)
Box 1660
New York, New York 10021
(212-570-5434)

faculty: Dorothy Vislocky, dance coordinator; Lorraine Colasanto, Dorothy Indenbaum, Bruce King, Barbara Manilla, Beatrice Montros, Charles Moore, Albert Reid, Kathleen Sumler, Pauline Tish

Graduate program
for information, contact:
Graduate Admissions
Hunter College of the City University of New York
695 Park Avenue (69/70th Street)
New York, New York 10021
(212-570-5512) Dance Therapy Department

Continuing-education program
Classes in ballroom dancing, ballet, modern dance, tap, and modern jazz; also dance appreciation (including discussions with professionals and three evenings of performances by the Joffrey Ballet, the New York City Ballet, and the Alvin Ailey American Dance Theatre). Most courses are offered in the evening and range in cost from $60 to $110 per semester.

for information, contact:
Hunter College Center for Lifelong Learning
466 Lexington Avenue (45/46th Street), Room 1313
New York, New York 10017
(212-949-4361)

JUILLIARD SCHOOL

B.F.A. degree with performing arts dance major; professional diploma in modern dance and ballet also offered

for information, contact:
Admissions Office
Juilliard School
Lincoln Center Plaza
New York, New York 10023
(212-799-5000)

faculty: Martha Hill, director of dance department; Alfredo Corvino, Robert Dennis, Bernadette Hecox, Wendy Hilton, Kazuko Hirabayashi, Hanya Holm, Airi Hynninen, Daniel Lewis, Billie Mahoney, Gloria Marina, Michael Maule, Helen McGehee, Genia Melikova, Calvin Morgan, Janis Pforsich, Doris Rudko, Marian Șeldes, Craig Shuler, Janet Mansfield Soares, Anna Sokolow, Alfonso Solimene, Stanley Sussman, John West, Ethel Winter, Hector Zaraspe

MARYMOUNT MANHATTAN COLLEGE

B.A. and B.F.A. degrees in dance; continuing-education program

for information, contact:
Office of Admissions
Marymount Manhattan College
221 East 71st Street
New York, New York 10021
(212-472-3800)

faculty: Glorianne Jackson, department chairperson; Enid Britten, Norman Fields, Ken Fischer, Dalienne Majors

Continuing-education program
Classes are the same as those for the matriculating students in the bachelors' program. Nonmatriculating and full-time students pay the same tuition rate of $85 per credit.

NEW SCHOOL FOR SOCIAL RESEARCH

continuing-education program only

for information, contact:
Choreographer's Theatre Dance Department
New School for Social Research
66 West 12th Street
New York, New York 10011
(212-741-5630)

faculty: Laura Foreman, director; Kathy Burke, Kat DeBlois, Felice Lesser, Annie Oleske, Jill Richards, Linda Robbins, Julie Sandler, Charles Sheek, Satoru Shimazaki, Peggy Spina

Continuing-education program
Classes include "a dance sampler," modern dance technique, combined classical ballet and modern dance workshop, classical ballet, jazz/musical-comedy dance, tap dancing, folk dance, pantomime, exercise, movement workshop, improvisation, and introduction to dance therapy. Most classes are given in the evening. All courses are $110 except for dance therapy, which is $120.

NEW YORK UNIVERSITY, SCHOOL OF THE ARTS

B.F.A. and M.F.A. degrees, dance majors in modern dance and ballet with an emphasis on performance and choreography

for information, contact:
Director of Admissions
New York University
Tisch Building, Room 905, Box D
40 West 4th Street
New York, New York 10003
(212-598-3595) Admissions Office
(212-598-2401) Dance Department

faculty: Stuart Hodes, dance department chairperson; André Bernard, Robert Blankshine, Nenette Charisse, Denise Jefferson, Deborah Jowitt, Rachel Lampert, Nicholas Lyndon, Clarice Marshall, Ritha Devi Mukerjea, Bertram Ross, Tryntje Shapli, Linda Tarnay

NEW YORK UNIVERSITY, SCHOOL OF EDUCATION

B.S., M.A., PhD., and EdD. degrees in dance, with an emphasis in dance education and therapy; continuing-education program

for information on undergraduate and graduate programs, contact:
Patricia A. Rowe, Chairperson
Department of Dance and Dance Education
School of Education, Health, Nursing and Arts Professions
New York University
675 Washington Square
New York, New York 10003
(212-598-3459)

faculty: Patricia A. Rowe, chairperson; full-time faculty: Laura R. Brittain, Marcia B. Leventhal, Judith G. Schwartz; also Margaret Beals, André Bernard, Michelle Berne, Nada Diachenko, Morse Donaldson, Ellen Kogan, Genevieve Oswald, Mariano Perra, Janis Pforsich, Virginia Reed, Iris Rifkin-Gainer, Doris Rudko, Ernestine Stodelle

Continuing-education program
Classes in ballet, modern dance; jazz dance workshop, body language workshop, T'ai Chi Ch'uan workshop, body awareness workshop using videotape. All courses are given in the evening and costs range from $85 to $125.

for information, contact:
Admissions Office
New York University Continuing Education
and Extension Services
40 West 4th Street
New York, New York 10003
(212-598-2742)

PRATT INSTITUTE

M.F.A. degree with emphasis in dance therapy offered in department of art therapy; continuing-education program

for information, contact:
Sharon Kenny, Dance Coordinator
Pratt Institute
East Building
Brooklyn, New York 11205
(212-636-3775)

faculty: Sharon Kenny, dance coordinator; James Cunningham, Michele Geller, Henry Yu

Continuing-education program
Saturday classes were begun last spring in ballet for children and modern dance for adults (physical fitness through dance). Call the department for the fee schedule.

QUEENS COLLEGE

B.F.A. degree in theatre-dance; continuing-education program

for information, contact:
Coordinator of Theatre/Dance Program
Department of Health and Physical Education
Queens College
Flushing, New York 11367
(212-520-7212)

faculty: Dr. Mildred Spiesman, department head; Margaret Calvano, Ella Noornietz, Istvan Rabovsky

Continuing-education program
Classes offered in modern dance, the language of body movement, and dance and imageology (communication through use of expressive movement). All classes are scheduled in the evening and cost $40 for 12 sessions; same faculty as the B.F.A. program.

for information, contact:
Continuing Education Programs
Queens College
65-30 Kissena Boulevard
Flushing, New York 11367
(212-520-7597)

SARAH LAWRENCE COLLEGE

B.A., M.A., and M.F.A. degrees with majors in dance

for information, contact:
Sharon Bouck, Director of Dance Program
Sarah Lawrence College
Bronxville, New York 10708
(914-337-0700)

faculty: Sharon Bouck, director; Marie Adair, Norma Dalby, Carol DeSimone, Jennifer Donohue, Richard Dunham, Elizabeth Keen, Don Redlich, Marcia Siegel, Rose Ann Thom

STATE UNIVERSITY OF NEW YORK-COLLEGE AT PURCHASE

B.A. and B.F.A. degrees with performing arts majors in ballet and modern dance; continuing-education program

Undergraduate program
for information, contact:
Penny Robbins, Dance Applicants
Admissions Office
S.U.N.Y. College at Purchase
Purchase, New York 10577
(914-253-5046)

faculty: Jacques d'Amboise, dean of dance division; William Bales, Royes Fernandez, Carol Fried, Kazuko Hirabayashi, Aaron Osborne, Ann Parson, Rosanna Seravalli, Carol Sumner, Mel Wong

Continuing-education program
Open classes for adults in ballet, modern dance, jazz, tap, T'ai Chi Ch'uan, and body education (anatomy and massage); graded ballet classes in Russian (Vaganova) technique for children and young adults ages 5 and up, as well as student performances. Most adult classes are scheduled in the evening, while children's classes are given in the late afternoon. Fees range from $70 to $200, according to the length of the course and the number of class sessions per week.

for information, contact:
Office of Continuing Education
State University of New York
College at Purchase
Purchase, New York 10577
(914-253-5000)

Other classes of interest

Body conditioning

American Center for the Alexander Technique
142 West End Avenue
New York, New York 10023
(212-799-0468)
"Physical problems result not from ***what*** we do, but rather from ***how*** we do what we do," maintain the disciples of Frederick Matthais Alexander, an Australian actor who invented the Alexander Technique in the early part of this century. Among his grateful followers were Aldous Huxley, George Bernard Shaw, and John Dewey. Under the personal observation and supervision of a trained instructor, students of the Alexander Technique learn to replace faulty muscular habits that are causing pain, fatigue, and poor coordination with healthful new ways of moving that allow the body to function with greater ease, efficiency, and pleasure. This is achieved through correct posture (in particular, the proper positioning of the head on the spine) and the conscious "rethinking" of habitual movement patterns. People come to the center for both the treatment of injury-related problems and general self-improvement. It offers a range of services, including introductory advisory consultations, private lessons, small group classes, intensive weekend courses, and teacher-training courses. The staff recommends that new students attend at least three to five sessions before deciding whether or not to continue.

Milton Feher School of Dance and Relaxation
200 West 58th Street
New York, New York 10019
(212-246-4144)
Classes are given in body alignment and therapeutic exercises, as well as dance exercises for singers.

Pilates Studio for Body Conditioning
29 West 56th Street
New York, New York 10019
(212-974-9511)
The late Joe Pilates, an ex-boxer from Düsseldorf, Germany, devised a system of highly concentrated exercises based on the use of specially designed machines for body building and physiotherapy. He worked with both nondancers and dancers, attracting such artists as Ruth St. Denis, Hanya Holm, Alexandra Danilova, and Zorina. The gym is now run by Pilates's former pupil, Romana Kryzanowska. Studio regulars, who include premier danseur Jacques d'Amboise, claim that the Pilates program is the purest, most effective form of exercise. "It gets right down to where you need it," one satisfied client told us. "You have to use your body weight and muscles to make the machines work, not the other way around. If you're new, they run you through

the exercises once to see what your body needs, and go from there." The Pilates studio offers individually supervised workouts for relaxation and body conditioning. They do realignment work to straighten out the spine, and also physical therapy and corrective exercises for injuries. Sessions are by appointment only.

Elaine Summers
537 Broadway (Spring Street)
New York, New York 10012
(212-966-3367)
Summers, an experimental choreographer, teaches special exercises for muscle relaxation and the correction of postural misalignment.

Joyce Suskind
200 West 70th Street
New York, New York 10023
(212-362-0135)
Joyce Suskind has been teaching the Alexander Technique for thirty-five years. Her own mentor, Alma Frank, was trained by F.M. Alexander himself and was one of the first teachers of his method in the United States. Suskind says that the Alexander Technique is often used therapeutically to counter the effects of bad dance training, injuries, or injury-related problems. But many of her students come "just to feel better, improve their posture, and get in touch with their bodies. Basically what we do here is get people to understand and appreciate their own unique body structure rather than fight it," she says. "We teach them to carry their weight in a balanced and healthful way and to get the most out of their physical assets; and we do this through sensory awareness exercises and touching techniques, which get them to relax the holding tensions in the body." Suskind gives private and group lessons. "Alexander always worked individually with his students, so group classes are a relatively new development. But many people cannot afford to pay for the private lessons, and there is individual supervision in the groups, too."

Carola Trier Studio
200 West 58th Street
New York, New York 10019
(212-CO5-1697)
This studio specializes in body conditioning, spot-reducing, correction on technique and body placement, and therapeutic and corrective exercise for injuries; sessions are by appointment only. European-born Carola Trier studied with Kurt Jooss and Rudolf Laban in Germany and was a student of the late Joe Pilates. Her special exercises, which are done with and without machines, are aimed at improving posture and breathing while "helping the body to function in an integrated way to full capacity." Trier works with dancers (ballerina Allegra Kent is among her faithful clientele) and nondancers alike. She seems to elicit both harsh criticism and high praise: some clients say Trier is temperamental. Others feel she has helped them enormously. An

editor friend of ours who has been working out at Carola's swears it's changed her life. "Just one hour a week gets amazing results," she says. "You feel like you've done very little, but it's all very efficient and you see an improvement almost immediately."

Movement studies and improvisation

American Mime Theatre
192 Third Avenue (20th Street)
New York, New York 10003
(212-777-1710)

The American Mime Theatre offers a complete course in mime—including technique, performance, script-writing, directing, stage and costume design, teaching, and administration. Students must commit at least three months to study. The school is also the headquarters of a professional mime troupe established by Paul Curtis in 1952.

Dalcroze School of Music
161 East 73rd Street
New York, New York 10021
(212-TR9-0316)

Although this is primarily a music school, its curriculum is based on eurhythmics, a method of teaching rhythm by translating sounds into body movement which was devised by Swiss composer Emile Jaques Dalcroze (1865-1950). Eurhythmics had a great impact on European modern dance and modern ballet, influencing such artists as Marie Rambert, Vaslav Nijinsky, Kurt Jooss, Mary Wigman, and Hanya Holm. The Dalcroze School offers classes in rhythmic movement and improvisation for children ages 3½ and up, and adults. It also sponsors teacher-training courses. Scholarships are available.

Dance Notation Bureau
505 Eighth Avenue (35th Street)
New York, New York 10018
(212-736-4350)

The Dance Notation Bureau is best known as an archive of recorded dance works and a training ground for Labanotation, a widely used method of analyzing and scoring choreography which was invented by German movement theorist Rudolf Laban. But it also sponsors an assortment of interesting classes on related areas of study and historic dance forms. In the past these have included courses in body alignment, effort/shape, anatomy and kinesiology, teaching dance, ballet, Balinese dance, eighteenth-century baroque dance, eurhythmics, and modern dance improvisation and composition.

Laban Institute of Movement Studies
151 West 19th Street
New York, New York 10011
(212-924-8755)

The Laban Institute of Movement Studies was founded by Irmgard Bartenieff, a former student of Rudolf Laban who has applied his principles of movement analysis to her own work in the fields of physical therapy, dance therapy, and anthropology. An "interdisciplinary center for seeing, writing, and experiencing movement," the institute offers classes in effort/shape, movement observation and labanotation, dance therapy training, eurhythmics, injury prevention, creative movement for adults, baroque and renaissance dance, movement for actors, and movement choir. Intensive courses, such as the recent "career alternatives in movement fields," are also given.

Noyes School of Rhythm Foundation
36 East 61st Street
New York, New York 10021
(212-TE8-6919)

Rhythmic movement and old-style interpretive dancing à la Isadora Duncan are taught here. Although it is no longer a full-time teaching facility, since 1919 the Noyes School of Rhythm, founded by Florence Fleming Noyes and now directed by Valeria Ladd, has operated a summer camp for women in Portland, Connecticut, called Shepherd's Nine. Guests sleep in tents, drink fresh spring water, eat wholesome home-cooked meals, and wear flowing tunics to classes. Activities at this charmingly anachronistic retreat include daily movement classes, art lessons, swimming, and other outdoor sports. In the evening there are performances of dance dramas, masques, and group dances choreographed by the faculty. The Noyes junior camp for girls is located nearby.

School for Creative Movement in the Arts
265 West 87th Street
New York, New York 10024
(212-724-3520)

Classes in creative movement and improvisation at the School for Creative Movement have a strong psychological orientation. According to directors Jack and Hattie Wiener, the teaching objective is "not to teach technique per se, but to develop the dancer's individual style of movement." A combined program of art and dance classes is offered for children. There are also classes for adults.

Levy-Shea Studio: Yoga and Creative Movement
100 East 16th Street
New York, New York 10003
(212-677-5690)

Founded by two former social workers, the Levy-Shea method utilizes stretching, relaxation, and breathing exercises "to create a constant energy flow necessary to health and well-being." Students are encouraged "to expand their own range of physical potential." The studio also features special lunch-hour sessions which combine a thirty-minute yoga class with a low-calorie health food lunch, all for the price of $4.

A preschool movement class at the School for Creative Movement in the Arts.

Gymnastics

Alex and Walters Studio
30 West 56th Street
New York, New York 10019
(212-265-7270)

Alexy's Studios
4475 Henry Hudson Parkway
Riverdale, New York 10471
(212-884-2400)
Alex Drovinsky, Director

Alzerreca's Gym
254 Fifth Avenue (28th Street)
New York, New York 10001
(212-683-1703)
George Alzerreca, Director

Goddard Community Center
468 Riverside Drive (119th Street)
New York, New York 10027
(212-873-6600)
Fred Johnson, Director

The Gym for Gymnastics
305 East 47th Street
New York, New York 10017
(212-753-3553)
Gary Novickie, Director

Harlem Branch, YMCA
180 West 135th Street
New York, New York 10030
(212-281-4100)
Mel McCain, Director

Kounovsky Physical Fitness Center
25 West 56th Street
New York, New York 10019
(212-246-6415)
Nicholas Kounovsky, Director

Lexington Avenue YWCA
610 Lexington Avenue (52nd Street)
New York, New York 10022
(212-755-4500)
Rosemary Stanfield, Director

Manhattan Gymnastic Center
405 East 73rd Street
New York, New York 10021
(212-737-2016)

McBurney YMCA
215 West 23rd Street
New York, New York 10011
(212-741-9216)
Red Langton, Coach

Musawwir
41 Worth Street
New York, New York 10013
(212-226-2283)
Toby Towson, Director

New York Turnverein
152 East 85th Street
New York, New York 10028
(212-TR9-8834)
Henry Schroeder, Director

River East Health Club
614 Second Avenue (34th Street)
New York, New York 10016
(212-689-4043)
Jeff Nayer, Director

Sutton Gym for Physical Fitness and Gymnastics
410 East 54th Street
New York, New York 10022
(212-PL1-8318)
Bill Ladick, Director

West Side YMCA
5 West 63rd Street
New York, New York 10023
(212-787-4400)

Dance Companies Based in New York

New York City is the home of over 150 professional dance companies, most of whom perform here regularly, offer classes or operate schools, and hold auditions for new members. Besides internationally recognized troupes such as American Ballet Theatre, the Martha Graham Dance Company, and the Paul Taylor Dance Company, there are a host of established smaller groups such as those of Lar Lubovitch, Kei Takei, and Eleo Pomare, and a number of up-and-coming young companies such as Rachel Lampert and Dancers and Rosalind Newman and Dancers. You can go see a performance of George Balanchine's ***Concerto Barocco*** by the New York City Ballet one evening, and a satire of it performed in drag by the Ballets Trockadero the next; or you can see the Multigravitational Aerodance Group dance on the walls and ceilings. There are the ethnic-flavored Dance Theatre of Harlem and the Ballet Hispanico, and for musical comedy fans, the American Dance Machine's lively reconstruction of the best in Broadway dance. The post-Cunningham generation of avant-garde choreographers is well represented by such artists as Kenneth King, Lucinda Childs, and David Gordon.

What follows is a listing of dance companies that have worked consistently in the city for several years. In most instances we have supplied the names and addresses of their management agents, who should be able to answer inquiries about upcoming performances, classes, and auditions, or refer you to the proper source.

ACME DANCE COMPANY

Artistic Director: James Cunningham
Company Manager: Pentacle Dance Management
200 West 72nd Street, Suite 20
New York, New York 10023
(212-580-8107)

The Acme Dance Company's theatre pieces are fantastic "magic carpet odysseys" that combine dancing with acting, singing, dialogue, and mime, and a pageantlike use of elaborate costumes and masks. James Cunningham's eclectic choreography encompasses modern dance, ballet, jazz, acrobatics, rock dancing, yoga, improvisation, and even a touch of vaudeville. The repertory's colorful cast of characters are drawn from such diverse sources as ancient mythology (Dionysis, Lord Shiva, Osiris), contemporary culture (Mae West, Wonder Woman, Donald Duck, a Playboy bunny) and dance history (Isadora Duncan, the Swan Lake Ogre, Nijinsky's Faun and the Dying Duck). Humor permeates Cunningham's pieces, from slapstick to sophisticated satire. Cunningham is a native of Toronto, where he studied and performed both as an actor and dancer. He also studied acting, voice, and dance at the London Academy of Dramatic Arts. Since coming to New York in 1965, he has choreographed numerous concert works for performing spaces ranging from conventional proscenium theatres to the steps of the United States Treasury Building on Wall Street; some of his pieces employ up to 150 volunteer performers, both dancers and nondancers. Cunningham has received several grants for his work, including Guggenheim Foundation and National Endowment for the Arts grants. He has taught at a number of colleges, and for the last seven years has been on the dance faculty of Pratt Institute in New York. Among the perennial favorites of the Cunningham repertoire are ***The First Family: Isadora Duncan and Donald Duck, Aesop's Fables,*** and ***Mr. Fox Asleep.***

ALVIN AILEY AMERICAN DANCE THEATRE

Artistic Director: Alvin Ailey
Company Director: Edward Lander
1515 Broadway (45/46th Street), 3rd Floor
New York, New York 10036
(212-997-1950)

This enormously popular company was founded by Alvin Ailey in the late 1950s, and almost from its inception has drawn wide and enthusiastic audiences. Some of its City Center concerts resemble revival meetings, with viewers rising to their feet and clapping, knowing the dances by heart from having seen them so often. The Ailey style is an amalgam of the muscular modern dance technique of Lester Horton (with whose company Ailey performed), ballet, and jazz. Many of his dances are set to Negro spirituals, blues, jazz, popular, and gospel music; and Ailey's earliest works,

A scene from James Cunningham's fantasy satire, ***Dancing with Maisie Paradocks. Joel Gordon, courtesy of the Acme Dance Company***

such as ***Blues Suite*** and ***Revelations,*** draw on his personal experiences as a young black man growing up in the America of the 1940s and 50s. Other pieces, such as ***The Lark Ascending*** and ***Streams*** (to a Duke Ellington score), are lyrical works that have no ethnic specificity. Ailey's superlative dancers, who include Judith Jamison, Clive Thompson and Dudley Williams, are reason enough to see the group. The Alvin Ailey American Dance Theatre is also a repertory company that performs the work of other contemporary choreographers, such as George Faison, Rudy Perez, Talley Beatty, Louis Falco, Donald McKayle, Lar Lubovitch, Katherine Dunham, Pearl Primus, Lucas Hoving, as well as revivals of pieces by Lester Horton and Ted Shawn. Ailey has choreographed and appeared in several Broadway shows, and his formula for success is based on the first rule of the commercial theatre—always be entertaining. The Alvin Ailey American Dance Center, which has just moved to new headquarters, is the official school of the company (see Chapter Two).

ALVIN AILEY REPERTORY ENSEMBLE

Artistic Director: Sylvia Waters
Company Manager: William Burd
1515 Broadway (45/46th Street), 3rd Floor
New York, New York 10036
(212-997-1950)

The Alvin Ailey Repertory Ensemble is the sixteen-member junior company of the Alvin Ailey American Dance Theatre, consisting of advanced scholarship students from the Ailey school. It was established in 1974 to give performing experience to promising young dancers, develop new choreographers and offer dance programs to otherwise deprived institutions and communities along the East Coast. Under the direction of Sylvia Waters, a former principal with the Ailey troupe, the Repertory Ensemble performs pieces from the senior company's repertory as well as works by choreographers such as Dianne McIntyre and Ulysses Dove. The dancers are well trained and already accomplished performers.

Judith Jamison in Alvin Ailey's ***Cry.***
R. Faligant

FRANCES ALENIKOFF DANCE THEATRE COMPANY
Artistic Director and Company Manager: Frances Alenikoff
537 Broadway (Spring Street)
New York, New York 10012
(212-925-0880)

Performances by the Frances Alenikoff Dance Theatre Company are multimedia events synthesizing movement with dialogue, mime, tape collage, and film. Alenikoff often creates striking images that stay in the mind. The diversified repertory includes dramatic, lyric, abstract, and humorous pieces, solos as well as group dances. Among the group's best-loved pieces are ***Terns in Place, The One of No Way, In the Courtyard,*** and ***Episodes on the Edge.*** The company, which was formed in 1968, frequently performs at Alenikoff's loft, Eden's Expressway.

MANUEL ALUM DANCE COMPANY
Company Manager: Ralph Jackson
229 East 81st Street
New York, New York 10028
(212-744-3477)

Dramatic contrast is the hallmark of Manuel Alum's work. In it, "the freedom and expressiveness of modern dance are fused with the formal restraint and discipline of classical ballet. The music similarly ranges from the classical lyricism of Boccherini and Brahms to the tangos of Carlos Miranda to the contemporary expressionism of Penderecki, Berio, and Tal." A native Puerto Rican, Alum started dance training after coming to Chicago in 1959. But he found his chief mentors in New York: Paul Sanasardo, Margaret Black, Mia Slavenska, and Martha Graham. Alum was a leading dancer with the Paul Sanasardo Dance Company for ten years, during which time he choreographed several works for the group. He formed his own company in 1970. ***The Cellar,*** Alum's solo about the desperation of a cornered man, remains one of his most compelling pieces.

AMERICAN BALLET THEATRE
Artistic Directors: Antony Tudor and Nora Kaye
Company Manager: Joyce A. Moffatt
888 Seventh Avenue (56th Street)
New York, New York 10019
(212-757-7035)

This major ballet company began modestly in 1939 as the Mordkin Ballet, a showcase for the advanced students of Mikhail Mordkin's school (Mordkin was the Russian premier danseur who partnered Anna Pavlova). Under the leadership of Lucia Chase, who danced with the original company, and Oliver Smith, American Ballet Theatre grew to employ an internationally celebrated roster of dancers, which over the years has included Adolph Bolm, Patricia Bowman, Anton Dolin, Nora Kaye, Eugene Loring, Hugh Laing, Antony Tudor, Alicia Alonso, Jerome Robbins, Alicia Markova, Donald Saddler, Vera Zorina, Andre Eglevsky, Igor Youskevitch, Agnes de Mille, Leon Danielian, Maria Tallchief, Erik Bruhn, Violette Verdy, Melissa Hayden, Sallie Wilson, Bruce Marks, Toni Lander, Scott Douglas, Mikhail Baryshnikov, Natalia Makarova, Gelsy Kirkland, Anthony Dowell, Martine van Hamel, Gynthia Gregory, Rudolf Nureyev, and Fernando Bujones. The Ballet Theatre repertory is probably one of the most diversified in the world, containing works ranging from full-length classics such as ***Swan Lake, Giselle, The Sleeping Beauty,*** and ***Les Sylphides;*** to the psychological dramas of Antony Tudor; to George Balanchine's neoclassic ***Theme and Variations***, Agnes de Mille's American folk ballets, and Eugene Loring's ***Billy the Kid***; to pieces by Jerome Robbins and other contemporary choreographers such as John Neumeier, Glen Tetley, and Twyla Tharp. The Ballet Theatre Corps has earned an international reputation of its own. They are impeccably rehearsed and a joy to watch. The official training ground for the company is the American Ballet Theatre School (see Chapter Two).

AMERICAN DANCE MACHINE
Artistic and Executive Director: Lee Theodore
4 East 75th Street, 3rd Floor
New York, New York 10021
(212-879-5750)

The stated purpose of the American Dance Machine is to "reconstruct, preserve, instruct, and perform in a continuing repertory the important choreography of twentieth century American Musical Theatre and related media." It is a living archive of musical-comedy dance, culled from the memories of such Broadway veterans as Gwen Verdon, Buzz Miller, and Gemze de Lappe. Among the choreographers whose works are performed by the troupe are Jack Cole, Danny Daniels, Agnes de Mille, Ron Field, Bob Fosse, Peter Gennaro, Carol Haney, Michael Kidd, Joe Layton, Donald Saddler, Onna White, and Billy Wilson. The four-year-old company of dancer-singer-actors is highly polished and entertaining. Director Lee Theodore has appeared in numerous Broadway musicals, including ***The King and I*** and ***Damn Yankees.*** She is probably best remembered for having created the role of Anybody's in the original production of ***West Side Story.*** Theodore has also directed and choreographed several Broadway musicals. The American Dance Machine operates a school at the Harkness House for Ballet Arts on East 75th Street (see Chapter Two).

JERRY AMES TAP DANCE COMPANY
Company Manager: Herbert Barrett Management
1860 Broadway (61/62nd Street)
New York, New York 10023
(212-245-3530)

The seven-member Jerry Ames Tap Dance Company, founded in 1975, was the first ongoing professional troupe dedicated to the survival and growth of that indigenously American dance form. In some of the repertory pieces tap choreography is blended with ballet, jazz, or modern dance movement to give it greater range, and the numbers are performed to a variety of music—traditional, jazz, swing, pop, and Gershwin scores. Old-time hoofers make guest appearances with the company, and programs often include challenge matches or impressions of tap greats like Bill "Bojangles" Robinson and John Bubbles. Jerry Ames, who has made numerous Broadway and television appearances, teaches tap at the Theatre Teachers Alliance in New York (see Chapter Two).

Danny Daniel's witty Clog Dance from the Broadway musical ***Walking Happy***, performed by the American Dance Machine. ***Martha Swope***

ASAKAWALKER DANCE COMPANY
Artistic Directors: Takako Asakawa and
David Hatch Walker
77 Greene Street
New York, New York 10012
(212-925-4599)

Japanese-born Takako Asakawa and her Canadian husband, David Hatch Walker, were principal dancers with the Martha Graham company before forming their own group two years ago. Both choreograph for the company, whose repertory includes solos, duets, and ensemble pieces; and both draw heavily on the Graham movement vocabulary. The twelve members of the Asakawalker troupe are attractive and skillful performers, but most critics agree that on the whole the dancing outshines the choreography, which is still developing. The company's most successful works have been Asakawa's ***Reflections of Romance*** and Walker's ***Ritual.*** They recently opened a dance school in Lower Manhattan (see Chapter Two).

FRANK ASHLEY DANCE COMPANY
Company Manager: Sherry Chorney
Henry Street Settlement
466 Grand Street
New York, New York 10002
(212-766-9338)

The Frank Ashley Dance Company is an interracial modern dance group currently in residence at the Henry Street Settlement. The company's repertory is a blend of modern and jazz dance, and draws upon the folk heritage of the West Indies, Africa, and the black American experience, as well as on abstract and dramatic themes. Choreographer Frank Ashley performed with Yuriko and Eleo Pomare before establishing his own troupe in 1973.

BALLET HISPANICO OF NEW YORK
Artistic Director: Tina Ramirez
Company Manager: Natsu Ifill
167 West 89th Street
New York, New York 10024
(212-362-6710)

The Ballet Hispanico was founded in 1970 by Tina Ramirez "to provide a professional dance company that would reflect the cultural experience of Hispanic-Americans. Our purpose is to preserve the varied cultural heritages of Spain, Puerto Rico, and Latin America: the rhythms of the Caribbean, the festive dances of Mexico, the passionate soul of Spanish flamenco, the simple folk traditions of Latin America, as well as the street savvy of the cities and the contemporary expression of American modern dance and jazz." All the company's dancers come from Spanish-speaking regions of the United States. In addition to works by Miss Ramirez, the repertory contains pieces by American choreographers such as Geoffrey Holder, Talley Beatty, Alvin Ailey, Anna Sokolow, Louis Johnson, Lois Bewley, and Donald McKayle. The company's official school is located on Manhattan's Upper West Side.

BALLET THEATRE FOUNDATION PRESENTS THE BALLET REPERTORY COMPANY
Company Manager: Cynthia Gold
322 West 78th Street
New York, New York 10024
(212-799-1861/799-1940)

Ballet Repertory Company, the junior company of American Ballet Theatre, was formed in 1972 to provide professional performing experience to promising young dancers, and to offer first-rate ballet programs to communities that could neither afford nor accommodate the larger company. The group presents fully staged productions from the classical repertory, such as ***Le Corsaire Pas de Deux, Don Quixote Pas de Deux,*** and ***Bournonville Divertissement,*** as well as contemporary pieces, such as Lucas Hoving's ***Icarus*** and works by the group's Artistic Director, Richard Englund. Although the dancers are young, the caliber of performance is high.

Tarama Boumdiyeva (Sanson Candelaria) and Alexis Lermontov (Natch Taylor) in ***Swan Lake.*** ***John L. Murphy, courtesy of the Ballet Trockadero de Monte Carlo.***

BALLETS TROCKADERO DE MONTE CARLO
Artistic Director: Natch Taylor
General Director: Eugene McDougle
Associate Director: Anne Dore Davids
Box 46, Cathedral Station
New York, New York 10025
(212-865-7925/666-0506)

Les Ballets Trockadero de Monte Carlo (also known as the "Trocks") is an eleven-member all-male company that performs ballet classics as well as original burlesques ***en travesti***, with the men dancing both the women's and the men's roles. The group satirizes the styles and conventions of famous dancers, schools of dance, and choreographic styles. Included in the repertory are renditions of ***The Dying Swan, The Nutcracker, Pas de Quatre, Les Sylphides, Swan Lake, Don Quixote,*** and ***Giselle.*** All these pieces are performed on pointe and in full costume. Among the contemporary choreographers who are spoofed by the Trocks are George Balanchine (in ***Go for Barocco***), Isadora Duncan, and Martha Graham. In keeping with the company's tongue-in-cheek spirit all the dancers have facetious stage names like Ida Neversayneva and Igor Slowpokin. Although occasionally Trockadero pieces are too long, on the whole they are funny and illuminating. Since 1974, when it was formed, the group has toured widely and appeared on national television.

MARGARET BEALS IN CONCERT
Company Manager: Margaret Beals
228 West Broadway
New York, New York 10013
(212-431-3869)

Solo-dancer Margaret Beals is one of the truly original concert artists performing today. Her programs combine dance, music, and poetry, all delivered with a spellbinding intensity. The repertory ranges from dramatic to humorous dances and includes both choreographed and improvisational pieces. Recorded music, poetry recited by Beals herself, or live jazz improvisations by the musicians with whom she regularly works provide the accompaniment. Beals recently premiered a piece called ***Words*** at the popular nightclub, The Bottom Line, in which she created impromptu monologues and dance solos from audience suggestions. A self-taught dancer during her early years in Boston, Beals developed an individual approach to movement which eventually led her to the solo concert field. After coming to New York in her late teens, she performed with the companies of José Limón, Valerie Bettis, Jean Erdman, Paul Sanasardo, and Lucas Hoving. In the late sixties, she worked extensively in nightclubs and cabarets exploring the art of improvisation with jazz musicians. Beals has also taught dance at the American Dance Festival, Connecticut College, Barnard College, and the New York University School of Education. When time permits, she holds movement and improvisation workshops at her loft in Soho (see Chapter Two).

MARIA BENITEZ' ESTAMPA FLAMENCA
Company Manager: Renee Kaplan
HI Enterprises, Inc.
200 West 57th Street, Suite 1310
New York, New York 10019
(212-573-4303)

Maria Benitez' Estampa Flamenca offers a wide variety of Spanish dance, from traditional flamenco, Spanish classical, and regional folk pieces to a contemporary dance-drama integrating the poetry of Garcia Lorca. In all its works, however, the company adheres to the Spanish heritage and tradition, attempting to maintain a purity of style and interpretation of the traditional dance forms it performs. Benitez, a stunning performer who was trained in Madrid, has lately appeared at the American Dance Festival, the Delacorte Festival, the Sante Fe Opera, and on national educational television.

Margaret Beals in ***Stings. Philip Hipwell***

PEPSI BETHEL AUTHENTIC JAZZ DANCE THEATRE
Artistic Director: Pepsi Bethel
554 West 53rd Street, Suite A-24
New York, New York 10019
(212-265-4412)

The Pepsi Bethel Authenic Jazz Dance Theatre was organized in 1971 "to preserve and recreate those uniquely American dance forms that were created to jazz music." Their sources range from New Orleans to the West Indies to the Savoy Ballroom in Harlem. The eleven-member company is one of the few—if not the only one—that performs authentic minstrel dances, the original Cakewalk, and those marvelous jazz and ballroom steps of the 1930s and 1940s, like the Slow Drag, the Mooche, Snake Hips, The Bumps, and the Shortie George. These are set to music by Count Basie, Buddy Rich, Fats Waller, Frank Foster, and Frankie Lane, as well as original compositions and arrangements. Pepsi Bethel began his career as a Lindy Hopper at the famed Savoy Ballroom, and later trained as a modern dancer at Adelphi University, where he was a recipient of the Hanya Holm Dance Scholarship. He danced with Al Minns,

Pepsi Bethel (center) with his company. ***courtesy of the Pepsi Bethel Authentic Jazz Dance Theatre***

Leon James, Norma Miller, and Mura Dehn, and has appeared on Broadway in the hit musical ***Kwamina.*** Bethel also toured Africa with his company three times. He has taught at New York University and Sarah Lawrence College, and has been on the faculty of the Alvin Ailey American Dance Center and Clark Center for many years (see Chapter Two).

BHASKAR—DANCES OF INDIA
207 Columbus Avenue (70th Street), Suite F
New York, New York 10023
(212-362-1288)

Bhaskar, born in India, was trained there in the four styles of Hindu dance which dominate the company's repertory. The group, which was founded in 1956, tries to present "a palatable and entertaining" introduction to the dances of India and Southeast Asia. It also performs new works by Bhaskar which combine modern dance with traditional Hindu gesture.

TRISHA BROWN COMPANY
Company Manager: Elizabeth Rectanus
Performing Artservices
463 West Street
New York, New York 10014
(212-989-4953)

The Trisha Brown Company, established in 1967, is probably best known for its environmental pieces performed outdoors and in other unconventional places, such as art galleries, museums, and rooftops. Originally from Aberdeen, Washington, Brown studied dance composition with the late Louis Horst at Connecticut College, Ann Halprin in San Francisco, and Robert Dunn at the Merce Cunningham Studio. She later became one of the leaders of the experimental Judson Dance Theatre at the Judson Memorial Church in Greenwich Village. Most of Brown's material is derived from carefully structured improvisation, and makes use of natural gesture such as bending, straightening, or rotating parts of the body—what she calls "pure movement," as opposed to stylized dance steps. Brown's work has progressed through several distinct stages, from "structured events in the early 1960s to equipment pieces such as ***Man Walking Down the Side of a Building*** (1969), and elaborate formal compositions such as ***Accumulation*** (1971)." Her latest work consists of "extremely high energy dancing that falls in between improvisation and memory." The movement is memorized by her dancers but is at the same time "thoroughly organic, reckless, personal, and altogether unpredictable." Brown has received a Guggenheim Fellowship and a Creative Artists Public Service grant for choreography.

CARTOON OPERA MIMSICAL THEATRE
Artistic Directors, Patrick and Heather McDermott
Company Manager: Anne P. Kearns
Trinty Dance Management
162 West 56th Street
New York, New York 10019
(212-582-1760)

Established in 1974, the Cartoon Opera fuses mime, dance, live music, and song—or "mimsy," as they call it—in its repertory of performance pieces. Living cartoons present original stories as well as adaptation of Zen koans, Sufi stories, and other tales which feature unpredictable twists of fortune and surprise endings.

LUCINDA CHILDS
Company Manager: Performing Artservices
463 West Street
New York, New York 10014
(212-989-4953)

Lucinda Childs began her career as a choreographer and dancer in 1963, as an original member of the Judson Dance Theatre in New York. She performed her own work, mostly solos which used objects and spoken monologues in relation to movement, while also appearing with other experimental choreographers, such as Robert Morris, Steven Paxton, and Yvonne Rainer. Childs formed her dance company in 1973. Since that time, she has collaborated with Robert Wilson and Philip Glass on the opera ***Einstein on the Beach***, which was performed at the Metropolitan Opera House in 1976. She received a Creative Artists Public Service grant for her ***Solo for a Character on Three Diagonals*** and a ***Village Voice*** OBIE award for her performance. Childs also recently appeared with Wilson in his two-act play, ***I Was Sitting On My Patio This Guy Appeared I Thought I Was Hallucinating***. Her latest project is an evening-length collaboration piece with composer Philip Glass and visual artist Sol Lewitt, called ***Mirabel.*** It was premiered at the Brooklyn Academy of Music this fall. Here is how Lucinda Childs defines her work:

"My dances are set repeatable forms, danced without musical accompaniment. In dancing, however, distinct rhythmic patterns are both audible—through the sounds made in dancing: jumps, hops, pivot turns—and visible—in the manner that the body is used. Movement segments are subject to repetition or ordered in additive or permutational sequences. Even though phrases are repeated, they are never repeated in exactly the same manner. The dances exist in the time it takes to exhaust a given selection of variables that can be used while continuing to introduce the material from a different point of view."

ZE'EVA COHEN SOLO DANCE REPERTORY

Company Manager: Pentacle Dance Management
200 West 72nd Street, Suite 20
New York, New York 10023
(212-580-8107)

Ze'eva Cohen's solo dance program, initiated in 1971, offers a panoramic survey of contemporary dance, from modern to ballet to dances derived from her own Semitic folk roots. In addition to her own pieces, this charismatic dance-actress performs works by Anna Sokolow, Kei Takei, James Waring, Rudy Perez, Art Bauman, Deborah Jowitt, Frances Alenikoff, Phyllis Lamhut, and Viola Farber. Cohen was born in Tel Aviv, Israel, where she received her early training and made her stage debut at the age of sixteen. In 1963, she came to New York to study at the Juilliard School. She has danced as a soloist with the companies of Anna Sokolow, the American Dance Theatre at Lincoln Center, Dance Theatre Workshop, the New York Shakespeare Festival, and as a guest artist with Pearl Lang and Company. Cohen has also taught extensively and is currently a Lecturer in Modern Dance at Princeton University.

MERCE CUNNINGHAM AND DANCE COMPANY

Company Manager: Art Becofsky
463 West Street
New York, New York 10014
(212-255-8240)

Probably no single choreographer has been a greater influence on the current generation of modern dancers than Merce Cunningham. Although his work seems tame compared to that of some present-day avant-gardists, it is still provocative. His dances still enrage some viewers and delight others, and Cunningham himself is still a fascinating performer. As chronicler Don McDonagh has written in the ***Complete Book of Modern Dance,*** "Cunningham was among the first to challenge the conventions of the founding generation of modern dance [Martha Graham, Doris Humphrey, Charles Weidman and Hanya Holm] ." Cunningham's theatrical approach, McDonagh's continues, "was not dependent on the accepted need for story, character and dramatic mood. He was interested in pure movement and its inherent possibilities." Cunningham thought that dancers were interesting enough to watch as themselves, that an audience could take in several images at the same time, and that dances needn't have a central focus or frontal orientation—his could be seen from any angle. He also believed that everyday movements such as standing, sitting, or riding a bicycle had a place in dance. He felt that art should imitate life and used chance methods, like the toss of a coin, to structure his pieces. Music and scenic design for his works were created independently of each other and of the choreography. His movement style fused the fluid torso of modern dance with the quick footwork and linear clarity of classical ballet.

Cunningham first performed with the Martha Graham Company. By the mid-1940s he had begun to choreograph, and in 1947 he created a work for George Balanchine's company. Since founding his own troupe in 1953, Cunningham has collaborated with avant-garde musician John Cage, whose musical compositions often consist of electronic scores or witty anecdotes read aloud, and with contemporary painters such as Robert Rauschenberg, Jasper Johns, Andy Warhol, and Robert Morris. The Cunningham company performances may consist of a program of two or three individual pieces from the repertory, or an "event" in which the musicians select and perform music from their own and the company's repertory. For events the décor is most often the performance space itself. The combination of movement, music, and décor, as well as the arrangement of the choreographic material, are unique for each event. The Merce Cunningham Dance Studio at Westbeth is the company's official training facility (see Chapter Two), and the setting for events (see Chapter One).

DANCE THEATRE OF HARLEM

Artistic Directors: Arthur Mitchell and Karel Shook
Company Manager: Richard A. Gonsalves
466 West 152nd Street
New York, New York 10031
(212-690-2800)

The Dance Theatre of Harlem, established in 1969, is composed of thirty classically trained black dancers who perform works by George Balanchine, Jerome Robbins, Jack Mitchell, Geoffrey Holder, and Lester Horton, as well as lesser known black choreographers. The company's founder was Arthur Mitchell, the first black dancer ever to perform with the New York City Ballet. The Dance Theatre of Harlem's repertory contains ballet, modern, jazz, and ethnic pieces, and most of its versatile young dancers were trained at the official company school on 152nd Street (see Chapter Two).

Jude Bartlett in Irene Feigenheimer's ***Later Dreams. Frank Gimpaya, courtesy of Dancemoves***

DANCEMOVES/IRENE FEIGENHEIMER

Company Manager: Pentacle Dance Management
200 West 72nd Street
New York, New York 10023
(212-580-8107)

Since 1973 Irene Feigenheimer's five-member modern dance company has appeared in New York annually, presenting solos, duets, and group works created by Feigenheimer and occasionally other choreographers. She began her studies at age seven with Hanya Holm, a disciple of German expressionist Mary Wigman. Until the age of twenty Feigenheimer remained a pupil of Holm's, although she also studied ballet with Antony Tudor, Alfredo Corvino, and Margaret Craske, as well as modern dance at the Martha Graham school and the Merce Cunningham Studio. During the next ten years she danced a season with the Metropolitan Opera Ballet and performed with the companies of Anna Sokolow, Ruth Currier, Cliff Keuter, and Don Redlich. Feigenheimer is also an experienced teacher who has taught at the American Dance Festival in North Carolina and at Sarah Lawrence College. When she is in town, she gives technique and composition classes at her loft on Laight Street in Soho. Her most recent work makes use of ritualistic masks and delves into the realm of subconscious archtypes.

DANCERS
Artistic Director: Dennis Wayne
Company Manager: Taffy Wendelken
450 Avenue of the Americas (10/11th Street)
New York, New York 10011
(212-260-0453/260-0454)

Dancers is a repertory ensemble of fourteen dancers who are former members of American Ballet Theatre, the Joffrey, Harkness, Pennsylvania, and Boston Ballets, and other major companies. It was formed four years ago by Dennis Wayne with financial backing from actress Joanne Woodward. As its name implies, the company is intended to display the considerable talents of its dancers. The repertory is a bit uneven in quality, but it does offer a varied fare of contemporary works including pieces by Maurice Béjart, Todd Bolender, John Butler, Cliff Keuter, Brian Macdonald, Judith Marcuse, Frank Ohman, Igal Perry, Marcus Schulkind, François Szony, Rudi Van Dantzig, Hans Van Manen, Norbert Vesak, and Norman Walker. The official company school, Dancerschool, was founded in 1976 (see Chapter Two.)

CHUCK DAVIS DANCE COMPANY
Company Manager: Bess Pruitt
Bess Pruitt Associates
819 East 168th Street
Bronx, New York 10459
(212-589-0400)

The Chuck Davis Dance Company aims to present works which span black cultural heritage from Africa to America. The company, which was founded in 1968, has an ethnic and modern dance repertory. Choreographer Chuck Davis is a former member of the Eleo Pomare Dance Company.

LAURA DEAN DANCERS AND MUSICIANS

Company Manager: Jane Hughes Paulson
15 West 17th Street
New York, New York 10011
(212-741-2643)

Laura Dean's company is unique: all the performers are singers and musicians as well as dancers. Dean has been developing works based on steady pulse, repetitive movement, and structured patterns using spinning, stamping, and jumping, since 1968. The dancers chant as they whirl or execute simple floor designs. Additional accompaniment is sometimes provided by piano, autoharp, cello, violin, or synthesizer. Her works are long (from 37-70 minutes) and have a hypnotic or meditative effect on the audience. Dean studied at the School of American Ballet and the High School of Performing Arts. After two years of working on her own in San Francisco, she returned to New York in 1970 to present her own work—at which time she also began to compose music. Dean has been awarded choreography grants from the Guggenheim Foundation, the Creative Artists Public Service Program, and the National Endowment for the Arts. She has recently been commissioned jointly by the American Dance Festival and the Brooklyn Academy of Music to create a music-and-dance piece for performance during the 1979-80 season. Her writing has appeared in ***Drama Review, Dance Scope,*** and ***Contemporary Dance.***

Dennis Wayne's Dancers in Cliff Keuter's ***Of Us Two. courtesty of Dancers***

DOUGLAS DUNN AND DANCERS
Company Manager: Performing Artservices
463 West Street
New York, New York 10014
(212-989-4953)

Douglas Dunn grew up in Palo Alto, California. With a background in athletics and ballet, he came to New York in 1968 to dance. He has performed with Yvonne Rainer, Merce Cunningham, and the Grand Union, and in 1971 began presenting his own work—solo and group dances, as well as combined film and live performances. He and his four-member company have an easygoing style that makes intricate movements look deceptively simple. Dunn is also the director of ***Lazy Madge,*** an ongoing project begun in 1976, based on the concept of constantly evolving choreography designed to fill each individual space for any given performance. He has been the recipient of choreography grants from the Creative Artists Public Service Program, the New York State Council on the Arts, and the National Endowment for the Arts. Here's how a ***Dancemagazine*** reviewer described Dunn's movement style: "Kick, turn, push. There is a back roll, flip-flops, ***pas de chats*** and ***pliés.*** Slaps of sneakers rubbing along the floor, dragging in a turn, popping out in a squat thrust, punctuate the air. Up, turn, slither."

EGLEVSKY BALLET
Artistic Director: Edward Villella
Company Manager: David Wasman
P.O. Box 43
Massapequa Park, New York 11762
(516-541-5584)

Now in its nineteenth year, the Eglevsky Ballet has survived the death in 1977 of the founder, the great Russian premier danseur, André Eglevsky. (Eglevsky studied with Lubov Egorova, Alexandre Volinine, and Nicholas Legat in Europe and went on to become a principal dancer with the Ballet Russe, American Ballet Theatre, and the New York City Ballet. He was known for his virtuoso technique.) Under the direction of Eglevsky's widow, Leda, the company continued to present full-length ballet classics such as ***The Nutcracker, Sleeping Beauty, Coppelia,*** and ***Cinderella,*** as well as works by George Balanchine and other contemporary choreographers. For the most part the Eglevsky Ballet is a training ground for promising young dancers and students of the Eglevsky school, in Massapequa Park, Long Island. Artists who have made their professional debuts with the company include Patricia McBride, Gelsey Kirkland, Robert Weiss, and Fernando Bujones. Programs frequently feature guest soloists from leading ballet companies, such as the New York City Ballet's Patricia McBride and Peter Schaufuss. Edward Villella replaced Leda Eglevsky in August 1979.

LOUIS FALCO DANCE COMPANY
Company Manager: Andrew Bales
131 West 24th Street
New York, New York 10011
(212-691-0933)

After graduating from New York City's High School of Performing Arts, Louis Falco won critical acclaim as a principal with the José Limón Dance Company. As a choreographer he has taken the momentum-based Limón style to a daring extreme. His own dancing and that of his company is breathtakingly loose, expansive, and energetic. The seven-member Falco troupe has a glamorous image (he's been called the Mick Jagger of modern dance), and their works are primarily pure dance inventions rather than dramatic or philosophical statements. The music ranges from original compositions by Burt Alcantara to Béla Bartók to rock scores and electronic tape collages to Falco's experiments with verbal accompaniment by the dancers themselves. The company operates a dance school at Falco's Chelsea loft (see Chapter Two).

VIOLA FARBER DANCE COMPANY
Company Manager: Charles Markis
Trinity Dance Management
162 West 56th Street, Suite 201
New York, New York 10019
(212-582-1760)

The eight-member Viola Farber Dance Company performs a repertory choreographed by Farber. The accompaniment ranges from live electronic scores to jazz or classical music on tape. Farber frequently has music especially composed for her works by Alvin Lucier, David Tudor, Robert Ashley, and others. Often the music and dance become a collaboration between the artists. The group performs in proscenium theatres and nonproscenium spaces, including large studios and gymnasiums and outdoor plazas and malls. Farber studied music at the American University in Washington, D.C., ballet with Margaret Craske, and modern dance with Katherine Litz and Merce Cunningham. For twelve years she was a leading dancer with the Merce Cunningham Dance Company, and has also performed in concert with Katherine Litz and Paul Taylor. She formed her own company in 1968, and has toured extensively with them throughout the United States, Canada, and France. Although Farber's movement vocabulary is Cunningham-based, it is more eccentric (she is fond of nonsequiturs), and her brand of humor is more surreal than Cunningham's. Her dancers are strong, brisk movers like herself. Farber's works have been commissioned for the Repertory Dance Theatre of Utah, the Manhattan Festival Ballet, the Nancy Hauser Dance Company, and the Ballet Theatre Contemporain in Angiers,

France; she has also made an hour-long video dance for public television called ***Brazos River***, in collaboration with artist Robert Rauschenberg and composer David Tudor. She has taught at the Merce Cunningham Studio, the London School of Contemporary Dance, the International Summer Dance Academy in Cologne, the Margaret Jenkins Dance Studio in San Francisco, at universities throughout the United States, and is currently teaching at Larry Richardson's Dance Gallery (see Chapter Two).

ELIOT FELD BALLET
Company Manager: Cora Cahan
890 Broadway (19/20th Street)
New York, New York 10003
(212-777-7710)

Eliot Feld has been called the most talented American choreographer to come along since Jerome Robbins. The thirty-seven-year-old Feld has created twenty-nine ballets since he began choreographing in 1967. His twenty-two-member company is a fine group of classical dancers who perform a repertory chiefly composed of Feld's works. They have toured widely and appeared on national and public television. Some of their most popular pieces to date are ***Intermezzo, At Midnight, The Consort, Tzaddik, Early Songs***; Americana dances such as the ***Sante Fe Saga, Half Time,*** and ***The Real McCoy***; and Latin-flavored works such as ***La Vida*** and ***Danzon Cubano.*** Eliot Feld was trained at the School of American Ballet, the New Dance Group, and the High School of Performing Arts in New York. He made his stage debut as the boy prince in the New York City Ballet's production of ***The Nutcracker.*** Later Feld danced in the companies of Pearl Lang, Sophie Maslow, Mary Anthony, and Donald McKayle, and at age sixteen Feld joined the

The Eliot Feld Ballet in ***Half Time.***
Lois Greenfield

Broadway cast of ***West Side Story.*** He also appeared as Baby-John in the movie version. While a soloist with American Ballet Theatre, Feld created several works for that company. He has also mounted works for the Joffrey Ballet, the Royal Danish Ballet, the National Ballet of Canada, the Royal Swedish Ballet, the Royal Winnepeg Ballet, and the London Festival Ballet.

The forward-thinking Feld Ballet has recently initiated a free training program for New York City public school children (see Chapter Two) and has also bought the old Elgin movie theatre in Chelsea, with plans to turn it into a concert hall for contemporary dance companies.

5 BY 2 PLUS—MODERN DANCE REPERTORY COMPANY
Artistic Directors: Jane Kosminsky and Bruce Becker
Company Manager: Rena Shagan
5 East 16th Street
New York, New York 10003
(212-595-7328)

5 by 2 Plus presents a survey of modern dance through the revival of historical works, the remounting of pieces no longer in the active repertories of other companies, and by performing dances by new choreographers. Their repertory includes works by Helen Tamiris, Anna Sokolow, Daniel Nagrin, Cliff Keuter, Norman Walker, Paul Taylor, and Merce Cunningham, among others. The troupe was formed in 1972 by Jane Kosminsky, a former member of the Paul Taylor Dance Company, and partner Bruce Becker. The pair have since added three new members, hence the meaning of their rather cryptic name: 5 (pieces) by 2 Plus (the original two dancers plus the new members).

LAURA FOREMAN DANCE THEATRE
Company Manager: Annie Oleske
25 West 19th Street
New York, New York 10011
(212-989-2230)

Laura Foreman's work is a hybrid of dance and theatre which combines dramatic events, dialogue, dance, and song. Her husband, composer John Watts, creates many of the musical scores for the company. Space is a central theatrical element in all of Foreman's pieces and each one is shaped to the place where it is performed. Foreman has choreographed sky dances for Central Park, using skywriters to print choreography instructions overhead. She has also made dances for elevators, balconies, rooftops, and cliffs, as well as works that take place entirely in the audience. The company was established in 1968, and has been in residence at the New School for Social Research since that time.

EMILY FRANKEL
Company Manager: Emily Frankel
13 West 17th Street
New York, New York 10011
(212-255-1933)

Emily Frankel is a solo modern dancer who began her career with the Humphrey-Weidman Dance Company. She performs works by Todd Bolender, Norman Walker, and others to live or taped symphonic music. Frankel also choreographs one-act dance dramas which range from the humorous to the dramatic and serve as effective vehicles for her considerable acting talents. Her programs usually include two or three long pieces which contrast sharply in music, style, content, and choreographic approach. Frankel is married to Broadway star John Cullum, with whom she sometimes collaborates professionally.

ANNABELLE GAMSON, DANCE SOLOS
Company Manager: Ralph Hanes
Shaw Concerts, Inc.
1995 Broadway (67/68th Street)
New York, New York 10023
(212-595-1909)

Annabelle Gamson formed Dance Solos in 1974, primarily to recreate great modern dance solos of the past, such as those of Isadora Duncan and Mary Wigman. Her repertory contains Duncan's ***Marche Slave, Water Study,*** and ***Three Etudes,*** as well as Wigman's ***Witch Dance, Pastorale,*** and ***Dance of Summer.*** Gamson is an extraordinary performer who has won high critical praise for her ability to "fill the footprints" of these dance giants—something it seems no one else has been able to do. In addition, she performs her own pieces and the works of other contemporary choreographers.

MIMI GARRARD DANCE THEATRE
Company Manager: David Yaksic
155 Wooster Street
New York, New York 10012
(212-674-6868)

The nine-member Mimi Garrard Dance Company performs works that range from technically sophisticated multimedia pieces to pure movement explorations and comedy numbers. The musical scope includes classical as well as electronic and computer scores. Garrard danced with Alwin Nikolais before branching out into her own work, and like Nikolais's, her pieces are very visual. The spatial patterns and physical shape of the movement are the most important elements in the choreography, and she uses a computerized lighting system which makes elaborate lighting designs possible.

David Gordon and Valda Setterfield in ***An Audience with the Pope.*** *Lois Greenfield, courtesy of the David Gordon Pick-Up Company*

DAVID GORDON/PICK-UP COMPANY
Company Managers: Mimi Johnson and Penny Finkelman
Performing Artservices
463 West Street
New York, New York 10014
(212-989-4953)

David Gordon began dancing with James Waring's company in 1956. He studied dance composition with Waring and choreographed his first duet for himself and his wife, Valda Setterfield, in 1960. Gordon also studied composition with Merce Cunningham, and later with Judith and Robert Dunn, whose class eventually exploded into the Judson Dance Theatre. From 1962 to 1966 Gordon presented several pieces at the Judson Church, including ***Mannequin Dance, Helen's Dance, Random Breakfast,*** and ***Walks and Digressions.*** He gave up choreography altogether between 1966 and 1971, but continued dancing with Yvonne Rainer's company and the Grand Union, an experimental choreographers' collective which toured the United States and abroad until its disbandment in 1976. Since 1974 he has been presenting his own work again, with Setterfield and a small group of dancers. His wit and imagination have won accolades from two of New York's most respected critics:

"Working in repetitive patterns with words, actions, sometimes music, sometimes props, he sets up exhilarating tensions between elaborate structures and mundane tasks, pristine order and shambly movement, between what we see and what we assume it to mean, and then—suddenly—what else it can mean. . . .One leaves a performance of his spare pieces feeling as if one's brain has been tickled in a serious and seriously enjoyable way."

—Deborah Jowitt, *Village Voice*

"When it comes to feats of memory or feats of absurdity, Gordon and Setterfield are not to be outdone. They are my favorite off-Broadway comedians, but they have a serious core . . . they are the non-performers who have the most to teach about performance."

—Arlene Croce, *The New Yorker*

LOTTE GOSLAR'S PANTOMIME CIRCUS

Company Manager: Todd Randall
484 West 43rd Street, Apt. 44S
New York, New York 10036
(212-354-7850)

Lotte Goslar and her company, established in 1954, call themselves a Pantomime Circus to describe the scope and variety of their show. It is a dance and mime theatre that employs techniques which Goslar developed from classical and modern dance forms (she studied with Mary Wigman in Germany), as well as from pantomime and allied theatre arts. In addition to creating works for her own company, Goslar has choreographed for Hollywood films, children's theatre, and the Joffrey and Hartford Ballets. Although the Pantomime Circus's repertory is interspersed with a few serious works and pure dance numbers, its intention is largely comic—which makes it ideal entertainment for children of all ages.

MARTHA GRAHAM DANCE COMPANY

Company Manager: James Nomikos
316 East 63rd Street
New York, New York 10021
(212-832-9166)

Martha Graham is one of the founders of American modern dance and the originator of a movement technique that is performed and taught all over the world. Her company, formed in 1926, is the oldest extant professional dance troupe in America. Its active repertory includes Graham's works from 1930 to the present, many of which deal with Greek mythology, religious themes, or American history. Martha Graham was one of the first American choreographers to specially commission scores for her dances by contemporary composers such as Louis Horst, Hunter Johnson, Aaron Copeland, and Gian Carlo Minotti. She also commissioned set designs by modern artists such as sculptor Isamu Noguchi, who created the scenery for several of her greatest pieces. So many of Graham's works stand out as masterpieces—***Primitive Mysteries, Lamentation, Cave of the Heart, Letter to the World, Appalachian Spring, Clytemnestra, Errand into the Maze,*** and ***Diversion of Angels,*** to mention just a few. A number of distinguished choreographers and performers have come out of the Graham company, including Paul Taylor, Merce Cunningham, Erick Hawkins, Ethel Winter, Yuriko, and May O'Donnell. Superb dancing is still a hallmark of her group. The Martha Graham School at the same address has trained three generations of Graham dancers (see Chapter Two).

The chorus in Martha Graham's ***Night Journey. Martha Swope, courtesy of the Martha Graham Center of Contemporary Dance***

JOSÉ GRECO DANCE COMPANY
Artistic Directors: José Greco and Nana Lorca
Company Manager: Royce Carlton, Inc.
866 United Nations Plaza
New York, New York 10017
(212-355-3210)

The well-known José Greco Dance Company has been performing classical, regional, and flamenco dances of Spain since 1945. Greco, a unique personality as well as a top-flight artist, no longer appears with a large permanent company as he once used to. More often today he performs with "friends," such as Nana Lorca, and introduces and explains the pieces in the program. Recently he has shared concerts with symphony orchestras and has even played Count Dracula in a touring version of ***The Passion of Dracula.***

PASCHAL GUZMAN/DOWNTOWN BALLET
Company Manager: Robert Shuster
189 Lexington Avenue (31/32nd Street)
New York, New York 10016
(212-683-1967)

Although Paschal Guzman bases much of his choreography on classical ballet technique, his company also presents modern and ethnic dance pieces "in an eclectic, down-to-earth approach." Rock, jazz, classical, and contemporary music is used. The group, established in 1970, is purposely small, young, and predominantly Hispanic, but does not perform Hispanic dance per se.

HARRY/DANCE AND OTHER WORKS BY SENTA DRIVER

Company Manager: Anne P. Kearns
Trinity Associates
162 West 56th Street
New York, New York 10019
(212-582-1760)

Harry is a company of four who perform works by Senta Driver. The repertory includes dances, movement pieces, and pieces whose purpose is to be heard as well as seen. Driver has been working "to develop a dance idiom rooted in physical strength and characterized by wit, intellect, and physicality." Dances may be unaccompanied or have scores ranging from Gilbert and Sullivan to the music of contemporary composers to the sound of stop watches or various types of recitation by the performers. Driver began her dance training at Ohio State University and appeared for several seasons with the Paul Taylor Company. She is the recipient of two National Endowment for the Arts grants and a Guggenheim Foundation Fellowship for choreography, and has been commissioned twice by the American Dance Festival to create new pieces.

ERICK HAWKINS DANCE COMPANY

78 Fifth Avenue (14th Street)
New York, New York 10011
(212-255-6698)

Erick Hawkins is a major figure in American modern dance whose choreographic career has spanned over a quarter of a century. His ten-member company performs works in which movement, music, sets, and costumes are conceived and executed as an inseparable whole. Hawkins' pieces are meticulously crafted and rehearsed, and to the cultivated eye, deliciously subtle. From the time he first started choreographing, Hawkins has insisted on live musical accompaniment, and he has collaborated with composer Lucia Dlugoszewski on most of his pieces. Dlugoszewski performs her Eastern-influenced percussion scores in costume on stage with the company. Hawkins' dances, too, have a kind of oriental serenity and economy of movement. A Greek scholar from Harvard, he came to dancing late—in his early twenties. He trained at the School of American Ballet and danced briefly with the American Ballet and the Ballet Caravan, both forerunners of the New York City Ballet. Soon afterwards Hawkins became the first male member of the Martha Graham Dance Company, for whom Graham choreographed many important roles. (Incidentally, he and Graham were married for two years.) By the early 1950s Hawkins began to pursue his own choreographic ideas and he evolved an important modern dance technique based on kinesthetic awareness, a calm centering of the body, and an efficient, free-flowing use of the muscles. He and his company have been teaching at their studio on lower Fifth Avenue for a number of years (see Chapter Two).

Erick Hawkins, Lucia Dlugoszewski and Dena Madole in the 1964 work, ***Geography of Noon. Michael Avedon, courtesy of the Erick Hawkins Dance Company***

KAZUKO HIRABAYASHI DANCE THEATRE
Company Manager: Robert Swinston
Tornay Management
1995 Broadway (68th Street)
New York, New York 10023
(212-580-8696)

Kazuko Hirabayashi's choreography is a blend of traditional Japanese themes with the movement vocabularies of Western ballet and modern dance. She was a soloist with the Martha Graham Company and has taught at the Juilliard School for several years. The company was founded in 1969.

SAEKO ICHINOHE AND COMPANY
857 Ninth Avenue (55/56th Street)
New York, New York 10019
(212-246-4779)

Saeko Ichinohe and Company synthesize Japanese movement, costumes, props, and music with American modern dance. The company's eclectic repertory includes Ichinohe's solo, ***The Woman Who Loved Worms; Variations in the Kitchen,*** a whimsical piece for four women in traditional Japanese dress who do a series of kitchen chores to music by Haydn; and ***Cakewalk***, a showy work that employs ballet, modern dance, and jazz movement. The troupe was established in 1970.

THE JOFFREY BALLET
THE JOFFREY II
General Administrator: Peter Diggins
130 West 56th Street,
New York, New York 10019
(212-265-7300)

The youthful and popular Joffrey Ballet was established in 1964 by choreographer Robert Joffrey, chiefly to perform his works and those of other contemporary choreographers. Its repertory includes pieces by Gerald Arpino, Sir Frederick Ashton, Agnes de Mille, Kurt Jooss, Jerome Robbins, and Twyla Tharp. The company has also revived historic ballets, such as Leonide Massine's ***Parade*** (first performed in 1917 by the Diaghilev Ballets Russes) and, in collaboration with Rudolf Nureyev (containing two of Vaslav Nijinsky's greatest roles), ***The Afternoon of a Faun*** and ***Petrouchka.*** The Joffrey II is the Joffrey's junior company and a training ground for talented young dancers from the American Ballet Center, the company school (see Chapter Two). It performs some works from the parent company's repertory, as well as pieces by new choreographers.

Gary Chryst (foreground) and members of the Joffrey Ballet in Jerome Robbins' ***Moves. courtesy of the Joffrey Ballet***

ELIZABETH KEEN DANCE COMPANY
Company Manager: Patrick O'Rourke
360 West 21st Street
New York, New York 10011
(212-JU6-6300)

Ironic humor and drama are central to the work of modern dance choreographer Elizabeth Keen. Keen performed with the Tamiris-Nagrin and the Paul Taylor companies before starting her own group in 1966. She was also one of the experimenters working at the Judson Memorial Church in the 1960s, and has done street theatre, as well as choreographed off-Broadway productions. She likes to use live music and often incorporates social and period dances in her concert pieces. The company's recent repertory includes ***Rainbow Tonight,*** a work that uses ballroom dances of the 1930s and

1940s to express romantic yearning, and ***A Fair Greeting,*** a theme and variations piece set to Brahms music, which deals with interpersonal relationships.

BRUCE KING DANCE CONSORT
Artistic Director and Company Manager: Bruce King
160 West 73rd Street
New York, New York 10023
(212-877-6700)

The Bruce King Dance Consort is a three-member modern dance company which performs the works of Bruce King. The repertory is designed for proscenium theatres as well as less formal spaces, such as gymnasiums, studios, and art galleries. King is also a respected educator who has written extensively about dance instruction for elementary school children in ***Dancemagazine.*** His company was established in 1959.

CLAUDE KIPNIS MIME THEATRE
Company Manager: Barry Weissler
National Artists Management
165 West 46th Street, Suite 1202
New York, New York 10036
(212-575-1044)

The Claude Kipnis Mime Theatre, founded in 1967, performs a varied repertory, from solo to ensemble pieces, and silent to music-based pantomime. The seven-member company is proud to have been the first mimes to appear at the White House during the Ford administration. Kipnis, who is French, studied with Marcel Marceau and formed his own workshop in Israel before his much-acclaimed New York debut of ***Men and Dreams*** in 1966, a work which was praised for its incorporation of immediate human qualities of the characters into the mime. He is the author of ***The Mime Book.***

PAULINE KONER DANCE CONSORT
Company Manager: C.C. Conner, Jr.
444 East 84th Street
New York, New York 10028
(212-249-4847)

Now in her fifty-first year as a dancer and choreographer, Pauline Koner has a substantial following within the dance community. After retirement from the stage (she was a leading dancer with José Limón and Doris Humphrey) she spent several years teaching, but in 1975 she formed a seven-member company—chiefly composed of her students from the North Carolina School of the Arts. Their rapid success has once again put her in the limelight. Koner's works, which are very theatrical, show the influence of Limón and Humphrey, but also exert a unique choreographic thrust of their own. The recent repertory includes

The Farewell, a restaging of Koner's 1972 tribute to Doris Humphrey set to Mahler's ***Songs of the Earth; Mosaic,*** a lyrical piece to music by Bach; and ***Cantigas,*** a medieval masque set to a George Crumb score.

PHYLLIS LAMHUT DANCE COMPANY
Company Manager: Leigner Management
1860 Broadway (61/62nd Street), Suite 1610
New York, New York 10023
(212-582-5795)

The Phyllis Lamhut Dance Company, formed in 1969, performs works by Phyllis Lamhut ranging from solos to duets to group pieces. Lamhut excels in comedy, but her dances also venture into the dramatic and the abstract. Dialogue and song are incorporated into some of the repertory pieces, and in some works she combines ballroom steps with modern dance movement. Improvisation is also used. Lamhut's dancers are effective in her style. Lamhut was trained at the Henry Street Settlement Playhouse by Alwin Nikolais, with whose company she performed for many years. She has also appeared with the Murray Louis Dance Company. Although Lamhut is youthful and energetic, she has been making dances for thirty years.

RACHEL LAMPERT AND DANCERS
Company Manager: Pentacle Dance Management
200 West 72nd Street
New York, New York 10023
(212-580-8107)

Rachel Lampert is definitely one of the up-and-coming young choreographers to watch in New York. With a background in theatre and musical comedy as well as ballet and modern dance, she skillfully combines dance with music, theatre, and spoken dialogue (which she writes herself). Entertaining yet sophisticated, the group's repertory encompasses abstract, pure dance, and subdued mood pieces; but their special contribution is terse, slice-of-life dance-drama such as ***Issue,*** a tragicomic portrait of the psychodynamics of family life, ***The Frog Princess,*** a 1950s version of Agnes de Mille's ***Rodeo,*** and ***Bloody Mary Sunday***, about the trials and tribulations of two college roommates. Lampert's musical tastes run from Sergio Cervetti's contemporary scores to Mozart, Bach, Leadbelly, Cole Porter, and 1950s and 60s popular music. Before forming her seven-member group in 1975, Lampert danced in the companies of Valerie Bettis, Elina Mooney, Phoebe Neville, and Dorothy Vislocky, and in Broadway and off-Broadway shows. She has choreographed for summer stock, television, off-Broadway, and industrial shows, and has also mounted works on the Connecticut and Hartford Ballets. Lampert is on the dance faculty of the New York University School of the Arts (see Chapter Two).

PEARL LANG AND DANCE COMPANY
Company Manager: Frank Lackner
382 Central Park West (98th Street)
New York, New York 10025
(212-840-8520)

Pearl Lang was a leading dancer with the Martha Graham Dance Company, and her work is largely derivative of the Graham style. The repertory ranges from baroque to abstract dances to contemporary dramatic pieces. Most of the musical scores are by contemporary American composers. Lang's dancers are strong, and her own performances still thrill audiences. Lang is also coartistic director of the Alvin Ailey American Dance Center, where she teaches advanced classes in Graham technique. Her seventeen-member troupe was founded in 1969.

Rachel Lampert (top), Carl Tillmanns and Holly Harbinger in *Issue. Philip Hipwell, courtesy of Rachel Lampert and Dancers*

DANIEL LEWIS DANCE REPERTORY COMPANY
Artistic Director: Daniel Lewis
Resident Choreographer: Anna Sokolow
Company Manager: Maria O'Neil
32 Jones Street
New York, New York 10014
(212-989-1644)

The Daniel Lewis Dance Repertory Company, formerly known as the Contemporary Dance System, is a twelve-member troupe that performs the modern dances of Daniel Lewis, Anna Sokolow (including her best known works, ***Rooms*** and ***Dreams***), and young choreographers Hannah Kahn and Matthew Diamond, who have both danced with the company. In addition, the group restages major works by Doris Humphrey, Lucas Hoving, and José Limón, with whose company Lewis performed for ten years. After Limón's death, he took over his classes at Juilliard and has remained on the faculty since that time. Lewis has also staged the pieces of José Limón and Doris Humphrey for the Batsheva Company in Israel, the Royal Swedish Ballet, the Royal Danish Ballet, the Alvin Ailey American Dance Theatre, the American Ballet Theatre, the National Ballet of Canada, and the American Dance Festival.

JOSÉ LIMÓN DANCE COMPANY
Artistic Director: Carla Maxwell
Company Manager: Judith Hankins
HI Enterprises, Inc.
200 West 57th Street, Suite 1310
New York, New York 10019
(212-573-4303)

This company, formed in 1946, has survived the death seven years ago of its founder and choreographer, José Limón, to become not only the chief repository of his works but a modern dance repertory ensemble that performs revivals of other important historical pieces. It has also begun presenting the works of contemporary choreographers. Among the pieces which the company performs are Limón classics such as ***The Moor's Pavane, The Traitor, There is a Time, Missa Brevis,*** and ***Psalm***; Kurt Jooss' ***The Green Table;*** and Doris Humphrey's ***Passacaglia and Fugue.*** Recent programs have featured guest appearances by Erik Bruhn (performing Limón's role in ***The Moor's Pavane***), Joyce Trisler's Danscompany (doing a couple of Denishawn reconstructions), and Murray Louis (in his own work). The group is currently under the artistic direction of a long-time member and one of its finest dancers, Carla Maxwell.

The Murray Louis Dance Company in ***Hoopla,*** a work that pays tribute to Louis' mentor, Alwin Nikolais. ***Agor***

MURRAY LOUIS DANCE COMPANY
Company Manager: Anthony P. Micocci
33 East 18th Street
New York, New York 10003
(212-777-1120)

Murray Louis is one of the world's most beloved modern dancers and choreographers. He was a featured performer with Alwin Nikolais for many years, and organized his own company in 1953. Louis's work primarily consists of pure dance inventions and movement studies. Kinetic humor—which comes from eccentrically disjointed body movement, crisply defined space, split-second timing, and skillful miming—is his forte. (***Junk Dances, Hoopla,*** and ***Dêjá Vu*** are prime examples.) Louis's musical accompaniment ranges from Brahms and Tchaikovsky to an electronic score by Alwin Nikolais, a jazz composition by Dave Brubeck, and a Cole Porter score. The company of nine dancers has toured nationally and internationally, several times under the sponsorship of the United States Department of State. Louis's works are also performed by the Royal Danish Ballet, the José Limón Dance Company, and the Berlin State Opera; and he has created solos for Rudolf Nureyev and Erik Bruhn. Murray Louis and Alwin Nikolais share a school, the Louis-Nikolais Dance Lab, where technique and composition are taught (see Chapter Two).

LAR LUBOVITCH DANCE COMPANY
Company Manager: KLS Management
853 Broadway (17/18th Street)
New York, New York 10003
(212-674-8170)

Lar Lubovitch is a young choreographer whose work grows finer and more distinctive all the time. His company of ten superb dancers do his supple, undulating movement to perfection. Lubovitch's musical tastes run from Mozart, Bach, and Scriabin to Stravinsky, Ellington, and contemporary composers Steve Reich and Philip Glass. Lubovitch began dance training at the Juilliard School, where his teachers were Antony Tudor, Anna Sokolow, José Limón, and members of the Martha Graham Dance Company. While still in school he performed with Pearl Lang, Donald McKayle, Glen Tetley, and John Butler. Before forming his own company in 1968, Lubovitch also appeared with the Manhattan Festival Ballet and the Harkness Ballet. He has been awarded several grants from the National Endowment for the Arts, a Creative Artists Public Service grant, and a Guggenheim Fellowship for choreography. Lubovitch's dances are in the repertories of American Ballet Theatre, the Alvin Ailey American Dance Theatre, the Pennsylvania Ballet, Ballet Rambert in England, the National Ballet of Holland, and the Bat-Dor Dance Company in Israel. Among his most popular pieces are ***The Time Before the Time After (After the Time Before),*** a dramatic duet; ***Whirligogs,*** a paranoid fantasy visually reminiscent of the paintings of Hieronymus Bosch; ***North Star***, a pure dance piece; and the lyric solo, ***Scriabin Dances.*** The Lubovitch company occasionally offers workshops at its studio on 18th Street.

SOPHIE MASLOW DANCE COMPANY
Company Manager: Hope Moss
New Dance Group Studio
254 West 47th Street
New York, New York 10036
(212-245-9327)

Sophie Maslow was a soloist with the Martha Graham company for many years and established her own company in 1959. Her works—dramatic, satirical, and lyric pieces that combine poetry, music, and dance—are often based on American and Jewish folklore themes. Maslow was one of the socially conscious second-generation modern dancers who came out of the post-Depression years, and a founding member of the New Dance Group Studio. She still teaches there today.

Choreographer Lar Lubovitch (center) and company. ***Jack Mitchell, courtesy of the Lar Lubovitch Dance Company***

MATTEO ETHNOAMERICAN DANCE THEATRE
Company Manager: Judith Hankins
HI Enterprises, Inc.
200 West 57th Street, Room 1310
New York, New York 10019
(212-573-4303)

The Matteo Ethnoamerican Dance Theatre, founded in 1967, explores ethnic dances that have influenced our American cultural heritage—including those of India, Spain, Japan, Polynesia, Africa, China, Arabia, Latin America, and the American Indian.

PATRICIA MCBRIDE, JEAN-PIERRE BONNEFOUS AND COMPANY
Company Manager: Bruce Michael
327 Central Park West (92/93rd Street), Suite 2C
New York, New York 10025
(212-662-5118)

This fifteen-member chamber group was established two years ago by New York City Ballet principals Patricia McBride and Jean-Pierre Bonnefous. The repertory consists of well-known pieces by George Balanchine, such as ***Concerto Barocco, Who Cares, Bugaku,*** and ***Valse Fantasie***; Jerome Robbins's ***Afternoon of a Faun***; and works by Bonnefous.

Patricia McBride and her husband, Jean-Pierre Bonnefous. ***courtesy of Patricia McBride, Jean-Pierre Bonnefous and Company***

NANCY MEEHAN DANCE COMPANY

Company Manager: Charles Markis
Trinity Dance Management
162 West 56th Street, Suite 201
New York, New York 10019
(212-582-1760)

Like Erick Hawkins, with whom she performed for nearly a decade, Nancy Meehan's movement style is fluid and effortless; but it is bigger and dynamically more varied. Also like Hawkins, she commissions original musical scores for her works, which are played live at performances. Since 1970 Nancy Meehan has received a Guggenheim Fellowship and a Creative Artists Public Service grant for choreography. Greatly respected as both a teacher and dancer, she has been on the faculty of the Erick Hawkins School, Hunter College, and the American Dance Festival. She currently teaches at her own studio in Westbeth (see Chapter Two).

Nancy Meehan. ***Johan Elbers, courtesy of the Nancy Meehan Dance Company***

MEREDITH MONK/THE HOUSE

Company Manager: KLS Management
853 Broadway (17/18th Street)
New York, New York 10C03
(212-674-8170)

Meredith Monk is a multifaceted choreographer whose talents extend to musical composition, singing , and writing. (Her vocal scores are so extraordinary that they have been used by other choreographers, such as Merce Cunningham and Phoebe Neville.) The House, formed in 1969, is a group of performers who also have diverse backgrounds in dance, drama, music, film, painting, and science. Their work is an integration of several arts and "resembles Oriental Theatre more than any Western form." Monk's pieces, such as ***The Education of the Girlchild, Chacon,*** and ***Quarry***, have been described as "a theatre of images" and "nonverbal opera." Her style blends, in a simple and direct manner, abstract movement, mime, and natural gesture, and her dances combine mythic with intensely personal content. The pace is often slow so that each image can be fully taken in. Monk works with both highly trained and untrained dancers, in a variety of performing environments: proscenium and non-proscenium theatres, museums, and outdoor locations. Her dance background includes the study of eurythmics, ballet, and modern dance with various teachers, and composition with Judith Dunn, Ann Halprin, and Beverly Schmidt.

RICHARD MORSE MIME THEATRE
Company Manager: Rasa Allan
224 Waverly Place
New York, New York 10014
(212-242-0530)

The Richard Morse Mime Theatre, established in 1972, presents commentary on contemporary life. It also dips freely into the past, aided by masks, period costumes, and music. While comedy plays a dominant part in the repertory, serious pieces are blended in "with the same overall intention of enhancing an awareness of our human experience."

JENNIFER MULLER AND THE WORKS
Company Manager: John Philip Luckacovic
131 West 24th Street
New York, New York 10011
(212-681-3803)

Jennifer Muller is a virtuosic dancer who was a principal with the José Limón Dance Company for nine years. She has interesting choreographic ideas that employ theatre and dialogue, and are obliquely laced with humor. Like her contemporary Louis Falco, who also worked with Limón and with whom Muller has collaborated in the past, her dance style is very physical, performed with daring and high energy. Even when her pieces ramble on a bit, Muller and her company of eight dancers are strong and exciting to watch. The group gives workshops from time to time at their loft in Chelsea.

Meredith Monk/The House performing ***Chacon. courtesy of Meredith Monk/The House***

Kay Gainer and Bronya Weinberg in ***Silver Scream Idols. Ken Karp, courtesy of the Multigravitational Aerodance Group***

MULTIGRAVITATIONAL AERODANCE GROUP
Artistic Director: Stephanie Evanitsky
Company Manager: Barbara Salz
234 East 23rd Street, #1RE
New York, New York 10010
(212-889-5089/888-2604)

The seven-member Multigravitational Aerodance Group performs suspended by various systems of elastic tightropes, harnesses, trapezes, webs, and vinyl sacks. Their air-dancing is a synthesis of dance, gymnastics, aerial trapeze work, theatre, and sculpture. "The dancers attempt to free themselves of the usual orientation to the floor, creating new theatrical perspectives with their suspended vertical and horizontal paths of motion. Visual images, sometimes dream-like or surreal, convey such choreographic themes as male/female relationships, the origins of magic, the rise and fall of superstars, and an homage to Picasso." The group was founded in 1969 by choreographer Stephanie Evanitsky, an art graduate from Pratt Institute and a former student of Alwin Nikolais. They offer classes intermittently.

MUSAWWIR GYMNASTIC DANCE COMPANY
Artistic Directors and Company Managers: Toby Towson and Richard Martin
41 Worth Street
New York, New York 10013
(212-226-2283)

The Musawwir Gymnastic Dance Company—Musawwir means "the Giver of Shape and Form"—attempts to bridge the gap between dance and gymnastics "by combining the skill and strength of highly trained athletes with the grace and sensitivity of dancers," and by "probing the similarities and differences between gymnastics and dance." They perform a style of acrobatic dance based on floor exercise, gymnastics, tumbling, classical ballet, and modern dance. The nine-member company was formed in 1974 by two former national collegiate gymnastics champions, Toby Towson and Richard Martin. Although this young group is still experimenting and has yet to find its own choreographic voice, it is becoming more and more dance oriented, and performances have a consistently polished look. They plan to augment their repertory with works from outside choreographers. The company gives gymnastics classes at their loft on Worth Street.

DANIEL NAGRIN, DANCE SOLOIST
Company Manager: Keith J. King
Nagrin Dance Foundation
550 Broadway (Prince Street)
New York, New York 10012
(212-226-3551)

Daniel Nagrin has been exploring the solo dance form since 1948, while he was still codirecting a company with the late Helen Tamiris. He is well-known in dance circles for his

Daniel Nagrin in ***Jazz Three Ways.***
Beverly Owen

deeply personal and affecting performances and his volatile "urban jazz" style, which is epitomized by the work, ***Strange Hero,*** a shrewdly etched portrait of a 1940s gangster. Nagrin studied modern dance with Tamiris, Hanya Holm, Martha Graham, and Anna Sokolow, and in addition, is a trained actor who has appeared on and off Broadway. He has also choreographed for off-Broadway theatre and film. Though varied, Nagrin's pieces share a common theme: "the mystery of what it is to be human in our time." His recent repertory includes such works as ***Untitled, Fragments, Getting Well, Silence is Golden, 19 Upbeats,*** and ***Word Game.*** He has been on the faculty of C.W. Post College and New York University, and he occasionally conducts workshops at his studio on lower Broadway.

PHOEBE NEVILLE DANCE COMPANY
Company Manager: KLS Management
853 Broadway (17/18th Street)
New York, New York 10003
(212-674-8170)

Phoebe Neville is a minimalist whose condensation of movement and energy creates a building kinetic tension. Even the smallest gesture acquires great significance in her spare dances, which take place in a dreamlike, primordial world of their own. Although Neville's recent choreographic efforts involve more movement than in the past, all her pieces have a massive, weighted, sculptural quality about them. ***Caryatid, Cartouche, Triptych,*** and ***Mosaic*** have been some of her most popular works to date. Neville performed with the Tamiris-Nagrin company, worked with Kenneth King, Meredith Monk, and Carolee Schneemann at the Judson Dance Theatre, and has appeared with the Elina Mooney Dance Company. Her movement style has been influenced by modern dance, ballet, ethnic dance, and the Chinese discipline of T'ai Chi. Neville, who has been choreographing since 1961, formed her five-member company in 1975.

NEW YORK CITY BALLET
Ballet Masters: George Balanchine, Jerome Robbins, and John Taras
General Director: Lincoln Kirstein
Company Manager: Patricia Avedon Turk
New York State Theatre
Lincoln Center Plaza
63rd Street and Broadway
New York, New York 10023
(212-877-4700)

The New York City Ballet has the singular distinction of having as artistic directors two of the greatest choreographic geniuses in the world today—George Balanchine and

Jerome Robbins—and a company of dancers who perform their work to perfection. The City Ballet troupe was founded in 1948 by Lincoln Kirstein and George Balanchine, though its forerunners, The American Ballet Company and Ballet Society, had existed fifteen years prior. Balanchine's and Robbins's ballets are sublimely musical, with movement that is among the most beautiful ever created. The Balanchine dancer—cool, sinuous, and athletic—has come to epitomize streamlined, space-age America, and Balanchine's neo-classical, plotless ballets are performed by major companies all over the world. The City Ballet's repertory is large and varied, spanning half a century of creative activity. Though it is primarily known for Balanchine's abstract works such as ***Agon, The Four Temperaments,*** and ***The Stravinsky Violin Concerto,*** it also performs full-length story ballets such as ***A Midsummer's Night Dream, Coppelia,*** and ***The Nutcracker***; the romantic ***Serenade*** and ***Vienna Waltzes***; pure dance pieces such as ***Theme and Variations, Jewels, Other Dances,*** and ***Concerto Barocco***; dramatic works such as ***The Cage, Prodigal Son, Afternoon of a Faun,*** and ***Dances at a Gathering***; and patriotic jaunts such as ***Stars and Stripes*** and ***Union Jack.*** Most of the New York City Ballet's dancers are products of the School of American Ballet (see Chapter Two).

Rosalind Newman. ***Lois Greenfield, courtesy of Rosalind Newman and Dancers***

ROSALIND NEWMAN AND DANCERS

Company Manager: Thomas Borek
124 Chambers Street (between Church Street and
West Broadway)
New York, New York 10007
(212-962-1327)

Though her company is still young, Rosalind Newman has already earned a great deal of critical praise and several grants for choreography, including a Guggenheim Fellowship, two grants from the National Endowment for the Arts, and a Creative Artists Public Service award. She began training at the age of five with Marjorie Guthrie, former Graham dancer and wife of folksinger Woody Guthrie. She also had a taste of circus life through her father's ten-year association with Ringling Brothers, Barnum and Bailey Circus. Newman then went on to study at the Martha Graham School, the University of Wisconsin, and with Merce Cunningham, Dan Wagoner, Viola Farber, Margaret Black, and Melissa Hayden. She performed with Wagoner, Farber, and Kathryn Posin before organizing her own company in 1972. ***Village Voice*** reviewer Deborah Jowitt has described Newman's work thus:

". . . the dancing swells, ebbs, and changes direction. The activity is constantly surprising, the lifts like nothing you've seen before . . . extremely beautiful dancing."

WALTER NICKS DANCE THEATRE

The Church of the Intercession
550 West 155th Street
New York, New York 10032
(212-787-4557/286-4438)

Walter Nicks has had a long and distinguished career as a performer and teacher. As a choreographer, he has researched authentic Afro-Caribbean dance forms and combined them with jazz and modern dance movement. Nicks organized his company in 1972 with support from the French Federation of Dance and the American Dance Festival. He was trained at the Karamu House in Cleveland, Ohio, and at the Katherine Dunham School of Dance in New York City, of which he later became associate director. He has since taught in several European countries , at the American Dance Festival and the University of Maryland, and has participated in the National Endowment for the Arts' Artists-in-Schools Program.* Having danced on Broadway and in television specials, Nicks still choreographs for theatre and television (notably the Harry Belafonte shows), as well as for his own group. Besides performances, the company offers workshops, lecture demonstrations, and dance instruction to the neighboring community.

NIKOLAIS DANCE THEATRE

Company Manager: William Bourne
Chimera Foundation for Dance
33 East 18th Street
New York, New York 10003
(212-777-1120)

Alwin Nikolais, the "Father of Multimedia," as he is called, is an acknowledged pioneer in the use of lighting design and imaginative stage props. In his dances he creates a total theatre of shape, sound, motion, color, and light. He not only invents the choreography, but the electronic music, costumes, and lighting design as well. For many years Nikolais was the resident choreographer at the Henry Street Settlement Playhouse. He also directed the dance school there, and in 1948 formed his first company out of his advanced students. "Alwin Nikolais is the P.T. Barnum, the Tom Swift, ***The Yellow Submarine*** of dance," writes Joseph Mazo in his book, ***Prime Movers*** (New York: William Mor-

*This is a federally funded program that brings professional dance performances, lecture-demonstrations, and classes to public schools throughout the nation.

row and Company, 1977). "His company travels with thirty-five spotlights, eighteen light dimmers on three boards, twelve projectors, and a sound system. Nikolais presents a theatre of color and shape, both of which change constantly. His dancers often are dressed in costumes that either alter or blur the lines of their bodies. Projected patterns, striking those costumes, further erase the outlines that separate people from the space they inhabit. A dancer may change color as he steps from one area of the stage to another, or he may execute a series of actions while a projector throws moving images on his stretching body. Movement plays upon movement, color alters color, shape defines and undefines shape." At present Nikolais codirects a dance school with his former protégé, Murray Louis, the Louis-Nikolais Dance Lab (see Chapter Two).

NIMBUS DANCE THEATRE COMPANY
Artistic Directors: Erin Martin and Jack Moore
Company Manager: Dove Arts Management
575 Madison Avenue (56th Street)
New York, New York 10022
(212-421-7633)

The Nimbus Dance Theatre Company performs the works of Erin Martin and Jack Moore. Moore is a painter as well as a gifted choreographer, and his dances have a keen sense of shape, color, composition, and texture (he designs the costumes and decor for many of his pieces). He studied dance composition with Hanya Holm, Doris Humphrey, and Louis Horst, and made his choreographic debut at the 92nd Street YM-YWHA. Moore has also performed with the companies of Martha Graham, Katherine Litz, José Limón, Jean Erdman, Merce Cunningham, and Anna Sokolow. He has taught at the Neighborhood Playhouse, the Juilliard School, the University of California at Los Angeles, Connecticut College, and is currently on the faculty of Bennington College. As a painter he has had one-man shows in New York, Washington, D.C., and Vermont. Our favorites among Moore's works are ***Songs Remembered, Ghost Horse Rocker, Three Netsukes,*** and ***Snow Shadow Garden.*** His latest pieces are Japanese-inspired in flavor, style, and movement. Erin Martin comes from a theatre background and is interested in combining dance with dialogue and acting. She has distinguished herself as a performer with American Ballet Theatre, in the companies of Jerome Robbins and Glen Tetley, and at the New York Shakespeare Festival and the Spoleto Festival. Martin has received a number of choreography grants, and is on the dance faculty at Adelphi University.

MAY O'DONNELL CONCERT DANCE COMPANY
439 Lafayette Street (Astor Place)
New York, New York 10003
(212-777-0744)

Now in her seventies, May O'Donnell suddenly finds herself the director of a successful young dance company. Although she has been choreographing since 1937, O'Donnell, who was a featured dancer with Martha Graham and José Limón, has primarily been known in recent years as a teacher of Graham technique (see Chapter Two). Four years ago she fashioned a company out of her advanced students which performed some old and new works. They were singled out for critical praise almost immediately. O'Donnell's dances, such as the eerie ***Suspension,*** surreal ***Drift,*** and entertaining ***Dance Energies,*** are characterized by calm energy—physical expansiveness, yet control. The company is magnificently trained by O'Donnell herself and music is by her composer husband, Ray Green.

GALE ORMISTON DANCE COMPANY
Company Manager: Jon M. Garness
Circum Arts Foundation
145 West 96th Street, #4A
New York, New York 10025
(212-866-7494)

The Gale Ormiston Dance Company has been performing since 1971. Ormiston danced with the Alwin Nikolais Dance Theatre, and like Nikolais, creates some of her own sound scores. A recurrent theme in her work is "the ironies of life, alternately humorous and sad." Ormiston's more recent repertory includes ***RePlay, Circum, Rondo, Criteria,*** and ***Pavane.***

MARIANO PARRA SPANISH DANCE COMPANY
Company Manager: Neil Fleckman
327 Central Park West (92/93rd Street)
New York, New York 10025
(212-662-5118)

The Mariano Parra Spanish Dance Company "seeks to preserve a dance and cultural tradition and to create new forms by exploring that tradition with contemporary vitality." The repertory encompasses classical and modern flamenco works, as well as eighteenth-century folk and contemporary Spanish dance. The company's approach is "one of restraint and discipline, refinement and nuance, always aiming for purity of form." Parra's intention is to "focus on the shape of the dance itself, its style and detail." The specially designed costumes are colorful yet authentic in line, and they reflect the company's eclecticism.

ELEO POMARE DANCE COMPANY
Company Manager: Virgil D. Akins
325 West 16th Street
New York, New York 10011
(212-675-1136)

The Eleo Pomare Dance Company, formed in 1958, is an integrated modern dance troupe of twelve to fifteen performers. The repertory extends from "neoclassical" pure dance works set to music by Bach and Handel, to contemporary dance-theatre pieces using jazz, blues, folk, or electronic music and spoken dialogue or poetry. Pomare is probably best known for his biting social commentary on city life, ***Blues for the Jungle.*** Many of his pieces draw on the cultural heritage and experience of the black American or Spanish themes which reflect Pomare's Latin ancestry. The company is technically proficient and they perform with electrifying intensity. Besides ***Blues,*** some of their most successful works have been ***Narcissus Rising, Hushed Voices,*** and ***Fallscape.*** Pomare was born in Cartagena, Colombia, South America, and lived in Panama before coming to New York at the age of ten. After graduating from the High School of Performing Arts, he went on to study with Louis Horst, Curtis James, and José Limón and, in Germany, with Kurt Jooss. Pomare organized a company in New York, which he disbanded in order to work in Europe under a John Hay Whitney Fellowship from 1962-64. On his return to the United States he revived and expanded his old troupe, which has since toured the country and appeared on national educational television. Pomare has also choreographed for the Alvin Ailey American Dance Theatre and the Dayton Contemporary Dance Company. He has received a Guggenheim Fellowship for choreography and a grant from the National Endowment for the Arts. A frequent lecturer on modern dance, Pomare helped organize the first Dancemobile program, a free concert series sponsored by the Harlem Cultural Council (see Chapter One). He and his company teach daily classes at the Vital Arts Center (see Chapter Two).

KATHRYN POSIN DANCE COMPANY
Company Manager: Sheldon Soffer Management
130 West 56th Street
New York, New York 10019
(212-757-8060)

The seven-member Kathryn Posin Dance Company, established in 1971, performs the work of Posin and occasionally that of Associate Director Lance Westergard. The group's style is eclectic, incorporating modern dance, rock, jazz, and ballet movement and using music that ranges from Bach to jazz/rock scores and original compositions by modern composers. At times the dancing is stronger than the choreography, but Posin has truly created a gem of a piece in ***Waves.*** She is a Bennington graduate who has performed with the companies of Anna Sokolow, Valerie Bettis, Dance Theatre Workshop, Lotte Goslar, and the American Dance Theatre at Lincoln Center. She has received choreography grants from Bennington College, the American Dance Festival, the National Endowment for the Arts, the New York State Council on the Arts, and the Jerome Robbins Foundation. Posin has mounted works on the Eliot Feld Ballet and the 5 by 2 Plus Dance Company. She has also choreographed for off-Broadway theatre and the New York Shakespeare Festival.

DON REDLICH DANCE COMPANY

Company Manager: Sheldon Soffer Management
130 West 56th Street
New York, New York 10019
(212-757-8060)

The Don Redlich Dance Company performs an entertaining repertory of pure dance, dramatic, and comic works. The group's five excellent dancers, led by the ageless, mimelike Redlich, have a keen rhythmic sense and an amazing ability to expand and contract the space around them. Over the years Redlich has earned a solid reputation as a choreographer, dancer, and teacher. He graduated from this country's first college-level dance program at the University of Wisconsin, where he studied with Margaret H'Doubler and Louise Kloepper. After moving to New York, Redlich trained with Hanya Holm, performed in Broadway musicals, and choreographed off-Broadway and television productions. He established his own company in 1966. They have toured extensively and are presently in residence at the 92nd Street YM-YWHA (see Chapter Two). Redlich has also been on the faculty of Adelphi University and Sarah Lawrence College.

LARRY RICHARDSON AND DANCE COMPANY

Company Manager: J. Antony Siciliano
40 Park Avenue (36th Street)
New York, New York 10016
(212-685-5972)

Larry Richardson and Dance Company, an eight-member modern dance troupe, performs pieces in Richardson's lyric style. The company was founded in 1967 and also teaches technique classes at its home base, Larry Richardson's Dance Gallery (see Chapter Two).

LUIS RIVERA SPANISH DANCE COMPANY
Company Manager: Sheldon Soffer Management
130 West 56th Street
New York, New York 10019
(212-757-8060)

The Luis Rivera Spanish Dance Company, formed in 1970, presents a panorama of Spanish dance—sixteenth-century court, folk, classical, semiclassical, modern, and flamenco. The music and dances are performed in the authentic style and costume of the period. Rivera, who was a leading dancer with José Greco, rivets the eye with his smouldering footwork, and razor-sharp body movement.

BARBARA ROAN PARADES AND DANCES
Company Manager: Pentacle Dance Management
200 West 72nd Street, Suite 20
New York, New York 10023
(212-580-8107)

In the early 1970s Barbara Roan was known for staging colorful, zany, paradelike dances peopled with characters from pop culture, New York City streets, the dance world,

Barbara Roan as the Bag Lady in ***The October Parade. Kathy Zaslov, courtesy of Barbara Roan/Parades and Dances***

and her own life. While she is still interested in exploring the parade form, she has lately gone back to choreographing smaller pieces—solos and trios performed to live jazz music. Aside from appearing in her own work, Roan has toured with the companies of Erick Hawkins, Rod Rodgers, Rudy Perez, and for many years, Don Redlich. Her choreography has been supported with grants from the National Endowment for the Arts, the New York State Council on the Arts, and the Creative Artists Public Service Program. She is also on the faculty of Bennington College. Roan is an extraordinary dancer. Probably the best description of her stage magic was written by ***Village Voice*** critic, Deborah Jowitt:

"Everything Roan does interests me . . . lyrical time-space-energy games she can do so gloriously. Her body is as powerfully calm as the core of a storm; her limbs slice up the air and reapportion it. Watching her is like seeing someone at the peak of happiness, vitality, and excitement."

ROD RODGERS DANCE COMPANY
Company Manager: Marilynn Maltby Smith
8 East 12th Street
New York, New York 10003
(212-924-7560)

The Rod Rodgers Dance Company, formed in 1964, was "one of the first American troupes under the direction of a black artist to be recognized for something other than exclusively ethnic or traditional Afro-American dance." Rodgers received a John Hay Whitney fellowship in 1965 and helped establish the Association of Black Choreographers. He has made dances for television as well as the concert stage. The company's repertory "includes abstract works in the modern dance idiom; works based on jazz, blues, and rock music; dramatic dance-theatre pieces, many of which relate to the black American experience; and percussion works (a company trademark), using complex African and Oriental rhythms." Though Rodgers' earliest training was in jazz and tap dance, he performed with the Erick Hawkins Dance Company before embarking on a choreographic career. One of his most popular works is ***Tangents,*** a piece in which he skillfully combines the fluid movement of the Hawkins style with compelling rhythms. Rodgers and his company of eleven dancers operate a dance school in lower Manhattan (see Chapter Two).

SARA RUDNER PERFORMANCE ENSEMBLE

Company Manager: Elizabeth Rectanus
Performing Artservices
463 West Street
New York, New York 10014
(212-989-4953)

Sara Rudner was a featured performer with the Twyla Tharp company from 1966 to 1974, and has also appeared with the Joffrey Ballet, the Pilobolus Dance Theatre, and the Paul Sanasardo Dance Company. She is an exceptional dancer, much admired for her clear and effortless virtuoso style. In her own work, which is Tharp-derived, Rudner collaborates closely with the dancers, visual artists, and musicians to create a tightly integrated "total piece." Some of her works are performed in silence, carried solely by the body rhythms of the movement. She has been choreographing since 1971 and has received grants from the Creative Artists Public Service Program, the New York State Council on the Arts, and the National Endowment for the Arts. Rudner occasionally teaches workshops in New York.

SOLARIS

Artistic Director: Henry Smith
Company Manager: Steven Keith
33 East 60th Street
New York, New York 10022
(212-752-7812)

Solaris is a group of actors, dancers, singers, musicians, and designers interested in experimental dance and theatre. The work of the company "integrates the dancer's control of shape and space, the actor's command of intention and intonation, and the musician's development of rhythm and phrasing." They have been together since 1974.

THE SOLOMONS COMPANY/DANCE

Company Manager: Nora Larke
Theatre Arts Concepts
152 West 42nd Street
New York, New York 10036
(212-582-1502)

Gus Solomons came to New York to study dance after graduating from MIT with a degree in architecture. He had jazz and tap training as a child and participated in amateur theatrical productions in his native Boston. In the years that followed, Solomons appeared with a number of dance companies, including those of Martha Graham, Donald McKayle,

Merce Cunningham, Joyce Trisler, and Pearl Lang. His experimental pieces have an architectural preciseness of design and composition, and Solomons's dancers share with him both strength and clarity of intention.

SOUNDS IN MOTION
Artistic Director: Dianne McIntyre
Company Manager: Steven Solder
290 Lenox (125th Street)
New York, New York 10027
(212-348-2460)

Sounds in Motion is a company of black dancers and musicians whose intent is "to present the life experiences of blacks, past and present, and to explore a contemporary mode of expression through collaboration with black musicians, poets, and designers." Choreographer Dianne McIntyre performed with Gus Solomons, Jr., before forming her troupe in 1972. She also directs the Sounds in Motion dance school (see Chapter Two).

STARS OF AMERICAN BALLET
Artistic Director: Steven Simmons
Company Manager: Howard Dando
2039 Broadway (72nd Street), Suite 4D
New York, New York 10023
(212-799-1893)

Stars of American Ballet is a flexible touring company which presents principal dancers and soloists from major American companies at popular prices. The troupe consists of a nucleus of twelve dancers, augmented by guest stars such as Suzanne Farrell, Patricia McBride, Helgi Tomasson, Peter Martins, Lawrence Rhodes, Cynthia Gregory, Marianna Tcherkassky, and Jacques d'Amboise, who appear with the company as their schedules permit. The repertory contains classical and modern ballets by such choreographers as George Balanchine, Antony Tudor, John Butler, Anton Dolin, Paul Mejia, Jerome Robbins, Maurice Béjart, August Bournonville, Kenneth MacMillan, and Marius Petipa.

ELAINE SUMMERS DANCE AND FILM COMPANY
Company Manager: Michele Bern
Experimental Intermedia Foundation
537 Broadway (Spring Street)
New York, New York 10012
(212-966-3367/226-9488)

As Don McDonagh writes in the ***Complete Guide to Modern Dance***: "The relationships between dance and film, and dance and its environment have been of passionate interest to Elaine Summers, who founded the Experimental Intermedia Foundation to foster creative exploration in the field." Born in Australia and raised in Boston, Summers attended art school before moving to New York to begin serious dance training. She studied at the Juilliard School, the Martha Graham School, and with choreographers Mary Anthony and Daniel Nagrin. In the early 1960s Summers took classes at the Merce Cunningham studio and became affiliated with the Judson Dance Theatre. In 1964 she founded her own company. Like other Judson experimenters, Summers likes to use natural movement in her dances, such as walking, standing, running, and jumping, with which she feels any audience can readily identify. Her eight-member group presents pure dance works in which the audience is often free to move around the dancers and "view them as kinetic sculpture;" intermedia pieces using film, slides and/or videotape; theatre pieces; and dance films. Summers feels that an important part of her work is taking on the challenge of building dances around unusual performing environments and she has made dances for museums, gymnasiums, the sculpture garden at the Museum of Modern Art, and even one piece in which her dancers scaled the wall beneath the Statue of Liberty. She uses live music most of the time.

An outdoor performance of ***Illuminated Workingman*** by the Elaine Summers Dance and Film Company. ***Babette Mangolte***

KEI TAKEI'S MOVING EARTH

Company Manager: Maldwyn Pate
19 Hudson Street
New York, New York 10013
(212-966-0562)

The avant-garde work of Japanese choreographer Kei Takei is among the most original and uncompromising of our time. Her company consists of ten to eleven performers of varied backgrounds in dance, theatre, music, and film, and from various parts of the world (Japan, the United States, France, Chile, and Wales, for example). This seems only fitting, since Takei's dances are nothing less than cosmic in scope. They speak directly to our collective unconscious through a series of powerful panoramic images. Using for the most part natural movement, Takei and her company perform with total concentration and a great deal of physical endurance. Rhythmic movements or spoken phrases provide accompaniment. Takei says she has of course been influenced by the traditions of Japanese dance, theatre, and culture, but does not "consciously try to synthesize East and West" in her work, "nor even to favor one over the other." Her themes "have their source in life, hence audiences relate to the work not in terms of execution of movement technique, but rather, based upon an understanding of their own life experiences." As one European critic noted, "clear things are said which cannot be said in words, and that is how it should be, for the body has a language of its own." Takei's most important work is an ongoing opus begun in 1969 called ***Light,*** for which fifteen parts have been choreographed. She spent her childhood in Tokyo, studying dance with the well-known Japanese teacher Kenji Hinoki. While teaching in Japan, choreographer Anna Sokolow saw Takei's work and encouraged her to come to the United States. This she did in 1967, when a Fulbright Scholarship made it possible for her to study at Juilliard. Within a month after her arrival Takei began to choreograph. The Moving Earth, which was formed in 1969, has toured the United States, Europe, and Japan.

Kei Takei's Moving Earth troupe performing in ***Light, Part 4.***
Don Manza

THE PAUL TAYLOR DANCE COMPANY

General Manager: Robert Yesselman
550 Broadway (Prince Street)
New York, New York 10012
(212-431-5562)

Linda Kent and Elie Chaib in Paul Taylor's ***Esplanade. Jack Vartoogian, courtesy of the Paul Taylor Dance Foundation***

Since its inception in 1956, the Paul Taylor Dance Company has established itself as one of the most popular yet truly sophisticated modern dance companies in the world. Taylor's very physical style, with its constantly flowing movement, swooping arms, and agile footwork has been described as "casual, barefoot classicism" by critic Clive Barnes. His choreographic scope is unusually broad, encompassing delightful pure dance works; dark odysseys into the human soul; and of course the Taylor trademark, frequent displays of irreverent humor. His thirteen-member company is wonderfully individual, yet tightly knit by a strong artistic vision. The current repertory contains revivals of old dances as well as new works, including ***Private Domain, Book of Beasts, Piece Period, Cloven Kingdom, Diggity, Airs, Esplanade,*** and ***Dust.*** The music ranges from Bach and Handel to modern scores by Cowell, Zenakis, Subotnick, and Poulenc. With a prior background in art and athletics, Paul Taylor received his first dance training at the Juilliard School. He also studied on scholarship at the Martha Graham School and the Metropolitan Opera Ballet School, and performed with Pearl Lang and Merce Cunningham. From the mid-1950s to early 1960s Taylor was a principal dancer with the Martha Graham Dance Company. In 1959 George Balanchine created a solo for him in the ballet ***Episodes,*** which was jointly choreographed by Graham and Balanchine and which both their companies performed. Although ***Episodes*** is still in the New York City Ballet's repertory, Taylor's solo has been dropped, since Balanchine felt that no other dancer could perform it as well. Paul Taylor's works have been seen on national television, and he has staged pieces for the Royal Danish Ballet, Rudolf Nureyev, and Mikhail Baryshnikov. When their schedule permits, the Taylor company offers a Christmas course and various workshops at their downtown studio.

TWYLA THARP DANCE FOUNDATION

Executive Director: Patricia Quinn
Company Manager: Roddy O'Connor
38 Walker Street
New York, New York 10013
(212-966-2590)

While a student at Barnard Collage, Twyla Tharp took outside classes with Erick Hawkins and Merce Cunningham. She also performed for two years with the Paul Taylor Dance Company before establishing her own group in 1965. In the beginning she experimented with minimal choreography, unaccompanied dances, and exhaustive explorations of the variations possible in a single movement phrase (at least they seemed exhaustive to some of us sitting in the audience). A far cry from the suave, entertaining, yet choreographically dense works we see today? Not really. Underneath Tharp's current jazzy loose-jointed style is the scrupulously ordered formal structure she was searching for in the early days. Her pieces have been performed to classical and pop music, and scores by jazz musicians such as Scott Joplin, Jelly Roll Morton, and Fats Waller. The thirteen dancers in Tharp's company (including Tharp herself) are marvels of rubbery virtuosity. They have developed works for various kinds of performing spaces, including outdoor sites, gymnasiums, proscenium and nonproscenium theatres, and for closed circuit and national television. Tharp has choreographed dances for American Ballet Theatre and the Joffrey Ballet, and her handiwork can also be seen in the film version of the Broadway musical ***Hair.*** Dance workshops are given intermittently at the Tharp studio.

Twyla Tharp (far right) and company in ***Eight Jelly Rolls. Tony Russell, courtesy of the Twyla Tharp Dance Foundation.***

THEATRE DANCE COLLECTION
Artistic Directors: Lynne Taylor, Rodney Griffin, and Jaclynn Villamil
Company Manager: Bonnie Arquilla
92 Horatio Street, #1A
New York, New York 10014
(212-243-4433)

Formed in 1972, the Theatre Dance Collection is a group of ten dancers who perform their own original works. Using ballet, modern, and jazz techniques, they have created a varied repertory which contains dramatic, abstract, and comedic dances. This is a company of fine individual performers with a highly theatrical approach. The recent repertory includes ***Semantically Speaking, Unremembering Lullaby, Crossroads,*** and ***An Evening at theTango Palace.***

THEATRE OF THE OPEN EYE
Artistic Director: Jean Erdman
Company Manager: Elizabeth Rudolf
316 West 88th Street
New York, New York 10024
(212-534-6363)

Founded in 1972, the Theatre of the Open Eye is a repertory company of dancers, actors, musicians, puppeteers, and designers who produce total theatre works. ***The New York Times*** has called it "a company which all around has an amazing mastery of a variety of mediums." Artistic Director Jean Erdman trained with Martha Graham and at the School of American Ballet. She was a principal dancer in the Graham company and jointly choreographed some pieces with Merce Cunningham, who was also working with Graham at the time. Erdman has choreographed a number of Broadway and off-Broadway plays, and her dance-theatre piece, ***The Coach with the Six Insides,*** which is based on James Joyce's ***Finnegan's Wake,*** has won several awards.

JOYCE TRISLER DANSCOMPANY
Company Manager: Renee Kaplan
HI Enterprises, Inc.
200 West 57th Street, Suite 1310
New York, New York 10019
(212-573-4303)

Before turning to choreography Joyce Trisler danced with Lester Horton and Alvin Ailey, and her company, established in 1973, is well trained in Horton technique. The group performs Trisler's intense, energetic dances as well as works by Donald McKayle and Alvin Ailey, and revivals of pieces by earlier artists such as Ruth St. Denis, Ted Shawn, Doris Humphrey, Lester Horton, and James Waring. Unfortunately, as we were going to press we learned of Joyce Trisler's untimely death at age forty-five. A spokesperson for the company said they would continue to perform, though as yet a new artistic director had not been chosen.

THE TRUST COMPANY/BILL DUNAS
Company Manager: Ross Harting
Ambrose Arts Foundation
457-9 Broome Street, #4R
New York, New York 10013
(212-966-1704/473-5666)

Bill Dunas is concerned with acting and theatre as much as dance, and his avant-garde solos have a stark, emotionally raw quality that hammers away at the audience. One reviewer described them as being "evening-long meditations." For the most part Dunas uses natural, unstylized movement, and his dances are performed to silence, recorded music, dialogue, or various other sound scores of his own devising. Dunas is a native New Yorker who attended C.W. Post College and Brooklyn College. He studied ballet with Alfredo Corvino, Mia Slavenska, and Don Farnworth, and modern dance with Paul Sanasardo, Merce Cunningham, and Daniel Nagrin. He has taught at the University of Wisconsin and New York University.

DAN WAGONER AND DANCERS
20 East 17th Street
New York, New York 10003
(212-929-1018)

Dan Wagoner was a principal dancer with Paul Taylor and Martha Graham before organizing his eight-member company in 1970. Wagoner's dances, like the man, have a warm, good-humored air about them. Choreographically they often deal with "various uses of space, energy and structure," as well as the individual way that each performer handles the material. Accompaniment ranges from taped music to silence to spoken words. Wagoner and his fine dancers have an interestingly weighted, loping movement style. Some of their most popular pieces are ***Taxi Dances, Songs,*** and ***Summer Rambo.*** Wagoner teaches intermediate and advanced technique classes at his loft on 17th Street (see Chapter Two).

Quick-reference index

The Dance Lover's Blackbook

One evening last spring a dancer we had just interviewed was leaving our office when we noticed that she was about to forget a small, ragged notebook lying on a nearby desk. When asked if it was hers she gasped, "Oh thank you, my life is in there!" This chapter contains those can't-get-by-without names, addresses, and phone numbers which most people painstakingly acquire by word-of-mouth recommendations, hand-passed scribblings on tiny scraps of paper, and years of experience living in New York.

Dance in print

For in-depth coverage of dance, consult these periodicals:

- ***Ballet Review***
  Marcel Dekker, Inc.
  270 Madison Avenue
  New York, New York 10016
  (212-889-9595)
  subscriptions:
  Marcel Dekker Journals
  Box 11305
  Church Street Station
  New York, New York 10249
  Robert Cornfield and Nancy Reynolds, Editors.
  quarterly; $17.50/year

Ballet Review was founded by Arlene Croce to encourage dance criticism and scholarship and open up a "lively discussion of the state of the art." Intelligent and well written, it contains an interesting mix of interviews, critical reviews, and analyses as well as articles of current interest. The book reviews are exceptionally well done, and the new editor, Robert Cornfield, has instituted a monthly report card in which various dance critics give A-F grades to recent performances. Articles are long and thorough. Recent issues have included an interview with Suzanne Farrell, a piece on the School of American Ballet, and critical exploration of the works of Doris Humphrey and Paul Taylor.

• ***Dance Chronicle***
Marcel Dekker, Inc.
270 Madison Avenue
New York, New York 10016
(212-889-9595)
subscriptions:
same as for ***Ballet Review,*** above
Jack Anderson and George Dorris, Editors.
quarterly; $17.50/year

Dance Chronicle has a strong historical emphasis and is geared to academic tastes. In the extreme, the subject matter can get obscure, as in a recent article entitled, "Theatrical Dancing in the Territory of Utah, 1848-1868"; but to be fair, the journal has also done pieces on the turn-of-the-century American dancer Maud Allan, the Paris Opera, Indian ritual dancing, and it has devoted an entire issue to the life and works of contemporary modern dance choreographer Bella Lewitsky.

• ***Dance Herald***
P.O. Box 686, Ansonia Station
New York, New York 10023
William Moore, Editor.
$3.00/year; 75¢/issue

Dance Herald is a six-page black dance newsletter that is published sporadically throughout the year. It includes a directory of schools and companies.

• ***Dance Life***
158 East 7th Street
New York, New York 10009
(212-533-5727)
David Lindner, Editor.
annual; $6.00/3 issues and $2.50/issue

This "anti-glamour and anti-trivia" magazine is probably the most practical of all the dance publications. It deals with important, real-life issues that concern most dancers. Articles range from reviews of ballet, modern dance, and avant-garde performances to interviews and discussions of dance training. ***Dance Life*** also explores related fields, such as mime, martial arts, and dance photography. Two of our favorite ***Dance Life*** articles have been "Dancer's Pain," on prevention and treatment of dance injuries, and "Nomadism in Modern Dance," about the increasingly high turnover of performers in modern dance companies.

- ***Dancemagazine***
  Danad Publishing Company
  1180 Avenue of the Americas
  New York, New York 10036
  (212-921-9300)
  William Como, Editor-in-Chief
  Richard Philp, Managing Editor.
  monthly; $18.00/year, $34.00/2 years, $2.00/issue
  Dancemagazine is the world's largest dance publication and the best source of current dance news. It contains a voluminous news section, lengthy concert calendars (for both New York City and around the country), dozens of performance reviews, a national dance school directory, and a plethora of ads for upcoming events. The magazine also covers regional ballet, college dance, summer festivals, dance camps, as well as dance teacher conventions, plus feature articles and columns on a variety of subjects, including dance personalities, dance film, history, education, notation, books, health and injury prevention, and dance technique. It is written for a general audience. Lots of nice photos by Herb Migdoll.

- ***Dance News***
  119 West 57th Street
  New York, New York 10019
  (212-PL7-6761)
  Helen V. Atlas, Editor.
  monthly except July and August; $9.00/year
  Dance News is a sixteen-page newspaper that contains short articles on dancers and dance companies, festivals, and concert reviews; there are also some book reviews and ads for forthcoming activities.

- ***Dance Scope***
  American Dance Guild
  1133 Broadway, Room 1427
  New York, New York 10010
  (212-245-4833)
  Richard Lorber, Editor.
  quarterly; $8.50/year, $15.50/2 years, $2.50/issue
  A quality journal, ***Dance Scope*** covers a diversity of dance-related subjects, from book reviews and critical writings to historical pieces, biographies of prominent dance figures, and articles on dance reconstruction and therapeutic techniques, such as the Sweigard and Alexander methods. Sparsely but nicely illustrated.

- ***The Drama Review***
  51 West 4th Street, Room 300
  New York, New York 10012
  (212-598-2597)
  Michael Kirby, Editor.
  quarterly; $12.50/year, $22.50/2 years, $4.00/issue
  Originally founded as the ***Tulane Drama Review*** in 1955, ***The Drama Review*** is now edited by playwright Michael Kirby and affiliated with the New York University School of the Arts. It is devoted to the scholarly research and documentation of contemporary and historical avant-garde theatre, including experimental dance. Each issue focuses

on a single topic—for example, "Rehearsal Procedures," "Theatre and Therapy," and "Post-Modern Dance and Visual Performance." Among the contributors to the magazine have been Simone Forti, Richard Foreman, Deborah Hay, Richard Schechner, Lucinda Childs, Nikolai Foregger, and Noel Carroll.

- *New York On Stage*
  Calendar Department
  Theatre Development Fund
  1501 Broadway, Room 2110
  New York, New York 10036
  Marcia O'Dea, Editor.
  Eve Rodriguez, Assistant Editor.
  monthly; free to TDF voucher subscribers, and also sold separately by subscription

  A calendar of TDF-sponsored dance, music, and theatre events in New York City; includes photos.

- *Performing Arts Journal*
  928 St. Marks Place
  New York, New York 10009
  (212-260-7586)
  Bonnie Marranca and Gautam Dasgupta, Editors
  triannual; $9.50/year, $3.50/issue

  Since 1976 the ***Performing Arts Journal*** has been covering theatre, dance, music, opera, video, and film the world over. Most recently there have been interviews and articles on celebrated dance figures such as Edwin Denby, Kenneth King, Bob Fosse, Jerome Robbins, Merce Cunningham, Jiri Kylian, and Lee Theodore; concert and book reviews; and reports on dance festivals and conferences. Illustrated.

The following weekly trade papers publish audition notices for dance companies, and nightclub and theatrical productions:

- *Back Stage*
  165 West 46th Street
  New York, New York 10036
  (212-581-1080)
- *Show Business*
  136 West 44th Street
  New York, New York 10036
  (212-586-6900)

These local newspapers and magazines will keep you abreast of dance events in the city. They publish listings of upcoming dance concerts as well as concert and theatre reviews. Audition notices (mostly for modern dance companies) can also occasionally be found in the ***Village Voice.*** The ***Voice*** and the ***Soho Weekly News*** have the best coverage of modern and avant-garde dance.

- *The New York Times*
- *Village Voice*
- *Soho Weekly News*
- *New York Post*
- *Cue—New York*
- *New York Magazine*
- *The New Yorker*

Where to buy dance books and periodicals

New York has more bookstores and mail-order houses that stock dance publications than any other city in the world. Almost every bookseller has at least a few titles on the subject, but the following ones specialize in dance.

- **The American Dance Guild Book Club,** P.O. Box 109, Princeton, New Jersey 08540, (609-924-2244). This is the only bookclub exclusively for dance. Members get advance descriptions of the monthly selections and alternatives, and buy books at a discount.
- **The Ballet Shop,** 1887 Broadway (62/63rd Street), New York, New York 10023, (212-581-7990); open Monday-Saturday, 11:00 A.M. to 8:00 P.M. Located near Lincoln Center, The Ballet Shop has the most complete collection of dance books and periodicals in New York.
- **Barnes & Noble,** 105 Fifth Avenue (18th Street), New York, New York 10003, (212-255-8100); open Monday-Friday, 9:45 A.M. to 6:45 P.M. and Saturday 9:45 A.M. to 6:00 P.M.

Frank Gimpaya

Bloomsday Bookshop, 2259 Broadway (81st Street), New York, New York 10024, (212-724-0120); open Monday-Friday, 9:00 A.M. to 11:00 P.M.; Saturday, 9:00 A.M. to 1:00 A.M.; and Sunday, 10:00 A.M. to 12 midnight. Browsers are welcome in this neighborhood bookstore. There is a coffee shop on the second floor.

Book Branch East, 63 East 8th Street (at Broadway), New York, New York 10003, (212-260-3999); open Monday-Thursday, 10:00 A.M. to 11:00 P.M.; Friday-Saturday, 10:00 A.M. to midnight; and Sunday, 1:00 to 9:00 P.M. A good selection of hardcover and softcover dance books and periodicals. There is a 15% discount on all hardcover titles.

Books & Company, 939 Madison Avenue (72nd Street), New York, New York 10021, (212-737-1450); open Monday-Sunday, 10:00 A.M. to 7:00 P.M.

Brentano's, 20 University Place, New York, New York 10003 (212-674-3490); open Monday-Thursday, 10:00 A.M. to 11:00 P.M.; Friday-Saturday, 10:00 A.M. to midnight; and Sunday, 12:30 to 7:30 P.M. Also at 586 Fifth Avenue (47th Street), New York, New York, 10036, (212-PL7-8600); open Monday-Friday, 9:45 A.M. to 6:45 P.M. and Saturday, 9:45 A.M. to 6:00 P.M.

Coliseum Books, 1771 Broadway (57th Street), New York, New York 10019, (212-757-8381); open Monday-Friday, 8:00 A.M. to 11:00 P.M.; Saturday, 8:00 A.M. to 11:30 P.M.; and Sunday, 8:00 A.M. to 8:00 P.M.

B. Dalton Book Seller, 666 Fifth Avenue (52/53rd Street), New York, New York 10017, (212-247-1740), open weekdays, 9:30 A.M. to 8:00 P.M., Saturday, 9:00 A.M. to 6:00 P.M.; and Sunday, noon to 5:00 P.M. Dance books are on the Fifth Avenue level of this mammoth new reader's supermarket.

Dancemagazine, 1180 Avenue of the Americas (46th Street), New York, New York 10036, (212-921-9300); Besides putting out the world's largest dance publication, *Dancemagazine* makes back issues and reprints of articles available by mail order. It is also the publisher of the ***Dancemagazine College Guide, Raoul Gelabert's Anatomy for the Dancer,*** and the ***Dancemagazine Annual***, a directory of professional dance services—all of which can be purchased at the above address.

The Dance Mart, Box 48, Homecrest Station, Brooklyn, New York, 11229, (212-NI5-9607; Sells current and out of print books on all aspects of dance, by mail order only. Send away for a free catalog.

Dance Notation Bureau, 505 Eighth Avenue (35th Street), New York, New York 10018, (212-736-4350); Books on dance notation and movement analysis.

Doubleday Book Shop, 724 Fifth Avenue (57th Street), New York, New York 10019. (212-953-4868); open Monday-Saturday 9:30 A.M. to midnight. Also at 673 Fifth Avenue (53rd Street), New York, New York 10022, (212-953-4805).

The Drama Bookshop, 150 West 52nd Street, New York, New York 10019, (212-582-1037); open Monday-Friday, 9:30 A.M. to 6:00 P.M. and Saturday, 1:00 to 5:00 P.M. Since 1923 The Drama Bookshop has offered an excellent selection of hard and softcover books on theatre, music, and dance. Benches are provided for your browsing comfort.

Footnotes, F. Randolph Associates, Inc., Attention: Frank Derbas, 265 West 30th Street, New York, New York 10001, (212-947-3929); ***Footnotes*** is a performing arts shopper through which hundreds of dance books, as well as films, records, supplies (such as dance flooring), and novelty items may be ordered directly by mail or phone. Reduced rates are offered to members of their Discount Club.

The Gotham Book Mart, 41 West 47th Street, New York, New York 10036, (212-757-0367); open weekdays, 9:30 A.M. to 6:30 P.M. and Saturday, 9:30 A.M. to 6:00 P.M. Books on art, theatre, music, and dance, including out of print titles.

The Juilliard School Book Store, Lincoln Center Plaza, 66th Street and Broadway, (1st floor), New York, New York 10023, (212-799-5000); open Monday-Saturday (call for hours); closed on school holidays.

The Library and Museum of the Performing Arts Sales Shop at Lincoln Center, 111 Amsterdam Avenue (64th Street), New York, New York 10023, (212-799-2200, ext. 242); open Monday-Saturday, hours vary.

The Madison Avenue Bookshop, 833 Madison Avenue (70th Street), New York, New York 10021; (212-535-6130); open Monday-Saturday, 9:30 A.M. to 6:00 P.M. Small collection of current hardcover and softcover dance books.

Marboro Bookshops, 104 West 57th Street, New York, New York, 10019, (212-757-9286); open daily, 9:00 A.M. to midnight. Also at 750 Third Avenue (46/47th Street), New York, New York 10017, (212-682-4661); open daily, hours vary.

The Marloff Paperback Corner, 10 Sheridan Square, (West 4th Street at Seventh Avenue), New York, New York 10014, (212-924-5864); open Sunday-Thursday, 10:00 A.M. to midnight and Friday-Saturday, 10:00 A.M. to 1:00 A.M. Good selection of softcover books and dance periodicals.

The New Yorker Book Shop, 250 West 89th Street (at Broadway), New York, New York 10024, (212-799-2050); open Monday-Friday, 9:00 A.M. to 9:45 P.M.; Saturday, 10:00 A.M. to 9:45 P.M.; and Sunday, 10:00 A.M. to 8:00 P.M. A modest but stable dance selection, including the periodicals *Dance and Dancers* and *Dancemagazine.*

Three Lives and Company, 131 Seventh Avenue South (at West 10th Street), New York, New York 10014, (212-741-2069); open Monday-Saturday, 1:00 to 10:00 P.M. and Sunday 2:00 to 6:00 P.M. Has a well-stocked dance shelf of hardcover and softcover books and calendars; also carries the journal *Dance Life.*

New Morning, 169 Spring Street, New York, New York 10012, (212-966-2993); open daily, hours vary.

New York University Book Center, 18 Washington Place, New York, New York 10003, (212-598-2255); open Monday-Saturday, hours vary. Dance books are located in both the general book collection and downstairs with the textbooks under specific dance courses.

Rizzoli International Bookstore, 712 Fifth Avenue (55/56th Street), New York, New York 10022, (212-397-3700); open Monday-Saturday, 10:00 A.M. to midnight.

Scribner's Book Store, 597 Fifth Avenue (49th Street), New York, New York 10017, (212-486-4070); Scribner's is another old and stately bookseller that stocks mainly hardcover books. Their dance selection is smaller than that of most of the other stores listed here.

Strand Book Store, 829 Broadway (12th Street), New York, New York, New York 10003, (212-GR3-1452), open Monday-Saturday, 9:30 A.M. to 6:30 P.M.

Womrath Bookstores, 1144 Lexington Avenue (79th Street), New York, New York 10021, (212-737-5023); open Monday-Friday, 9:30 A.M. to 7:00 P.M. and Saturday, 9:30 A.M. to 5:30 P.M. Also at 1158 Madison (86th Street), New York, New York 10028, (212-RE7-9330); open Monday-Saturday, 9:00 A.M. to 6:00 P.M. and Sunday, noon to 6:00 P.M.

A unique experience: The Library and Museum of the Performing Arts at Lincoln Center

111 Amsterdam Avenue (at 64th Street)
New York, New York 10023
(212-799-2200); hours: dance, music and theatre collections: 12:00 to 6:00 P.M., Tuesday, Wednesday, Friday, Saturday, and 12:00 to 8:00 P.M., Monday and Thursday; Rogers and Hammerstein Sound Archives: 12:00 to 6:00 P.M. Monday through Saturday; Children's Library: 2:00 to 5:00 P.M. Monday through Friday, 1:00 to 5:00 P.M. Saturday. Garage parking is available. To go by subway, take the Seventh Avenue IRT Number 1 Train to the 66th Street, Lincoln Center stop; the Number 104 Broadway bus also stops there.

The Library and Museum of the Performing Arts at Lincoln Center is alone worth a visit to New York City. Comfortably and attractively designed, it houses the only public archive in the world exclusively devoted to theatre, music, and dance. Here, briefly, is what it offers.

The Dance Collection reading room. *courtesy of the New York Public Library*

The Dance Collection (third floor) is the world's largest library of dance literature, memorabilia, and iconography. Every aspect of dance is covered: ballet, modern, theatre, ethnic, ritual, and social dance. Also included are materials from the private collections of Isadora Duncan and Gordon Craig, Ruth St. Denis and Ted Shawn, Doris Humphrey and Charles Weidman, Agnes de Mille, Lincoln Kirstein, Hanya Holm, Ruth Page and Jerome Robbins. Special photographic or historical exhibits are often on display in the reading room, and the atmosphere is wonderfully informal. It's not unusual to see a college student working on a term paper seated right next to a well-known critic researching his latest book or a ballet superstar boning up on a new role. Walter Terry is a frequent visitor, as are dance reviewers Anna Kisselgoff and Don McDonagh. Natalia Makarova and Dame Margot Fonteyn have both been seen there recently.

The Dance Collection contains over 28,000 books and pamphlets, including biographies, critical writings, notebooks and memoirs, dictionaries, anatomy studies, and works on dance history, technique, education, and notation. There are rare manuscripts and a healthy selection of newspaper clippings, old programs, scrapbooks, and other memorabilia. Current and back issues of all the widely read dance periodicals are on hand too, from ***Dancemagazine*** and ***Square Dancing*** to journals such as ***Dance Chronicle*** and ***Dance Scope***; from the British publication, ***Dance and Dancers*** to the German magazine ***Der Tanz.*** It's great fun to skim a vintage issue of ***Dancemagazine*** (formerly called ***American Dancer***) or thumb through a 1911 copy of ***Dancing Times.*** In addition, the research library holds an extraordinary dance print collection containing thousands of historical photographs and lithographs, many original drawings, and hundreds of costume and set designs.

Perhaps the most exciting of all the Dance Collection's holdings is its film library, which emcompasses straightforward records of performances, as well as films on dance training and appreciation, and dances made expressly for the film medium. Among the archive's treasures is some rare footage shot by Douglas Fairbanks of Anna Pavlova while she was on tour in California, and a 1908 short subject called "Animated Picture Studio," which is believed to feature Isadora Duncan. There is José Limón dancing with Pauline Koner and Lucas Hoving in Limón's masterpiece, "The Moor's Pavane"; Agnes de Mille starring in her own ballet, "Three Virgins and a Devil"; and one of Twyla Tharp's early choreographic efforts, "Tank Dive." Anyone can arrange a private film or videotape screening by making an appointment two weeks in advance. It is suggested, however, that viewers make a preliminary trip to look through the library's catalog listings beforehand, because some films have union restrictions or can only be seen with the choreographer's permission.

Another invaluable research tool is the Dance Collection's oral history archive, comprised of hundreds of recorded interviews with celebrated dance personalities. You can listen to Martha Graham discuss her method of choreography, for example, or hear Kirov ballerina Natalie Dudinskaya reminisce about the great Russian teacher, Agrippina Vaganova, at a 1964 interview taped at the Russian Tea Room restaurant in New York.

The Theatre Collection (third floor) encompasses every aspect of theatre—stage, motion pictures, radio, television, circus, vaudeville, burlesque, magic, marionette, and nightclub. It also contains prompt books and acting copies of scripts, as well as material on musical comedy choreography.

The Music Collection (third floor) covers a wide range of music across the ages, from primitive to folk, rock, jazz, popular, chamber, symphonic, opera, musical comedy, contemporary, and experimental.

The Rogers and Hammerstein Archives of Sound (third floor) is the largest listening library in the world, containing over 200,000 recordings.

The Children's Library: Small fry have their own selection of books and records on dance, theatre, and music at the Children's Library on the second floor. The furniture is scaled down, and nearby in the Hecksher Oval, story hours, puppet shows, and other programs are presented especially for youngsters. A reference collection of children's books is also available for teachers.

The Circulating and Information Library: Located on the first floor (or plaza level) is material on dance, drama, and music which may be used on the premises or borrowed with a New York City Public Library card. Included are books, periodicals, screenplays, clippings, musical scores, concert programs, and records. Borrower's cards are issued free to everyone who lives, works, or studies in New York. A nonresident's library card may be obtained at a nominal charge.

Special Exhibits and Displays: There are several exhibition halls in the library building, which display original designs for costumes and stage sets, drawings, models of theatres, photographs, posters, and lithographs from the library's collections and those of other New York City museums. The largest exhibition space is the Vincent Astor Gallery on the second floor, which shows material from the research libraries—photographs, autographed scores, and other memorabilia.

Gift Shop: The Library and Museum Gift shop is on the first floor near the main entrance to the building. Books, periodicals, cards, posters, and novelty items pertaining to the performing arts are sold. It's open Monday through Saturday; hours vary.

Free Performances: Music, dance, and dramatic readings are held in the library's auditorium, on the lower "A" level. Admission is free.

Dance organizations

AMERICAN DANCE GUILD
1133 Broadway, Room 1427
New York, New York 10010
(212-691-7773)
Elizabeth Zimmer, Executive Director

A forum for dance professionals, teachers, and organizations, the American Dance Guild sponsors various research projects and conferences, and a dance book club which offers monthly selections at a discount. It also publishes the journal ***Dance Scope,*** as well as a monthly newsletter containing dance news, job listings, and reviews of books, films, and concerts. Two of the Guild's major projects are the promotion of dance in education and the establishment of public school work-study programs whereby dancers can get academic credit for performing and training at professional dance schools. Most of the members of this organization are dance teachers, studios, schools, and libraries. Dues are lower for students and retirees. Anyone can join the American Dance Guild Book Club.

AMERICAN DANCE THERAPY ASSOCIATION (ADTA)
2000 Century Plaza, Suite 230
Columbia, Maryland 21044
(301-997-4040)
Judith Bunney, President

(The ADTA does have a New York chapter, but inquiries should be directed to the above address; please include a self-addressed, stamped, legal size envelope.)

The American Dance Therapy Association was founded in 1966 to establish and maintain high standards of professional education and competence in the field. It defines dance therapy as "the psychotherapeutic use of movement as a process which furthers the emotional and physical integration of the individual." The ADTA holds an annual conference and publishes ***The American Journal of Dance Therapy,*** various monographs and pamphlets, a code of professional ethics, and a newsletter. Its helpful brochure, "Educational Opportunities in Dance Therapy," contains a current listing of approved graduate and undergraduate degree programs in dance therapy, as well as dance therapy training centers, institutions that offer internships, and ongoing courses and workshops. The Association also keeps a bibliography of relevant books, articles and films. One of its most important functions is the maintenance of a registry of dance therapists who have met its professional standards of education and clinical practice. (Registered dance therapists are identified by the initials "D.T.R." after their names.) In addition, the ADTA operates a speakers bureau, through which dance therapists are available to make presentations on the field to interested organizations and schools. There are full members (practicing dance therapists), associate members (individuals, organizations, libraries and institutions), and student members of the ADTA.

ASSOCIATION OF AMERICAN DANCE COMPANIES (AADC)
162 West 56th Street
New York, New York 10019
(212-265-6824 or toll free 800-223-6573)
Norma Munn, President

A nationwide organization that brings American dance companies together—through annual conferences, regional meetings, seminars, and its newsletter—to discuss mutual problems and learn from each other. The AADC presents a united voice in behalf of dance companies to government and private funding sources. It promotes dance in the press and through such activities as National Dance Week. It pools efforts and saves money for member companies on travel expenses and medical insurance, and also provides information and assistance on management, funding, and other matters.

BLACK THEATRE ALLIANCE
410 West 42nd Street
New York, New York 10036
(212-564-2266)

Located on recently renovated Theatre Row in the Times Square area, the Black Theatre Alliance publishes monthly listings of black dance and theatre events in the Metropolitan area. It also occasionally sponsors dance classes: last December choreographers Raymond Sawyer, Eleo Pomare, and Walter Nicks taught modern dance and jazz there. Call or write for free inclusion on their mailing list.

CHOREOGRAPHERS THEATRE (CT)
25 West 19th Street
New York, New York 10011
(212-939-2230)

In the past CT was an active producer of modern dance concerts, but at present its activities are limited to running the dance department at The New School for Social Research, and producing the Laura Foreman Dance Company, based there. Members have access to CT's sizeable record and tape library of contemporary music, file of job openings and auditions, and video equipment (when it is not being used by the Foreman company).

COMMITTEE ON RESEARCH IN DANCE (CORD)
Dance Department
Education 675D
New York University
35 West 4th Street
New York, New York 10003
(212-598-3459)

A center for dance research whose membership chiefly consists of university and secondary school teachers. Through its publications and annual conferences, CORD promotes the exchange of dance research, resources and ideas. Its conferences include workshops, lecture-demonstrations, panel discussions, and performances. CORD also puts out the ***Dance Research Journal*** and the ***Dance Research Annual.***

COUNTRY DANCE AND SONG SOCIETY OF AMERICA
505 Eighth Avenue (35th Street)
New York, New York 10018
(212-594-8833)
Nancy White Kurzman, Executive Director

The Country Dance and Song Society has fifty regional branches. It sponsors research, classes, concerts, dances, and demonstrations on American and English folk dances. Since 1930 the Society has operated Pinewoods, a summer camp for adults and children located in Plymouth, Massachusetts. Campers learn country, contra, and square dances along with their seventeenth, eighteenth, and nineteenth-century forerunners. Live music is provided for all classes. There are also folk song sessions and evening dance parties at Pinewoods.

DANCE FILMS ASSOCIATION
250 West 57th Street, Room 2201
New York, New York 10019
(212-586-2142)
Susan Braun, President

The Association publishes a dance film catalog and sponsors an annual dance film festival in New York. It also helps find film sources and acts as a consultant in setting up dance film series throughout the country. Its education department contains a lecture bureau.

DANCE NOTATION BUREAU
505 Eighth Avenue (35th Street)
New York, New York 10018
(212-736-4350)
Herb Kummel, Executive Director

The Bureau documents choreography, does research in movement analysis, gives related courses, and trains professionals in dance notation and reconstruction. Its library contains hundreds of recorded dance works, as well as a complete history of the art of dance notation. The Dance Notation Bureau also reconstructs dance pieces for performing companies.

DANCE THEATRE WORKSHOP (DTW)
at American Theatre Laboratory
219 West 19th Street
New York, New York 10011
(212-691-6500)
David White, Director

An extremely valuable membership group for new and established dance companies and choreographers, DTW helps local and out-of-town artists organize New York performance seasons (about 12 percent of its members are from other parts of the country). In addition, it produces its own concert series (see the Dance Theatre Workshop listing in Chapter One). For an annual fee of $25, members have access to DTW's computerized mailing list, a well-researched press kit noting key media contacts, discount advertising rates in major New York periodicais, graphic design services, low-rental rehearsal space, a telephone reservation service, and videotape documentation. Besides all this, DTW offers advice on management problems, including legal and unemployment counseling. It also serves dancers and dance audiences by sponsoring special seminars, film showings, dance workshops, and classes open to the general public. Rudy Perez, Annabelle Gamson, Phyllis Lamhut, and Jane Goldberg have taught there in the past. The DTW staff is friendly, helpful, and in close contact with the New York dance world—which makes this organization a good place to visit if you're new in town and in need of advice on classes and performing opportunities. The Workshop's large bulletin board, located near the front entrance, is always packed with notices of concerts, classes, auditions, workshops, lectures, and even apartment sublets.

NATIONAL ASSOCIATION FOR REGIONAL BALLET (NARB)
1860 Broadway (61/62nd Street)
New York, New York 10023
(212-757-8460)
Doris Hering, Executive Director

Unlike some wide-ranging organizations, the NARB is not a paper tiger. It has done a great deal to raise the standards of dance training and performance across the nation. It periodically evaluates the performance level and training of its 120 member companies, and sponsors annual festivals where they meet for master classes, seminars, and performances. It also conducts summer choreography workshops, and publishes the ***Dance America*** newsletter. The Association has a scholarship program and serves as a liaison between regional companies and state and national arts organizations. The NARB office in New York acts as a central information center for dancers and teachers around the country: Time permitting, the dedicated staff tries to answer individual inquiries and when possible, recommend good dance teachers, schools or college programs. NARB President David Howard is a highly respected ballet teacher with a school only a few blocks away from the office. Doris Hering, Executive Director, is a writer and critic for ***Dancemagazine,*** and has been active in the regional ballet movement for many years.

NATIONAL DANCE ASSOCIATION (NDA)*
American Alliance for Health, Physical Education, and Recreation (AAHPER)
1201 16th Street, NW
Washington, D.C. 20036
(202-833-5557)
Dr. Margie Hanson, Executive Director

*Although this group is not based in New York, we've included it here because of the useful services it provides.

An organization dedicated to raising the level of dance education in this country and promoting dance in the American educational system. It grants interest-free loans to students preparing for dance-teaching careers, holds conventions, and publishes a number of periodicals on dance, covering such subjects as dance therapy, aesthetics, careers in dance, children's dance, and a directory of college programs in dance (they will send you a complete list of their dance publications on request). The NDA also maintains a library of oral tapes of outstanding dance educators.

TECHNICAL ASSISTANCE GROUP (TAG)
463 West Street
New York, New York 10014
(212-691-3590)
Margaret Wood, Executive Director

The Technical Assistance Group both produces dance concerts—the New York Dance Festival at the Delacorte Theatre in Central Park, and the Dance Umbrella, a festival that is presently being held at the Camera Mart/Stage One—and provides a central pool of technical assistance and managerial services to dance companies and organizations across the country. The group is staffed by experienced professionals in the fields of production, company management, lighting design, stage management, and tour coordination. TAG also gives on-the-job training in these areas through its intern program. In addition, it maintains an open file of technical specification sheets on 600 performing spaces in the United States and abroad. On occasion the TAG staff travels to regional meetings and conferences, conducting workshops on dance management and concert production.

THEATRE DEVELOPMENT FUND (TDF)
1501 Broadway (44th Street)
New York, New York 10036
(212-221-0013)

TDF is a nonprofit organization founded in 1967 to stimulate the production of worthwhile plays in the commercial theatre. Since then it has broadened its scope to support nearly every aspect of theatre, music, and dance in New York. The Fund offers low-cost admissions to a wide variety of plays, music, and dance events through its audience mailing list, discount voucher program, and the operation of two half-price ticket booths (see Chapter One). In addition, TDF helps develop similar programs throughout the country (there are currently four). It also makes the 48,000 costumes in its costume collection available to nonprofit organizations for a nominal rental fee.

Professional Unions*

American Guild of Musical Artists (AGMA), 1841 Broadway (60th Street), New York, New York 10023, (212-265-3687). For professional dance companies. Publishes an annual wage scale that is used for the National Endowment for the Arts Dance Touring Program.

Actor's Equity Association (EQUITY), 1500 Broadway (43/44th Street), New York, New York 10036, (212-869-8530). Also has offices in Los Angeles and Chicago. For actors, singers, and dancers in live musical theatre: Broadway shows, stock tents, regional theatre, and dinner theatres.

American Guild of Variety Artists (AGVA), 1540 Broadway (45th Street), New York, New York 10036, (212-765-0800). For performers in live variety entertainment, at hotels, nightclubs, lounges, and circuses. Well-known examples are Disney on Parade and Ice Capades.

*Adapted from ***The Poor Dancer's Almanac*** by Margie Simkin and Ted Striggles (New York: Association of American Dance Companies, 1976), an excellent survival manual for what the authors call "the nonartistic side of dancing in New York." It covers housing, health care, unemployment insurance, funding and dance production needs, among other things. You can get a copy from Dance Theatre Workshop, 219 West 19th Street, New York City 10011.

American Federation of Television and Radio Artists (AFTRA), 1350 Avenue of the Americas (54/55th Street), New York, New York 10019, (212-265-7700). For television, radio and record performers.

Screen Actors Guild (SAG), 551 Fifth Avenue (45/46th Street), New York 10036, (212-687-4623). For all performers in films, from industrial movies to major motion pictures.

Dance gear

What with Discomania and the American physical fitness craze, dance apparel seems to be ubiquitous these days. Apart from inveterate manufacturers like Capezio, Danskin, and Selva, practically every fashion retailer in the city—from small hosiery shops and boutiques to department stores—has gotten into the dance business. Not to mention the intermission gift stalls that are thriving at theatres like City Center, New York State, and the Metropolitan Opera House. Whether you want to dance or just feel like a dancer, the variety of styles, colors, materials, and prices available is simply mind-boggling. To give you an idea, there is Frederick Freed of London, whose pointe shoes are worn by thousands of professionals; there are Rudi Gernreich's high-chic designs at Capezio's, as well as Herbert's dancewear at bargain basement prices, and even a store called Little Leapers that features leotards and tights for tiny tots. Danskin clothes, which are sold all over New York, come in both lightweight fabric for streetwear and recreational use, and heavyweight for serious dancers and professionals who need more durability. Many of the city's department stores, such as Bloomingdale's, Macy's and Alexander's, also stock leotards, tights, and leg warmers (usually in their hosiery departments); however, they tend to be more expensive and don't always carry a full line. The following suppliers specialize in dancewear and are thus likely to have the best selection.

Albert's Dancewear, 2113A Broadway (72nd Street), New York, New York 10023, (212-595-5860); shoes, tights, leotards, leg warmers, body warmers.

Albert Hosiery Stores: 609 Madison Avenue (57th Street), New York, New York 10022, (212-PL5-6483); 26 East 23rd Street, New York, New York 10010, (GR3-6247); 20 West 43rd Street, New York, New York 10036, (LO4-5644); 658 West 181st Street, New York, New York 10027, (LO8-8600); 925 Lexington Avenue (68th Street), New York, New York 10021, (988-1195); 49 Nassau Street, New York, New York 10038, (CO7-7526). All branches carry Danskin tights and leotards; some other brands too.

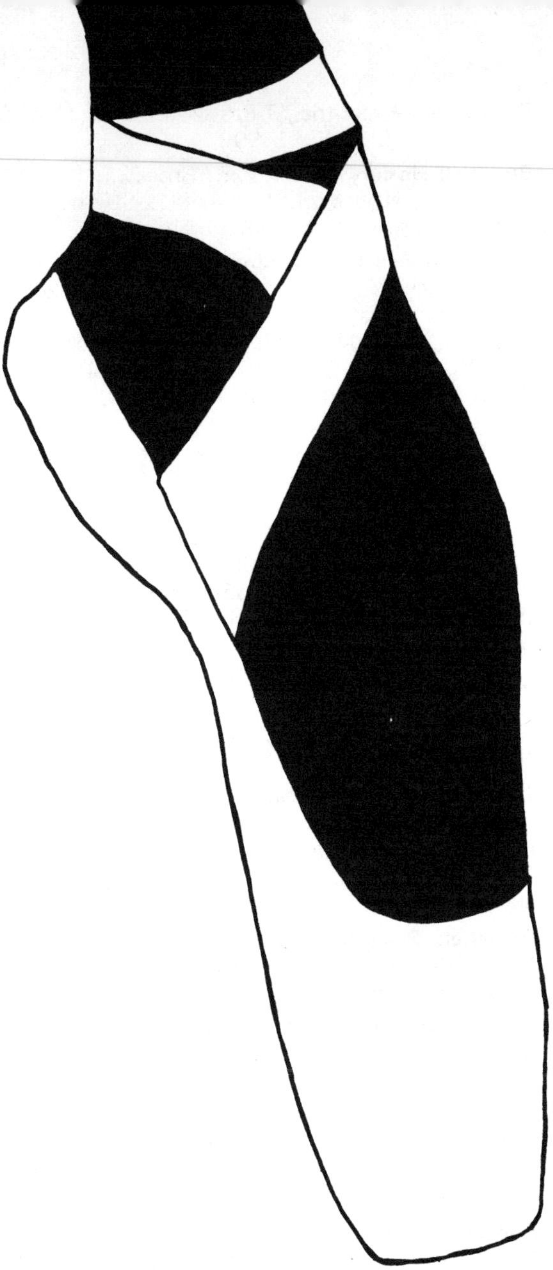

Bal-Toggery Knits Inc., 7 East 20th Street, New York, New York 10003, (212-477-1400).

Buy Well Hosiery Center, 2357 Broadway (85/86th Street), New York, New York 10024, (212-SU7-6211); discounts on Danskin seconds and other brands.

Capezio Dance-Theatre Shops: 755 Seventh Avenue (50th Street), New York, New York 10019, (212-245-2130); 16 West 61st Street (at Broadway), New York, New York 10023, (246-4944); 177 MacDougal Street (8th Street), New York, New York 10011, (477-5634); 136 East 61st Street (at Lexington Avenue), New York, New York 10021, (758-8833). Capezio probably has the largest selection of dance apparel and shoes in New York. All stores give a 10% discount to teachers; to obtain a catalog of Capezio products, send fifty cents to Capezio Ballet Makers, Department DM-379, 1860 Broadway, New York, New York 10023.

Chatila & Company, 5719 18th Avenue, Brooklyn, New York 11204, (212-BE6-6155); manufactures leotards and tights, recital costumes, jump suits, and toe, tap and ballet shoes.

Dale's Hosiery Store, 120 West 57th Street, New York, New York 10019, (212-757-4284); located near Carnegie Hall; carries most of the Danskin line, sometimes at a discount.

Danskin Inc., 1114 Avenue of the Americas (42/43rd Street), New York, New York 10036, (212-869-9800); offers a large line of dancewear for all occasions, plus accessories and fabric; also supplies many department stores, hosiery shops, and boutiques in the city.

Frederick Freed Ltd. of London, 108 West 57th Street, New York, New York 10019, (212-489-1055); shoes, leotards, tights, warmers.

Grace Costumes Inc., 254 West 54th Street, New York, New York 10019, (212-586-0260); custom-made theatrical costumes only.

Herbet Dancewear, 902 Broadway (20/21st Street), New York, New York 10011, (212-677-7606); shoes, leotards, tights, skirts, warmup clothes; not always the best quality, but probably close to the lowest prices in town.

Eileen Holding, 110 West 18th Street, New York, New York 10011, (212-CH2-4797); this personable English woman sells custom-made leotards, tights, and unitards; prices range from $15-$35.

Huguette Hosiery Shop, 1414 Avenue of the Americas (58th Street), New York, New York 10019, (212-486-9744); full line of Danskin leotards and tights.

Lady Orva Hosiery Store, 404 Park Avenue South, New York, New York 10016, (212-LE2-3551); full line of Danskin leotards and tights, and ballet shoes.

La Ray Boot Shop, 320 West 48th Street, New York, New York 10036, (212-757-4545); custom-made theatrical

footwear, toe and ballet shoes, opera hose, leotards, tights, and dance accessories.

Little Leapers, 2709 Broadway (104th Street), New York, New York 10025, (212-864-0508); leotards and tights for children.

Pavlova's Pointe Ltd., Ballet Shop and Boutique, 35 West 8th Street, New York, New York 10011, (212-260-7885); "Dancewear designed by dancers for dancers" is the motto of this beautiful little shop owned by ballet dancer Nadine Revene and partner Carl Lau. Their apparel, which comes in fifteen scrumptious colors, is functionally designed, meticulously crafted, and of sophisticated fashion. They sell leotards, unitards, knitted body suits and warmers that really fit, dance skirts, pants, and accessories for adults and children.

The Pavlova's Pointe showroom, complete with dance floor, barre and mirror (left). ***courtesy of Pavlova's Pointe, Ltd.***

Rivoli Shoe Repair, 166 West 50th Street, New York, New York 10019, (212-247-4850); fastening of taps, rubberizing of soles; discounts for students, dancers, and companies.

Selva, 1776 Broadway (57th Street), New York, New York 10019, (212-586-5148); shoes, tights, leotards, recital costumes, practice records; gives discounts to students, dancers, and companies.

S & S Hosiery, 156 West 50th Street, New York, New York 10019, (212-586-3288); low prices; also gives discounts.

Tantara, 19 Christopher Street (between Greenwich and Seventh avenues), New York, New York 10014, (212-242-7196); dance shoes and apparel; discounts available.

The dancer's face

Theatrical makeup

Most dancers wouldn't think of giving up the fun of making up their faces before a show (it also steadies the nerves), but lately there has been a trend toward the natural look, both on stage and off. More and more performers are discarding their false eyelashes (which were always such a nuisance anyway) in favor of ordinary mascara, and using liquid foundation instead of pancake on their skin. Since heavy "war paint" looks out of place in the small and informal theatres that have become popular, often a combination of street and theatrical cosmetics is worn. Some of the companies listed below stock both.

Bibi, 135 West 72nd Street, New York, New York 10023, (212-362-8840); no theatrical makeup per se, but they carry two brands of heavy night makeup which work well on stage; free skincare analysis and samples; open daily.

Brant Chemists, 275 Amsterdam Avenue (73rd Street), New York, New York 10023, (212-362-5480/362-2220); open seven days a week and holidays until midnight.

The Garden Pharmacy, 1632 Broadway (49/50th Street), New York, New York 10019, (212-265-3546). The Garden Pharmacy, which has been in business over forty years, calls itself "the largest retailer of theatrical makeup in the country." (Even a competitive distributor told us, "everyone in New York buys there.") They carry M. Stein, Mehron, Max Factor, and Leichner Stagelight cosmetics, among other brands—which makes them the ideal place for comparison shopping. Open until midnight.

Bob Kelly Cosmetics, 151 West 46th Street, New York, New York 10036, (212-245-2237). Located in the heart of the theatre district, Bob Kelley Cosmetics has been supplying show business personalities for over fifteen years. Their large inventory includes wigs, false noses, scars, and other facial disguises. Customers can try on samples.

Leichner Stagelight Cosmetics, 630 Ninth Avenue (44/45th Street), New York, New York 10036, (212-757-4851). These cosmetics are made in England and sold at Capezio stores, Macy's Department Store, and the Garden Pharmacy.

The Make-up Center, Ltd., 150 West 55th Street, New York, New York 10019, (212-977-9494). This store sells a wide variety of cosmetics and offers lessons for beginners.

Mehron Marketing, Inc., 250 West 40th Street, New York, New York 10018, (212-997-1011). This half-century-old firm manufactures a full range of theatrical cosmetics which are carried by over two hundred retail stores around the country (including Capezio shops, The Makeup Center, and the Garden Pharmacy in New York). Although it is primarily a wholesaler, Mehron sells its products retail to individual patrons. If you drop by the offices, you'll also be given expert advice. But the major advantage of buying directly is the assurance that you'll be seeing the entire line and paying the suggested retail price (other outlets may charge more). A color catalog is available for serious customers.

M. Stein Cosmetic Company, 430 Broome Street, New York, New York 10013; mail order only. For nearly a century the Stein Cosmetic Company in Soho has been supplying stage, film, and television artists with everything from pancake makeup and eyebrow pencil to black tooth wax and stage blood (amusingly enough, the latter comes in pints). Its huge inventory offers hundreds of items in dozens of shades and colors, and includes complete makeup kits for male, female, and dark-skinned performers. Stein's products are available through some local dealers, but may also be obtained by mail order at the above address. Even if you're not a performer you'll get a kick out of reading their free thirty-two-page makeup guide, which shows how to apply basic, corrective, and character makeup. You may even want to buy a few things just for fun.

Skincare

The mixture of sweat, skin oils, urban pollution, and studio grime can wreak havoc on even the most creamy complexions. For basic maintenance or an occasional treat, these salons specialize in deep-cleaning facials, light body massage, skincare and makeup consultations, and they all sell skincare products and makeup.

Elizabeth Arden Salon, 691 Fifth Avenue (54/55th Street), New York, New York 10022, (212-486-7929); pampers clients with nine floors of makeup and beauty facilities, including skincare, exercise and hair salons, steambaths, and fashion boutiques.

Georgette Klinger Skin Care Salons, 501 Madison Avenue (52nd Street), New York, New York 10022, (212-838-3200); competent but expensive on the whole; they may try to sell you more skincare products and makeup than you need. I went there for a light moisturizer and ended up buying $80 worth of creams, masques, and cleansers, most of which are still sitting in my medicine cabinet untouched. My own fault, perhaps, but be prepared for a stiff sales pitch. Klinger offers a separate line of merchandise for men and women.

Marie Rallé European Skin Care Inc., 101 West 57th Street, New York, New York 10019, (212-265-0358). Here's a real find—quiet, unhurried, expert care at reasonable rates. The skincare products really work, but Marie doesn't try to push them on you.

Christine Valmy, 767 Fifth Avenue (58/59th Street), New York, New York 10022, (212-838-0775); a "unisex" salon which offers facial treatment, skincare and makeup consultations (new customers get a free session) and body massage. They sell their own brand of skincare products and cosmetics.

In sickness and in health

Moderate to severe sprains and strains, as well as suspected fractures and spinal injuries, should, of course, be examined by an orthopedic specialist. Chiropractors and masseurs can also help in treating some sprains, strains, and chronic physical conditions such as backaches and headaches. In addition to therapeutic work, they just plain make you feel good, by relieving muscular tension and improving posture and overall body efficiency. (See also Chapter Two for classes in therapeutic and corrective exercise.) But even licensed practitioners can do varying degrees of damage if they are not experienced in treating dancers, because dancers need more perfect results than the average person. The doctors, chiropractors, and masseurs listed in this section have earned the respect of their colleagues and the trust of New York's professional dancers, some of whom have staked their careers on their skill. These people are not infallible, though. If a diagnosis is made or a course of treatment prescribed that you are not satisfied with (especially in the case of surgery or drug therapy), do confirm it with a second opinion.

Orthopedic specialists

Dr. William Liebler's name is practically a household word: he's probably treated more turned ankles, torn knee cartilage and broken bones than any other physician in town. In a recent interview the doctor stated that many of his colleagues steer clear of treating dancers because they have a poor track record for paying their bills. Liebler says that he has personally accrued over $150,000 worth of unpaid bills over the past year, and "most doctors can't afford to carry that kind of liability." Attempts have been made to set up clinics for dancers, but for the most part doctors and hospitals have been uncooperative. Most dancers don't know that hospital clinics will charge them more than a private doctor, and that they may be turned away because they are uninsured or cannot pay the examination fee in advance. At present Liebler sets aside special office hours for them on Saturdays.

According to Liebler, of the vast number of practicing orthopedic surgeons in New York City there are only four who specialize in dancer's injuries, and these doctors have seen hundreds of dancers. It is only this kind of experience, Liebler says, that can make physicians knowledgeable about the effects of certain dance technique on the body, and qualified to treat injuries which are peculiar to dancers or to recommend the right physical therapist.

Dr. William G. Hamilton
343 West 58th Street
New York, New York 10019
(212-765-2262)

Dr. Barnard Kleiger
1150 Fifth Avenue (96th Street)
New York, New York 10028
(212-289-1216)

Dr. William Liebler
742 Park Avenue (72nd Street)
New York, New York 10021
(212-RE4-7477)

Dr. Edward Nicholas
29 Claremont Avenue
New York, New York 10027
(212-866-6745)

Chiropractors

Chiropractors relieve pain and tension and release pinched nerves and muscular blockage by restoring normal nerve flow throughout the body. They do this by pressing and manipulating the spinal vertebrae into correct alignment (x-rays may be taken first in injury cases). Dr. Louis Savas, a good-natured, fatherly man who has been treating dancers for years, says many go to him for regular "tune-ups," even if they aren't having any specific problems. When the bones are correctly aligned, the body moves freely. There are various chiropractic methods, some of which use more force than others in making spinal adjustments. Ask about the procedures in advance, and if you're a little nervous because it's your first time, ask the chiropractor to go slowly.

Richard E. Carnival
141 East 55th Street
New York, New York 10022
(212-355-5136)

Seymour Goldstein, M.D.
3102 Avenue R
Brooklyn, New York 11229
(212-336-7444)
Hours: Monday-Friday 8:15 A.M. to 8:15 P.M.

John A. Mazzaferre
55 West 42nd Street
New York, New York 10036
(212-947-6045); Emergency (201-337-7953)

Dr. A. Alessandro Pireno
Chiropractic Arts Building
64 East 34th Street
New York, New York 10016
(212-689-2024/689-2025)

Alan H. Pressman
31 Washington Square West
New York, New York 10011
(212-228-5600)
Also gives nutritional advice.

Louis Savas
251 West 92nd Street
New York, New York 10025
(212-874-2200)
Hours: Monday-Friday 7:00 A.M. to 6:00 P.M.

Dr. Rose M. Smart
39 West 55th Street
New York, New York 10019
(212-582-1139)
New patients must be referred by current patients.

Dr. Barbara Vedder
710 Kennedy Boulevard
Bayonne, New Jersey 07002
(201-823-0448)

Masseurs

Healthy dancers often go to masseurs—like chiropractors—just to relax or to relieve stiffness, soreness, and fatigue. They claim that massage increases their body awareness, enabling them to work more deeply with the muscles. Massage therapy also helps ease the pain and swelling of injuries, stimulates circulation, reduces muscle spasm, and keeps muscles supple while they are healing. But check with your physician first, since it is not good for all types of injuries. As in chiropractic, there are various massage techniques, ranging from light, general workovers to the deep, localized, close-to-the-bone kind that can be painful and leave you a bit sore. Talk it over with your masseur or masseuse. Some will progress from light to deeper massage gradually, over several sessions, as your body is able to tolerate more and more. Authorities agree that an essential ingredient in successful treatment is the rapport between the masseur and the client.

We first heard of Armando Zetina from a dancer whose calf muscles had turned to rock from strain and overwork. He could barely take a step without his lower leg muscles cramping painfully. Within two sessions Zetina had kneaded and stretched out the tight calves. He also traced the problem to a faulty stance, and after correcting his posture, our friend was dancing better than ever. Later we learned that Zetina is considered to be one of the best masseurs in the city; his clientele has included Mikhail Baryshnikov, Wayne Cilento of ***Dancin'***, and singer Bette Midler.

Zetina says that there are actually only a handful of qualified masseurs practicing in New York, and it is difficult to find them because the legitimate ones don't advertise for fear of attracting the wrong clientele. "Particularly with regard to injuries, massage can be a very scary thing if the masseur isn't absolutely clear about what he is doing," Zetina points out. He feels that most masseurs do not have the proper combination of knowledge and intuition needed for good results. "This must be very carefully and slowly nurtured. It takes years to train an assistant," he says. Zetina was trained by Alfred Kagan, as was Ben Benjamin. Benjamin in turn trained Joan Witkowski and Terry Ross. Zetina feels that along with a few others who are honest, conscientious workers, this small core of masseurs who have worked under Kagan are the experts on treating dancers. The following practitioners were recommended by either Zetina or a consensus of the dancers we consulted:

Ben E. Benjamin
910 West End Avenue (105th Street)
New York, New York, 10025
(212-866-2069)
Benjamin believes that massage should be part of a total body care program that includes education and corrective exercise. He heads the Institute for Muscular Therapy and

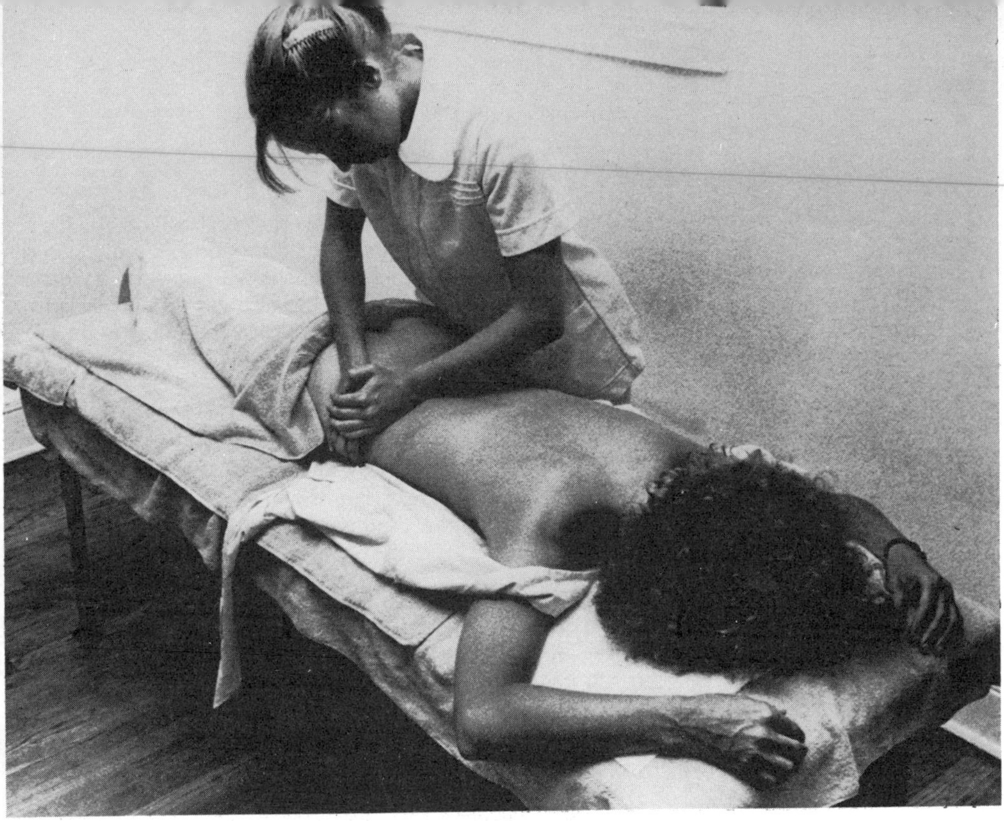

Masseuse Conni Brunner at work. ***Frank Gimpaya***

has written a self-help book that explains his views called ***Are You Tense?*** Benjamin treats many members of the Alvin Ailey company. He charges $50 an hour for consultations and $36 for treatment; his assistants, who are also good, charge $15-20 per session.

Conni Brunner, Muscular Therapist
10 Bethune Street
New York, New York 10014
(212-242-4492)
Trained by Ben Benjamin, Brunner takes a careful history of her clients, analyzes postural problems, and prescribes corrective exercises as part of the treatment. A dancer herself, good-humored and easy to talk to, this slight young woman can give a surprisingly rigorous massage; but she works up to it slowly, and only when she feels the muscles are ready.

Rush Johnson
233 West 83rd Street
New York, New York 10024
(212-877-2332)
Johnson combines standard Swedish massage with Shiatsu, which he learned from the Japanese master Masunaga. He does deep body massage, using his elbows and knuckles as well as his hands. His fee is $20 for one and a half hours.

Alfred Kagan
161 West 54th Street
New York, New York 10019
(212-586-5900)
Armando Zetina calls Alfred Kagan "one of the best." Kagan trained Zetina and Benjamin, and is so much in demand that getting an appointment with him can be as hard as getting in to see the mayor. He sees lots of Broadway dancers and treats several members of the Ailey group.

Robert LeGrand
155 West 68th Street
New York, New York, 10023
(212-787-0966)

LeGrand does a deep, rigorous massage, which he says is "too strong for many clients." Although he treats people from all walks of life, he is a dancer's favorite and the personal masseur for ballet teachers David Howard and Melissa Hayden. He has also worked on many members of the New York City Ballet, Rudolf Nureyev, Mikhail Baryshnikov, and Natalia Makarova.

Kevin Montgomery
255 West End Avenue (72nd Street), Apt. 21
New York, New York 10023
(212-873-1423)
Also an advocate of deep massage, Montgomery is often used by the Joffrey Ballet dancers and students at the American Ballet Theatre School.

Terry Ross
8 Spring Street
New York, New York 10012
(212-226-0520
Trained by two of the top masseurs in the city, Ross has taught therapeutic massage at the American Dance Festival for the past four summers. About 80 percent of his clients are dancers. Ross does a deep muscle massage because he feels that "dancers need deeper work than the average person." Although Ross ideally prefers clients to come for a series of sessions so he can "have the time to really make permanent changes," he doesn't insist on this since many dancers can't afford to come more than once or twice. He advises people to try different masseurs because "even if they practice the same technique, each one is an individual who works with a unique kind of energy and establishes a different kind of connection to the person they're working on." Ross's fee is $15 per session.

Ellen Saltonstall
87 Leonard Street
New York, New York 10013
(212-925-4718)
Ellen Saltonstall began studying with Ben Benjamin after he helped her recover from a dance injury several

years ago. She teaches dance, and along with massage, shows clients relaxation techniques and how to become aware of their own muscular tension patterns. Several dancers go to Saltonstall, including Rose Marie Wright of the Twyla Tharp Dance Company. She charges $20 an hour.

Shiatsu Education Center
52 West 55th Street
New York, New York 10019
(212-582-3424)
O'Hashi of the Shiatsu Education Center is acknowledged to be the leading practitioner of Shiatsu massage in the city. This Japanese method is based on the use of finger pressure applied at critical points on the body. He has treated Martha Graham, Ivan Nagy, and members of the New York City Ballet, among others.

Joan Witkowski
125 Christopher Street
New York, New York 10014
(212-691-9342)
Trained at the Ben Benjamin Institute for Muscular Therapy and the Swedish Institute of Massage and Allied Subjects, Joan Witkowski does what she calls "deep muscle therapy." She thinks of massage not just as a means of relaxing the body, but a healing process that entails deep work with the muscles. Witkowski says she "works with each person according to what they need as an individual. We work together, there has to be trust. I go only as far as each body can tolerate; if I feel the muscle contracting as I work on a particular spot, I'll ease up and work on the surrounding area. If a client is in pain from a back spasm or ankle sprain, I concentrate on breaking up the muscle spasm so they can move again—emergency first aid, really. On other people who don't have bad problems or whom I've seen before, we can go further. I can really start opening up the muscles and we can get into correcting whatever caused the problem—poor posture or lack of body awareness, whatever." When she feels it is appropriate Witkowski incorporates Alexander Technique, breathing exercises, or foot reflexology into treatments. She loves her work and goes for weekly massages herself. One session costs $25-$30.

Armando Zetina
211 West 56th Street, Apartment 3A
New York, New York 10019
(212-586-1342)
Armando Zetina blends several different styles of massage into his technique, including Swedish and Shiatsu. He says he likes to prepare clients by explaining his motions, and believes in using his voice to soothe and reassure. Zetina gives both light, general body massage and the deep, localized kind. His fees range from $20-$35 per session, depending on the kind of treatment required.

If you're new in town

Despite the inevitable snafus, subways are the fastest way to travel.
Frank Gimpaya

Getting around

Manhattan's grid design and numbered streets make finding your way around fairly simple. The Metropolitan Transit Authority (MTA) provides free subway and bus maps of the city, which are available at some subway token booths and major railroad depots such as Grand Central Station (East 42nd Street), and Pennsylvania Railroad Station (West 34th Street). You can also get them by sending a self-addressed, stamped envelope to Public Affairs Department, New York City Transit Authority, 370 Jay Street, Brooklyn, New York 11201. It should take about a week. In addition, the MTA operates a travel information service, and will give you directions by telephone to any street address in New York. Call 212-330-1234 (you may have to ring several times before your call is answered because the office is often deluged with inquiries).

If you aren't in a hurry, traveling by bus is far more pleasant than subway; but despite recent cutbacks in service, the New York subway system is still the fastest way to get where you're going. There has been a crime problem on the subway lately, so use some street smarts: Wait for trains in the center of the platform, near the turnstiles, and always ride in well-populated cars. Public transportation is half price on Saturday night (from 6:00 P.M. on) and all day Sunday. Ask your bus driver about other fare reductions for bus passengers, such as the "Night on the Town" and "Add-a-Ride" deals.

Where to stay

Visitors on limited budgets who plan a lengthy stay in New York soon discover that most acceptable housing is prohibitively expensive and that many residential hotels which charge reasonable rates are rather unsavory and dangerous places to live. Here are some time-honored solutions to the housing problem.

College dormitories: Good low-cost housing for the summer is available for young people at some local universities, where they will be with other students in a protected environment. Columbia University offers dormitory space for students over eighteen years old at $6 per night from May 25th to August 12th. Rooms may be reserved in advance. Proof of student status, in the form of a student I.D. card or letter from school, is required. For information write or call:

International Student Hostel
Columbia University
125 Livingston Hall
New York, New York 10027
(212-280-2775)

New York University also rents dorm space from June 4th to September 3rd for a season fee of $375. Priority is given to NYU students, but there are usually vacant rooms. For an application write to:

New York University Housing
54 Washington Square
New York, New York 10012
(212-598-2083)

Temporary residences: The American Ballet Theatre School recommends these temporary residences for out-of-town students:

Empire Hotel
Broadway at 63rd Street
New York, New York 10023
(212-265-7400)

Henry Hudson Hotel
353 West 57th Street
New York, New York, 10019
(212-CO5-6100)

Wellington Hotel
Seventh Avenue at 55th Street
New York, New York 10019
(212-CI7-3900)

Mayflower Hotel
Central Park West at 61st Street
New York, New York, 10023
(212-CO5-0060)

Westside YMCA
5 West 63rd Street
New York, New York 10023
(212-787-4400)

For women:

Barbizon Hotel for Women
Lexington Avenue at 63rd Street
New York, New York 10021
(212-TE8-5700)

St. Mary's Residence
225 East 72nd Street
New York, New York 10021
(212-249-6850)

YWCA Residence
135 East 52nd Street
New York, New York 10022
(212-753-4700)

Swiss Town House
35 West 67th Street
New York, New York 10023
(212-787-1130)

Milbank House
11 West 10th Street
New York, New York 10011
(212-GR5-9720)

Katherine House
118 West 13th Street
New York, New York 10011
(212-427-6000)

Sage House
49 West 9th Street
New York, New York 10011
(212-GR5-9861)

Parkside Evangeline
18 Gramercy Park South (East 21st Street)
New York, New York 10003
(212-677-6200)

The Evangeline
123 West 13th Street
New York, New York 10011
(212-CH2-2400)